MILESTONES IN SOIL MECHANICS

William John Macquorn Rankine 1820–1872

The distinguished practising civil engineer and mathematical physicist who made many significant contributions in the science of soil mechanics by making careful and thorough investigations of earth pressure and bearing load problems.

MILESTONES
IN SOIL MECHANICS

THE FIRST TEN RANKINE LECTURES

ISBN 0 7277 0010 3

D
624.1513
MIL

Published by Thomas Telford Ltd for the Institution of Civil Engineers

Printed by T. & A. Constable Ltd., Edinburgh

CONTENTS

The Rankine Lectures 1961–1970

In commemoration of the great engineer and physicist, William John Macquorn Rankine (1820–1872) the British National Committee of the International Society for Soil Mechanics and Foundation Engineering (now known as the British Geotechnical Society) arranged to hold a lecture annually in London, to be presented by an eminent soil mechanics specialist. The first ten lectures, of which this volume is made up, were given during 1961–1970 and were published annually in the June issues of Géotechnique, *the international journal of soil mechanics and foundation engineering. These lectures represent important milestones in the recent development of soil mechanics, as would be expected from the international standing of the Rankine Lecturers invited from all over the world.*

CONTROL OF SEEPAGE THROUGH FOUNDATIONS AND ABUTMENTS OF DAMS

A. Casagrande

"To pass judgement on the quality of a dam foundation is one of the most difficult and responsible tasks. It requires both careful consideration of the geological conditions and the capacity for evaluating the hydraulic importance of the geological facts which can only be obtained by a thorough training in the hydraulics of seepage."

Karl Terzaghi, 1929

I am deeply grateful to the members of the British National Committee for the great honour of inviting me to be your first Rankine Lecturer. The name Rankine was, of course, familiar to me in my student days. In my mind I had classified him in the same category with such eminent German engineers and teachers as Otto Mohr, Müller-Breslau, and Föppl. But until recently I had no conception of the enormous breadth and depth of Rankine's contributions in several areas of engineering as well as in pure science. And all this he accomplished in his short life span that I have exceeded already by 6 years. I could easily use the entire hour to talk about my impressions when reviewing Rankine's books and scientific papers. But may I mention just one item that concerns the conflict between theoretical science and engineering, a topic often discussed at the present time particularly in the United States where we are undergoing a period of critical review of engineering education and are groping for something new that nobody seems to be able to define clearly. As always in periods of uncertainty, there is a tendency to be over critical of past efforts; there is a danger of "throwing the baby out with the bath water"—at least that is the impression I have about certain changes which are being attempted in the teaching of civil engineering at some of our schools. Let me read two short paragraphs that bring out in essence what Rankine thought about this conflict that seems to have already existed in his days. My quotation is from his inaugural address when he accepted the professorship at the University of Glasgow, in 1856. This is what he said more than 100 years ago:

"In theoretical science, the question is—What are we to think?—and when a doubtful point arises, for the solution of which either experimental data are wanting, or mathematical methods are not sufficiently advanced, it is the duty of philosophic minds not to dispute about the probability of conflicting suppositions, but to labour for the advancement of experimental inquiry and of mathematics, and await patiently the time when these shall be adequate to solve the question.

"But in practical science the question is—What are we to do?—a question which involves the necessity for the immediate adoption of some rule of working. In doubtful cases, we cannot allow our machines and our works of improvement to wait for the advancement of science; and if existing data are insufficient to give an exact solution of the question, that approximate solution must be acted upon which the best data attainable show to be the

most probable.   A prompt and sound judgement in cases of this kind is one of the characteristics of a PRACTICAL MAN, in the right sense of that term."

This is, indeed, the best definition of the difference between theoretical science and engineering I have been able to find.   Also, it serves as an admirable introduction to the subject of
my Lecture in which I will make use of theory to supplement empirical knowledge and to
enhance "sound judgement".

CONTROL OF SEEPAGE THROUGH ROCK

INTRODUCTION

By control of seepage I refer to all measures which the design engineer has at his disposal
in order to protect a dam, its foundation, and its abutments against any undesirable or dangerous effects of seepage.   The seepage losses *per se* are more often than not of secondary consideration.   In fact, our control measures may cause a substantial increase in seepage rather
than a decrease.

The design assumptions for uplift beneath concrete dams 30 years ago were very conservative.   Gradually, on the basis of uplift measurements on numerous concrete dams, one
began to realize that with a combination of a grout curtain and a line of drainage holes the
uplift could be reduced to much smaller values than those assumed in the design.   Today the
largest builders of concrete dams in the United States, the U.S. Bureau of Reclamation, the
Tennessee Valley Authority, and the U.S. Corps of Engineers, use similar assumptions which
are a straight-line drop from reservoir level at the heel of the dam to a certain fraction of the
difference in head between reservoir and tailwater along the line of the drains; and from there
another straight line to tailwater elevation at the downstream toe.   The value of that fraction
at the line of drains was gradually reduced during the past 20 years and is now one-third for
the Bureau of Reclamation,[1] and one-fourth for the Tennessee Valley Authority.[2]   These
uplift values are assumed to act over 100% of the base area.   While several independent
organizations have arrived on an empirical basis at similar design assumptions, there is no
agreement among designers on the relative merits of the grout curtain and the line of drains.
I have noted in recent years a growing awareness that a grout curtain consisting of a single
line of holes may be very unreliable.   Leading engineers have expressed to me such views
privately, but they seem to be reluctant to state so publicly.   It seems as if they were afraid
of attacking something that is believed by a majority in the profession almost like a religious
dogma.   Others cloak their doubts in statements such as: "We consider the grout curtain
good insurance; but in our design we rely only on the drainage."

In 1952 the Tennessee Valley Authority published a book entitled "Civil and structural
design",[3] summarizing their design practice at that time.   From its chapter on "Foundation
cut-off and drainage" is reproduced Fig. 1 which shows typical uplift observations for a concrete gravity dam.   From a foundation gallery, drainage wells extend to a depth of about
40 ft, on 8-ft centres.   Not shown on the original Figure in that book is the grout curtain.   I
obtained that information from another source and added it on that drawing.   It consists of a
single line of 3-in. grout holes, 4–8 ft inside the heel of the dam, spaced at an average 5 ft, with
every third hole extending to a depth of 80 ft, the others to about 40 ft.

In the cross-section reproduced in Fig. 1, the measured uplift plots as a straight-line drop
from full reservoir level at the heel to tailwater elevation at the line of drain holes.   Downstream of the line of drain holes the uplift rises only very slightly above tailwater, such that
there is only an insignificant magnitude of uplift in the zone downstream from the line of

drain holes in excess of the tailwater level.   Later I will show that this type of uplift distribution can be readily explained by means of a theoretical analysis, provided that the drainage wells penetrate through the more pervious zone of the rock.   If the grout curtain would be reasonably effective, then the observed uplift between the heel and the line of drains should not be the practically straight line as indicated in this cross-section.

Although in the published design assumptions for uplift, the existence of a grout curtain is not even mentioned and seems to be ignored, that does not mean that the designers consider the grout curtain of secondary importance; on the contrary, in most publications primary stress is placed on the discussion of the grout curtain.   By comparison, discussion of the drain holes is usually very brief. When considering, in addition, that the drain holes are always spaced much farther apart than the grout holes, and that their depth is generally only about one-half of the depth of the grout curtain, I get the impression that the drain holes are treated like a step-child.   Certainly, the cost of such a line of drain holes is small as compared to the cost of the grout curtain.   Obviously there is a contradiction which is perhaps most easily explained by the fact that the relative merit of grout curtains and drainage holes has been a highly controversial subject for a long time.   The most frequent statement one finds in publications, and on which there seems to be some measure of agreement, is that the purpose of grouting is to control the rate of seepage beneath the dam and the purpose of drainage is to relieve uplift.   However, I cannot see how these two effects can be separated in this simple manner.   Any substantial reduction in seepage by means of a grout curtain must also reduce the uplift pressures downstream of the grout curtain.   If the piezometric surface between the heel and the drain holes is practically a straight line, as in Fig. 1, then the grout curtain is obviously not doing much good, while the drainage is doing an excellent job in controlling the uplift pressures in the area between the line of drains and the downstream toe.

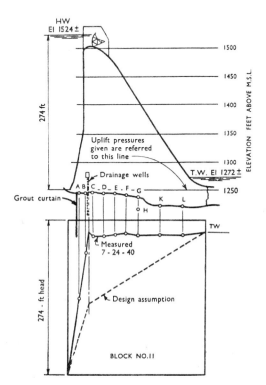

Fig. 1.   Foundation uplift pressures, Hiawassee Dam   (Reproduced from Fig. 54 of Ref. (3))

ANALYSIS OF DRAINAGE

The only theoretical analysis of the effect of drainage of rock beneath concrete dams with which I am familiar is that published by the late Dr Brahtz[4] of the Bureau of Reclamation, and which was later extended by the Tennessee Valley Authority.[5]   Fig. 2, reproduced from T.V.A. Technical Monograph No. 67, shows the theoretical results for various locations of a horizontal drain upon the uplift.   The rock is assumed semi-infinite in extent and of isotropic permeability, with Darcy's law valid.   The location of the drain closest to the heel gives, of

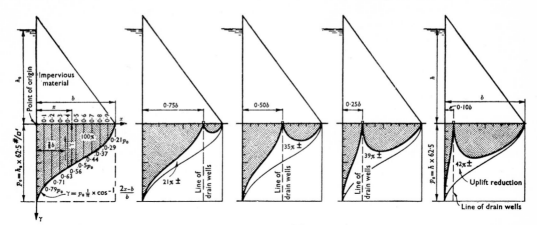

Fig. 2.   Theoretical uplift pressure reduction caused by a drainage system which is effective at the foundation level

(Reproduced from Fig. 36 of Ref. (5))

course, the largest reduction in uplift; but even for that case the reduction is far less and of different shape than the majority of actual uplift observations on concrete dams.   One should not really expect good agreement with this theoretical solution, because replacement of deep penetrating wells by a surface drain, and assumption that the rock is of uniform permeability to great depth, are excessive deviations from the usual conditions.

A more realistic analysis should not neglect the fact that the wells are intended and should penetrate through the zone of relatively pervious rock.   In addition, one should take into account that the hydrostatic pressure against the dam, which is transmitted into the foundation, may cause joints along the heel of the dam to open up and full hydrostatic pressure to extend more or less throughout the pervious zone of the rock along a vertical extension of the upstream face.   The joints need not be parallel to the dam axis; even an irregular system may develop such an effect.   If we make these assumptions, we arrive at the case illustrated in Fig. 3, consisting of a pervious foundation layer of limited depth with a vertical entrance face below the heel of the dam, and with a row of drainage wells located at a distance d from the heel.   One can readily see from this picture that the drainage wells should be effective in controlling uplift downstream from the line of wells, provided of course that the wells are deep enough to really penetrate the pervious zone.

In Fig. 4, I summarize my analysis on the basis of the assumptions just stated, namely a vertical entrance face, such as along a waterfront, into a confined pervious stratum of thickness D, with an infinite row of wells parallel to this entrance face at the distance d, with a well-spacing a, and a well radius r_w.   Basically, the solution of this problem is contained in Muskat's monumental book published in 1937.[6]   In terms of the drawdown s at any point (x, y) it can be expressed by the long equation at the top of Fig. 4.   From this general equation * one can derive several results which are of particular significance to our problem as discussed in the following paragraphs.

For any given difference in elevation h_c between reservoir and tailwater levels, and given

---

* Extensive use of the Muskat solution has been made by the Corps of Engineers in connexion with investigations of relief wells for earth dams and levees.   In that problem, as will be discussed in a later Paper, the main interest lies in the shape of the piezometric surface upstream of the wells and in the maximum head between the wells, because relatively large well-spacings are used.   However, beneath concrete dams, we are principally interested in the shape of the piezometric surface downstream of the line of drains and in the relative water levels in the drain holes and of the tailwater.

dimensions d, a, and r_w, there is a definite water level in the wells which will ensure that all seepage entering the pervious stratum is removed by the wells, and that the piezometric surface downstream of the wells will be horizontal. Only near the wells there is some flow also downstream of the wells, but which merely curves back into the wells. For practical purposes the horizontal piezometric surface is established beyond a distance of about one-half of the well-spacing downstream of the wells. The water level in the wells is h_w below the tailwater level, and halfway between the wells the piezometric surface is h_m above the tailwater level.*

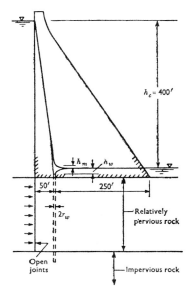

Well spacing a ft	Well diameter $2r_w$ in.	Area ratio $2r_w/a$ %	$\dfrac{h_w}{h_c}$ %	$\dfrac{h_m}{h_c}$ %
10	3	2·5	8·1	2·2
10	6	5	5·9	2·2
10	12	10	3·7	2·2
5	3	5	2·9	1·1
5	6	10	2·4	1·1

Fig. 3. Numerical examples for full control of uplift by single line of drainage wells

The piezometric surfaces plotted in Fig. 4 were computed for $a = d$. If the well-spacing a is much smaller than d, as is generally the case in the foundation treatment of concrete dams, then h_m and h_w become very much smaller in relation to h_c than shown in Fig. 4. It is really the ratios h_w/h_c and h_m/h_c (for convenience expressed in per cent.) which are of primary interest to us. Working formulas for these ratios are given in Fig. 4. In their derivation certain mathematical simplifications were introduced, but which still ensure results of slide-rule accuracy, provided we keep the well-spacing smaller than $3d$, and the ratio of well radius to well-spacing smaller than 0·1. Both conditions are generally fulfilled for the foundation drainage below concrete dams. The "well-level ratio" h_w/h_c is a function of the dimensionless ratios a/d and $a/2r_w$. However, the "midwell-level ratio" h_m/h_c is only a function of the ratio a/d. It is independent of the well diameter because the well diameter only influences the shape of the drawdown surface close to the well and the water level in the well. Once h_c is given or assumed, the piezometric surface is determined, except close to the wells and in the wells, and the rate of seepage q_w toward each well is also determined. The thickness of the water-bearing stratum D has no effect on the piezometric surface, and only enters in the rate of seepage which can be expressed simply as the flow through the layer of thickness D under a hydraulic gradient of h_c/d. As shown by the equations in Fig. 4, the rate of seepage may be expressed either as rate of flow per unit width $\bar{q}$, or as rate of flow toward each well $q_w = a\bar{q}$

* For convenience, tailwater is used as reference plane for measuring h values. The positive sign is used for h values above tailwater elevation, and the negative sign for h values below tailwater elevation. The signs for s are opposite those of h.

In the Table in Fig. 3 are listed numerical results for a 400-ft-high concrete dam, for the line of wells arranged 50 ft from the heel, and computed for two cases of well-spacings, namely 10 ft and 5 ft, and for well diameters of 3 in., 6 in., and 12 in.   For a well-spacing of 10 ft and well diameter of 3 in.—which is probably the most common combination for concrete dams in the United States—the water level in the drain holes must be kept about 8% of h_c below

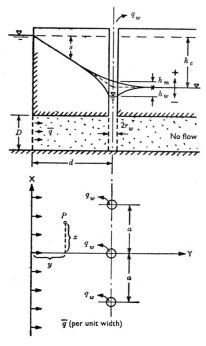

$$s = \frac{q_w}{2\pi k D} \, ln \, \frac{\cosh 2\pi(y+d)/a - \cos 2\pi x/a}{\cosh 2\pi(y-d)/a - \cos 2\pi x/a}$$

(Muskat, 1937)

Known or assumed: h_c, a, d, r_w, D, k

Determine: h_m, h_w, q_w, or $\bar{q}$

Working formulas (slide rule accuracy) for h_w and h_c when $\dfrac{a}{d} < 3$ and $\dfrac{r_w}{a} < 0{\cdot}1$:

$$\frac{h_w}{h_c} = -\frac{a}{2\pi d} \, ln \, \frac{a}{2\pi r_w} = -0{\cdot}366 \, \frac{a}{d} \, \log_{10} \frac{a}{2\pi r_w}$$

$$\frac{h_m}{h_c} = \frac{a}{2\pi d} \, ln2 = 0{\cdot}110 \, \frac{a}{d}$$

$$\bar{q} = k h_c \frac{D}{d} \quad \left(\text{Shape factor} = \frac{D}{d} \right)$$

$$q_w = k h_c a \frac{D}{d}$$

Fig. 4.   Theoretical solution for line of drainage wells parallel to vertical entrance face and no seepage downstream of wells

tailwater level in order to eliminate all excess uplift downstream of the line of drains.   However, if for the same well diameter we reduce the well-spacing to 5 ft, then the water level in the drain holes needs to be only about 3% of h_c below tailwater level.   If we maintain the 10-ft spacing, but increase the well diameter from 3 in. to 12 in., the water level in the drains has to be depressed about 4%.   In other words, the 3-in. drain holes at 5-ft spacing are not only cheaper but somewhat more efficient than the 12-in.-dia. drain holes at 10-ft spacing. In all these examples the rise of the piezometric surface halfway between the drain holes is only about 1% or 2% of h_c, thus negligible.

In the above and subsequent numerical examples the head loss in the wells was disregarded. Under certain conditions this factor should not be neglected.

The mathematical solution of Fig. 4 can be expanded to include the case when the water level in the wells is at the same elevation as tailwater, or even higher.   Then a certain amount of seepage will continue beyond the line of drainage holes and some uplift in excess of tailwater will develop downstream of the line of drains.   This combination of flow can be solved by direct mathematical superposition of seepage through the pervious stratum under a uniform gradient and the solution presented in Fig. 4.   Such direct superposition is mathematically correct because both systems of flow are solutions of the Laplace differential equation. The results of the analysis, for the water level in the drain holes at tailwater level, and again

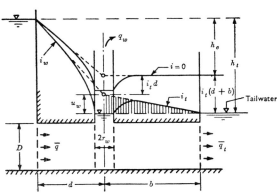

Known or assumed: h_t, a, d, b, r_w, D, k,

Determine: Uplift $u_w, \bar{q}, \bar{q}_t$

(1) Compute first auxiliary quantity h_c:

$$h_c = \frac{h_t}{1 + \dfrac{1}{2\pi} \cdot \dfrac{a}{d} \cdot \dfrac{b+d}{b} \cdot ln\, \dfrac{a}{2\pi r_w}}$$

(2) Compute hydraulic gradients i_t and i_w:

Downstream of wells: $\quad i_t = \dfrac{h_t - h_c}{b + d}$

Upstream of wells: $\quad i_w = \dfrac{h_c}{d} + i_t$

(3) Uplift at line of wells:
$$u_w = b \cdot i_t$$

(4) Seepage

Total flow: $\qquad \bar{q} \quad = kDi_w$

Flow passing wells: $\quad \bar{q}_t \quad = kDi_t$

Ratio passing wells: $\bar{q}_t/\bar{q} = i_t/i_w$

Fig. 5.   Theoretical solution for water level in drainage wells at tailwater level

with the limitations $a/d < 3$, and $r_w/a < 0.1$, to permit mathematical simplifications, are shown in Fig. 5.   It is convenient to compute first a fictitious tailwater h_c for which there is no flow downstream of the drains, and such that if one superposes a constant gradient i_t, the new tailwater elevation and the water level in the wells will coincide.   The total uplift downstream of the drainage line is the triangular hatched area, with the maximum u_w at the line of wells.   In Fig. 6 are shown the computed results for the same cross-section used before, for drain-hole diameters of 3 in., and the two well-spacings of 10 ft and 5 ft.   At the line of drains the uplift is 6·8% and 4·5% of the triangular uplift area for a straight-line drop from head to tailwater.   Thus, if the drainage gallery is located at the elevation of tailwater, the magnitude of the uplift downstream of the wells is still very modest.

In Fig. 7 is presented the solution for the case when the drainage gallery is at an elevation higher than tailwater.   This solution is useful for analysing some of the observed uplift data.

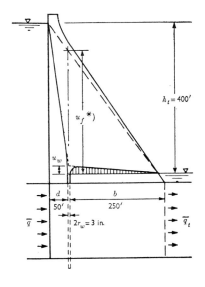

Well spacing a ft	Uplift u_w ft	$\dfrac{u_w}{u_f}$ %	$\dfrac{\bar{q}_t}{\bar{q}}$ %
10	22·5	6·8	1·2
5	15·0	4·5	0·8

$*)\ u_f = h_t \cdot \dfrac{b}{b+d}$

Fig. 6.   Numerical examples for water level in drainage wells at tailwater level

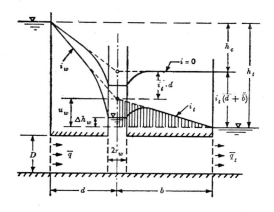

Known or assumed: $h_t, \Delta h_w, a, d, b, r_w, D, k$
Determine: uplift $u_w, \bar{q}, \bar{q}_t$

(1) Compute first auxiliary quantity h_c:

$$h_c = \frac{h_t - \Delta h_w \dfrac{b+d}{b}}{1 + \dfrac{1}{2\pi}\cdot\dfrac{a}{d}\cdot\dfrac{b+d}{b} ln \cdot \dfrac{a}{2\pi r_w}}$$

(2) Compute hydraulic gradients i_t and i_w:

Downstream of wells: $i_t = \dfrac{h_t - h_c}{b + d}$

Upstream of wells: $i_w = \dfrac{h_c}{d} + i_t$

(3) Uplift at line of wells:
$$u_w = b \cdot i_t + \Delta h_w$$

(4) Seepage
     Total flow: $\bar{q} = kDi_w$
     Flow passing wells: $\bar{q}_t = kDi_t$
     Ratio passing wells: $\bar{q}_t/\bar{q} = i_t/i_w$

Fig. 7. Theoretical solution with water level in drainage wells higher than tailwater level

ANALYSIS OF IMPERFECT CUT-OFFS

In an attempt to illuminate the question of efficiency of a grout curtain consisting of a single line of holes we make use of the theory of imperfect cut-offs which was published by Dachler (1936) in his book "Grundwasserströmung".[7] The solution shown in Fig. 8 expresses the efficiency of a very thin cut-off wall which has narrow slits. Whether the slits are horizontal or vertical is of no significance. If D is the total thickness of a pervious layer, d that portion which is made positively impervious by the cut-off, and $W = D - d =$ total width of open spaces, then d/D is called the cut-off ratio and W/D the open-space ratio. For example, a cut-off ratio of 0·99 would mean that 99% of the area does not let a drop through, and when we add up all the small openings that are not sealed, we obtain a total of 1% of the area, or an open-space ratio of 0·01. The cut-off efficiency E_c can be expressed as the ratio $(q - q_c)/q$, where q is the rate of flow without a cut-off, and q_c the rate of flow with the cut-off. When q_c is zero, we have a perfect cut-off, i.e. a cut-off efficiency of unity or 100%. For $q_c = q$, the cut-off efficiency is zero.

Dachler's equation for the cut-off efficiency E_c can be simplified for open-space ratios of $W/D < 0·1$, with slide-rule accuracy, to the working equation shown in Fig. 8 and plotted for $B/D = 1$, and for the number of openings $n = 20$ and $n = 120$. If we further consider only cases with large numbers of openings (say $n > 20$), and equal open-space ratio, it can be seen that the cut-off efficiency decreases approximately inversely proportional with the number of openings. (This paradoxical conclusion loses its validity when dealing with thick walls.)

THEORETICAL CONSIDERATIONS CONCERNING EFFICIENCY OF A SINGLE-LINE GROUT CURTAIN

A theoretical analysis of the hydraulic efficiency of a single line of grout holes in rock would require so many assumptions that the results would be of little value. However, the preceding analysis is useful to make plausible the reasons why single lines of grout cut-offs have proved inefficient in the majority of cases for which reliable observations are available. For example, we could resort to the following question: Is it reasonable to assume that a single-line grout curtain could be considered as good a cut-off as a steel membrane which has a slit $\frac{1}{16}$-in. wide spaced every 5 ft? This would correspond to an open-space ratio of 0·1%. Offhand,

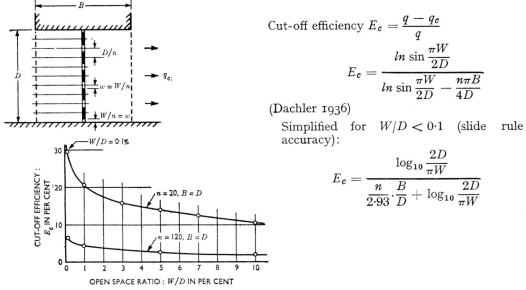

Cut-off efficiency $E_c = \dfrac{q - q_c}{q}$

$$E_c = \frac{\ln \sin \dfrac{\pi W}{2D}}{\ln \sin \dfrac{\pi W}{2D} - \dfrac{n\pi B}{4D}}$$

(Dachler 1936)

Simplified for $W/D < 0\cdot1$ (slide rule accuracy):

$$E_c = \frac{\log_{10} \dfrac{2D}{\pi W}}{\dfrac{n}{2\cdot93} \cdot \dfrac{B}{D} + \log_{10} \dfrac{2D}{\pi W}}$$

CUT-OFF EFFICIENCY : E_c IN PER CENT

$n = 20, B = D$

$n = 120, B = D$

OPEN SPACE RATIO : W/D IN PER CENT

Fig. 8. Theoretical efficiency of imperfect cut-off

one might well question whether such perfection could ever be achieved by means of a single-line grout curtain. Assuming $B = D = 100$ ft, the 5-ft spacing would make $n = 20$, and this would correspond to the upper curve in Fig. 8. For these assumptions the theoretical cut-off efficiency is 29%. In other words, 71% of the rate of flow without cut-off would still be going through these thin slits. If we divided the same $0\cdot1\%$ of the area into a larger number of smaller slits, the cut-off efficiency would drop to even lower values.

Based on a review of instances where reliable observations of the piezometric surface were made both sides of a single-line of grout holes in rock and not supplemented by additional grouting after filling of the reservoir, I have come to the conclusion that a 30% efficiency has rarely been exceeded in the past for most conditions. Could then a designer dare to rely on a single-line grout curtain, when analysing the safety of the dam? And when he considers seepage losses, the cases when a reduction of seepage by the order of 30% would warrant the high cost of a grout curtain would be a small minority. To achieve the same result in the case of a concrete dam with a wide base, one could simply move the line of drains farther downstream by one-third of its distance from the heel of the dam; e.g. instead of arranging the drains 30 ft from the heel, this distance could be made 40 ft, which would achieve the desired reduction in seepage in a more positive manner, and merely at the expense of a small increase in uplift. Or, one could provide an impervious zone or blanket upstream of the dam, as discussed later.

DISCUSSION OF HYPOTHETICAL EXAMPLES

Before proceeding to a presentation of a number of uplift measurements on concrete dams, it will be helpful to consider in Fig. 9 hypothetical uplift diagrams for different assumptions concerning the grout curtain, the line of drains, and the geologic conditions.

(a) A perfect grout cut-off through the pervious zone would result in full head upstream of the cut-off, then, at the cut-off line a sharp drop to the elevation of tailwater, and from the cut-off a horizontal line extending to the downstream toe.

(b) A reasonably effective grout cut-off through the pervious zone, but without drainage, would be reflected by an uplift diagram such as shown in (b). It is what I would hope to achieve under the most favourable conditions from a single line of grout holes. But it is not really "reasonably effective" from the standpoint of reduction in seepage, because with the slopes as shown in this sketch, the reduction of seepage would be only about 50%, and that I consider not good enough to justify the high cost of a grout curtain.

(c) If we add to (b) also a line of drain holes, then we obtain an uplift diagram which still shows a well-defined drop in head along the grout cut-off.

In Fig. 9 (d) and (e) are repeated the uplift diagrams for a line of drain holes of appropriate depth, but without a grout curtain. We are already familiar with these patterns from the preceding discussion, namely in (d) with water level in holes below tailwater, and in (e) above tailwater. The majority of the observed uplift diagrams show, in fact, good similarity with these two patterns.

Patterns (c), (d), and (e) are based on the assumption that the drain holes extend through the pervious rock stratum, and that there are no unusual geological complications. It is a surprising fact that the shallow drain holes which have been used on most dams are quite effective, as will be shown later. It indicates that at the majority of sites the pervious foundation zone is relatively shallow. This may not be true for abutments for which unfortunately very few observations are available.

In Fig. 9 (f), (g), and (h) are shown three examples of the deviations from the ideal pattern that one may encounter.

In (f) the drain holes are assumed to penetrate only partially into the pervious zone. That would cause a large bulge in uplift pressures downstream of the drains, similar to the Brahtz solution illustrated in Fig. 2.

In (g) stratified rock is assumed dipping upstream, with a pervious layer sandwiched between impervious strata, with the single-line grout curtain extending through the pervious

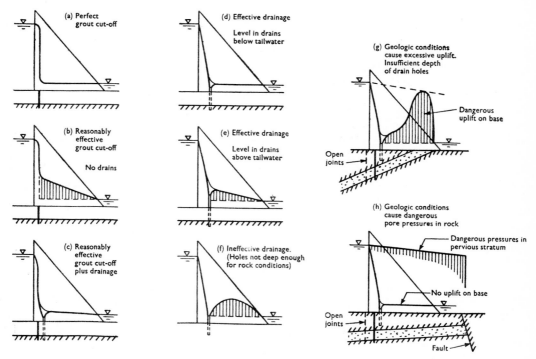

Fig. 9. Hypothetical examples

layer, but the drain holes stopping short of it.   As in the other cases, we also assume that entrance of water is gained just upstream of the dam by means of joints that open up under the effect of the hydrostatic pressure acting against the dam; and that the pervious layer meets the base of the dam in such a manner that drainage is prevented.   Such a combination may cause an uplift diagram which shows beneath a downstream zone of the dam uplift pressures almost equal to reservoir level.   If uplift measurements are made at a sufficient number of points in a cross-section, we might be warned in time of the development of this dangerous condition.   We could lower the reservoir, investigate the cause, and then extend the drain holes through the pervious layer.   We might also drill supplementary drainage holes near the downstream toe through the dam into the pervious stratum.

In (h) we assume a somewhat similar geological situation, except that the pervious layer does not come to the surface, and that downstream of the dam it is cut off by an impervious fault.   The drain holes will control the uplift along the base of the dam at approximately tailwater, particularly if a slightly more pervious surface zone should exist.   But such uplift observations along the base would create a false sense of security.   Actually, there exist dangerously high uplift pressures in the pervious stratum not far below the base of the dam, and which extend downstream of the dam.   Here again, drilling the drain holes much deeper could readily eliminate all danger.   Effective relief of the dangerous pressures could also be achieved by drainage wells drilled along the downstream toe of the dam through the pervious stratum.   To discover such conditions we would need not only uplift measurements along the base of the dam, but numerous piezometers extending to various depths into the rock.   A similar example was discussed by Terzaghi in the paper which he presented in 1929 before the American Institute of Mining and Metallurgical Engineers.[13]

From these hypothetical examples we may draw the following conclusions:

(1) Considering the low cost of drain holes, it seems logical that they should be drilled to a depth at least half the height of the dam, instead of 40 or 50 ft, as was used for most concrete dams in the past.   Local geologic conditions may indicate the need for still greater depths.

(2) Where the geologic conditions create the slightest doubt as to the control of hydrostatic pressures in various rock zones below the dam and in the abutments, not only uplift measurements along the base, but piezometer observations at many locations in the rock are needed.

For anyone with a good knowledge of engineering geology and of solving seepage problems by means of plotting flow nets, it is easy to invent combinations of geological details which can cause serious pressures in the rock foundation and abutments downstream of a dam.   I consider it such an instructive exercise that I encourage my students to indulge in this pastime.

UPLIFT OBSERVATIONS FOR TENNESSEE VALLEY AUTHORITY DAMS

The uplift diagram for the Hiawassee Dam, Fig. 1, consisting of a straight line from reservoir level to tailwater at the line of drains, and then practically a horizontal line at tailwater level for the area downstream of the drains, is an ideal example confirming the preceding theoretical analysis for the performance of drainage wells.   The Authors of T.V.A.'s book on Design[3] selected it as a representative uplift diagram.   The foundation rocks at this dam are steeply dipping, intensely jointed quartzites, and schists.

In Fig. 10,[10] are plotted the average uplift measurements for four T.V.A. dams (Fontana 480 ft, Hiawassee 307 ft, Cherokee 202 ft, and Douglas 175 ft).   Upstream of the drains the mean of the averages drops off from reservoir level in form of a slightly concave curve, with no indication of the location of the grout curtains.   The average water level in the drains is approximately at tailwater level.   The average uplift downstream from the drains is about 10% of a linear theoretical drop for the condition without drains.   This is certainly very safe

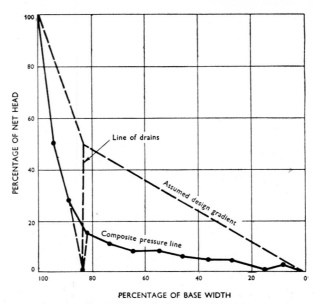

Fig. 10. Composite foundation uplift pressures for four dams of the Tennessee Valley Authority
(Reproduced from Fig. 17 of Ref. (10))

when compared with the original design assumptions for these dams. However, it also indicates that the depth of the drainage holes (a modest 40–50 ft) has not been quite deep enough, and that even better control could have been achieved easily and economically by carrying the drainage holes deeper.

Uplift diagrams on most of T.V.A.'s concrete dams are published in separate reports on each project. From the report on the Fontana Dam, published in 1953,[8] are reproduced the two diagrams in Fig. 11. The Fontana Dam is T.V.A.'s highest concrete dam. The foundation rock consists chiefly of intensely jointed quartzite. When I first saw the diagram in Fig. 11(a), I thought that I had at last discovered one clear-cut case of evidence for an effective grout curtain. From the heel to the first line of observation at A, the uplift along the base of the dam is almost equal to the full reservoir head. Then it drops abruptly to about one-fourth a short distance away, at point B; from there a further drop to the line of drains; and downstream of the drains a small rise which might indicate that the drains were not deep enough for fully effective control of uplift downstream of the drains. When examining this uplift diagram more carefully, I noticed that the grout curtain, which was carried out from the foundation gallery angling slightly in upstream direction, intersects the base of the dam in such a manner that observation points A and B are both located upstream of the grout curtain, and that between points B and C, where the grout curtain intersects the base, there is only a small drop in head. Therefore, the grout curtain can hardly be responsible for the sharp drop between A and B, but rather some local irregularity at the concrete-rock interface.

In the uplift diagram in Fig. 11(b), for another section of Fontana Dam, one can see a different pattern for two of the three observation dates. There is a sharp drop from the heel to point A, a very small drop from point A to point B, both points being located upstream of the grout curtain. However, for one set of observations there is a large continuous drop from the heel to point B, a small drop from B to C, and then a fairly large drop to the line of drains.

UPLIFT OBSERVATIONS FOR BUREAU OF RECLAMATION DAMS

Fig. 12 is a plot reproduced from the Paper by Keener,[9] which summarizes the averages of all measured uplift pressures for eight Bureau dams. The heavy line is the mean of all these averages and shows downstream of the drains about 25% of the theoretical straight-line uplift. This relatively high average is due to the high uplift pressures at Hoover Dam and one other dam before corrective measures were undertaken. When allowing for these changes (compare Fig. 14 (a) and (b)) the average uplift downstream of the drains reduces to the order of 10%, which is comparable to the average for the T.V.A. dams shown in Fig. 10.

In Fig. 13, reproduced from "Design criteria for gravity and arch dams",[1] typical uplift measurements at Grand Coulee and Shasta dams are compared with the original uplift design assumption for these dams and other design assumptions used more recently by the Bureau. At the Grand Coulee Dam the drainage gallery is about 50 ft below tailwater. Thus there is actually a negative uplift on the base of this dam, and some of the seepage pumped from the drainage gallery is being pulled through the foundation from downstream. (This case could also be investigated theoretically in a similar manner as shown in Fig. 5.) At the Shasta Dam there is practically no uplift downstream of the drains and this case may

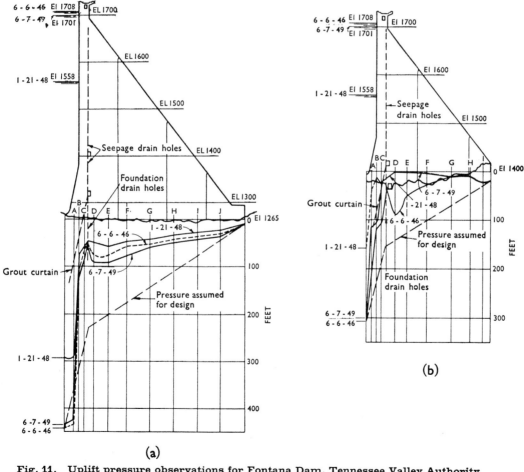

Fig. 11. Uplift pressure observations for Fontana Dam, Tennessee Valley Authority
(Reproduced from Ref. (8))

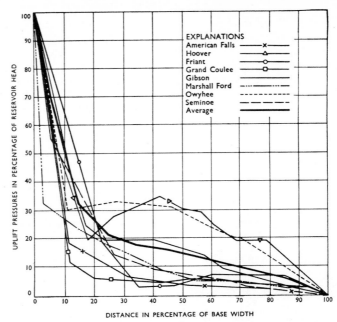

Fig. 12.   Average uplift pressures at the base of eight Bureau of Reclamation Dams
(Reproduced from Fig. 10 of Ref. (9))

be considered a good example for the theoretical analysis presented in Figs 3 and 4.   The observed uplift upstream of the drains shows no indication that the grout curtain has an important effect.

In Fig. 14, reproduced from Keener's Paper,[9] are shown the measured uplift pressures for the 726-ft-high Hoover Dam before (1938), and after (1947) extensive additional drainage and grouting operations were carried out.   The original grout curtain with holes on 5-ft centres, went to a maximum depth of 150 ft, sloping from the drainage gallery 15° from the vertical in upstream direction.   The drain holes were drilled vertical from the same gallery to a maximum depth of about 100 ft.   After the large uplift pressures developed, the following supplementary work was carried out.   A new grout curtain was made in the vertical plane of the drain holes, using and extending the existing drain holes to 400 ft deep.   A new line of drain holes was drilled from the gallery, sloping downstream at an angle of 15° to an average depth of 200 ft, with a spacing in part of 5 ft and in part of 10 ft.   Drain holes were also drilled in the powerhouse area.

From a comparison of the measured uplift pressures before and after the supplementary treatment, Fig. 14(a) and (b), one can see that the corrective measures have been fully success-ful.   Simonds[11] credits this to both the new grout curtain and the new lines of drains.   From the published details it is not possible to determine how the credit should be divided.   The low point of the pressures in Fig. 14 (b) seems to lie between observation pipes 1 and 2 which is located just about in a vertical plane placed through the lower ends of the new drainage holes.   The uplift observations just upstream and downstream of the new grout curtain, which lies in the vertical plane of the drainage gallery, show no significant effect of the grout curtain. On the other hand, Simonds also gives data on seepage measurements which would indicate that the new grout curtain has helped to reduce the rate of seepage.   From additional data supplied to the Author by the Bureau, the following information was extracted.   For approxi-mately equal reservoir elevations (El. 1180), the rate of foundation seepage from the drainage gallery in 1938 was about 200 gal/min. Starting late in 1938 and extending to 1944, the pro-gramme of supplementary work was carried out intermittently. During a few months in 1939, the rate of seepage increased sharply to about 2,000 gal/min and then dropped just as sharply to about 600 gal/min at the beginning of 1940. Much of this additional flow entered through new, deep grout holes. Inflows of 200–300 gal/min were encountered in a number of holes. Grouting against such inflow proved difficult and was finally accomplished by means of a new type of packer. From early 1940 to early 1944 the discharge diminished steadily when it reached about 200 gal/min. From 1944 to 1948 (when measurements were discon-tinued) the rate of discharge increased steadily to about 400 gal/min. The decrease in rate of flow between 1940 and 1944 was the result of the extensive additional grouting operations. The steady increase in flow since 1944 is not explained. It might be loss in efficiency of the grout due to leaching caused by hot alkaline waters which were frequently encountered in the drilling operations.

The foundation conditions at the site for the Hoover Dam were exceptionally unfavourable from the standpoint of control of seepage. Experience on this dam showed that with suffici-ently deep drain holes the uplift can be controlled satisfactorily even for such conditions. But control of rate of seepage required much more extensive grouting than the equivalent of a single row of grout holes.

MISCELLANEOUS COMMENTS ON GROUT CUT-OFFS

My overall impression from the data presented herein, and many similar cases of which I had included a number in my oral presentation, is that for the great majority of dam sites,

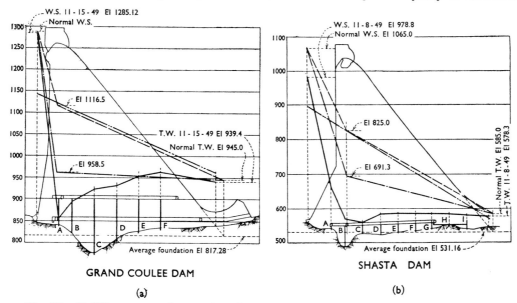

Fig. 13. Uplift pressure observations for Grand Coulee and Shasta Dams, Bureau of Reclamation

(Reproduced from Fig. 1 of Ref. (1))

——————— Measured uplift pressure.
——— · ——— Uplift pressure based on a gradient varying from full reservoir at the face of the dam to 30% of the full reservoir at the line of the drains, and from there to normal tailwater.
— — — Uplift pressure based on gradient varying from full reservoir pressure at the face of the dam to one-half the differential of normal water surface and normal tailwater at the line of drains, and from there to normal tailwater.
— · · — The original uplift design assumption.

irrespective of type of rock, strike and dip of strata, and faulting conditions, the pervious zone which requires seepage control is relatively shallow. Therefore, the relatively shallow depth of drain holes have been, by and large, reasonably effective in controlling uplift. The one outstanding exception is Hoover Dam.

The rate of seepage through the foundation for the majority of these concrete dams is small. This fact is sometimes cited as "proof" for the effectiveness of the grout curtains on these dams. What would be needed as a proof is an abundance of piezometer observations in the rock upstream and downstream of the grout curtain, at various depths, to enable one to analyse the seepage through the grout curtain. The few uplift measurements between the line of drains and the heel of concrete dams are not yet sufficient proof, although in my opinion an objective review of all available observations cannot but lead to the conclusion that a single-line grout curtain constructed before filling of a reservoir is frequently inadequate. In a few cases, extensive additional grouting with the reservoir in operation, thus permitting continuous evaluation of the effect of new grout holes, has eventually been successful.

The combination of a grout curtain and of a line of drainage holes in close proximity makes it difficult to evaluate the effectiveness of the grout curtain, unless a large number of piezometers are installed. It is much simpler to carry out an evaluation where a grout cut-off is used without drainage holes. For each case of this type which is credited in literature as a success, one could cite several instances where grouting failed to achieve the intended purpose and which, for that reason, are not publicized.

In May 1960, in the course on Engineering Geology at Harvard, Professor Terzaghi gave several lectures on grouting in which he summarized his own experience on a number of projects. With his consent I summarize in the following paragraphs his general comments on this subject and a few of his examples.

Professor Terzaghi started out by emphasizing that in many cases the owners are "penny-

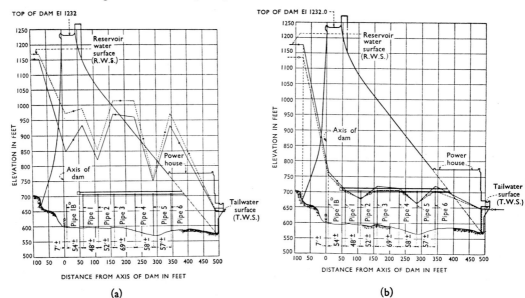

Fig. 14(a) and (b). **Uplift pressure observations for Hoover Dam, line B, Bureau of Reclamation**
(Reproduced from Fig. 13 and 14 of Ref.(9).)
In Fig. 14(a) = original Fig. 13 – "June 15, 1938" for the full drawn line; and "November 14, 1938" for the line of dashes.
In Fig. 14(b) = original Fig. 14 – "April 15, 1947" for the line of dashes, and "November 14, 1947" for the full-drawn line.

wise and pound-foolish" by spending much money on grouting and then little or nothing on the kind of observations which would clearly establish whether the grout curtain is effective. He said that if one observes small seepage, grouting is automatically given credit, whereas, in fact, one does not know whether the same flow would have occurred also without grouting, and one does not know whether one has wasted money for grouting. But when one observes excessive flow, then one knows that one has wasted one's money. Therefore, seepage observations are not sufficient to determine the effectiveness of a grout cut-off. He then described five projects for which he had insisted on accurate piezometer observations and which showed in each case that the grout curtain had little or no effect.

Terzaghi emphasized that the first requirement is to engage the most experienced and reliable grouting contractor one can find; but that one must not let him work alone. He must be constantly and closely supervised by a competent and independent engineer who also has a broad experience in grouting operations. Terzaghi pointed out that the trouble with grouting contractors, and often also engineers, is that they believe that the success of grouting can be measured by the amount of grout, or cement, that one succeeds in injecting, and he suggested that this reasoning is just as logical as when people believe that a medicine must be good because it tastes so awful. He expressed the opinion that even if all conditions are fulfilled for a satisfactory grouting job, one can still not be certain that the grouting will accomplish the intended purpose. Finally, he stated that on every project for which he had recommended grouting, the safety of the project did not hinge on the success of the grouting. He recommended grouting merely for the purpose of trying to reduce seepage losses; and he admitted that in every case it was a gamble and that some of these failed to accomplish the purpose.

In his lectures, Terzaghi discussed among a number of examples the following four cases:

Case 1.—In 1932, in connexion with his investigations for the Bou Hanifia Dam in North Africa, Terzaghi wanted to demonstrate the necessity for designing the dam such that it would be safe in case a proposed grout curtain in rock should prove ineffective. He performed laboratory tests with a diaphragm containing openings equal to 5% of the area. This diaphragm caused only very little reduction in flow and very little drop in head. Upon Terzaghi's suggestion, Dachler supplemented this investigation by a theoretical analysis[7] which is used in Fig. 8.

Case 2.—In connexion with his association with the Sasumua Dam in Africa, Terzaghi proposed to replace a grout curtain in volcanic rocks by a row of drainage wells. This suggestion was adopted, and after filling of the reservoir the total rate of seepage from the drainage wells was insignificant.*

Case 3.—The original design of an earth dam in South America included a grout curtain in jointed gneiss. Grouting tests, performed during the early construction stage, showed that the total quantity of grout which would be needed would be prohibitive in cost and time. Since loss of water by seepage would have been of relatively small importance, Terzaghi replaced the proposed grout curtain by a row of drainage wells. The total measured discharge from these wells is a small fraction of a cubic foot per second.

Case 4.—On another dam in South America, seepage developed through jointed gneiss, causing slides in downstream abutment slopes. In an effort to stop the seepage, 55 tons of cement were injected into more than 3,000 m of grout holes; but the effect of these grouting operations on the discharge of the springs was negligible. Later, when Terzaghi became connected with this project, he relied exclusively on drainage in order to cure the slide conditions.

One instructive case with which I am familiar is the 100-ft-high earth dam shown in Fig. 15.

* Karl Terzaghi, "Design and performance of the Sasumua Dam". Proc. Instn civ. Engrs, vol. 9 (Apr. 1958), p. 369.

It was built as a homogeneous compacted dam, of a residual sandy clay soil derived from underlying gneiss, with liquid limits ranging between 40 and 80.   The foundation consists of a similar residual soil, but because of its undisturbed structure it is several times more pervious than the compacted material in the dam.   The upper zone of bedrock, on an average 20 ft thick, is badly fractured and much more pervious than the overlying residual soil; but the gneiss below the fractured zone is practically impervious.   Therefore, the designer decided to make a grout cut-off through the badly fractured gneiss, continuing the cut-off well into the impervious gneiss.   For this purpose a trench, about 15 ft deep, was first dug into the residual soil and then a concrete wall was constructed which served as grouting cap, and which penetrated through the remaining thickness of the residual soil into the fractured gneiss.   The grouting was carried out by one of the world's leading grouting firms and was done with competence.   Detailed records were kept of all operations.   The holes were spaced as close as 2 ft on centres, but all in a single line.   The grout-take was high and erratic, as was to be expected.   In spite of a thorough job of grouting, we find that the piezometers which extend into the fractured rock, show a practically straight-line drop from reservoir level, at a location coinciding approximately with the upstream toe of the dam, to the downstream toe of the dam, and without the slightest indication that there might be an obstacle to seepage at the location of the grout curtain.   Similar results were observed in other cross-sections of this

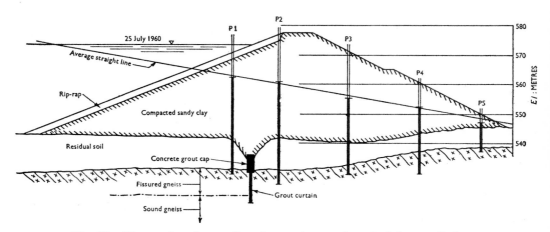

Fig. 15.   Piezometer observations in pervious rock underlying earth dam

dam.   These observations were, of course, a great shock to the designer who was convinced that the grout curtain would achieve a satisfactory impervious cut-off of the fractured rock.

Those who had implicit confidence in grouting then suggested that the seepage was probably passing through the relatively narrow, clay-filled cut-off trench, and then back into the residual soil and the fractured rock; in other words, that the seepage was bypassing the grout curtain by flowing over it.   If that were the case, the piezometric surface should be flatter on both sides of the grout curtain, and should show a steep gradient over that clay-filled trench where the flow lines would crowd through the much less pervious clay of the trench.   The observations do not support such a hypothesis.   Fortunately, the seepage losses are very small and in my opinion they do not in the slightest endanger the stability of this dam.   Also, there is not the slightest doubt in my mind that omission of this grout curtain would have resulted in a piezometric surface practically identical with the surface that has developed.

COMMENTS ON CONTROL OF SEEPAGE THROUGH ABUTMENTS OF THIN-ARCH DAMS

Unquestionably the most difficult problems of seepage control in rock are those which arise in connexion with the combination of a modern, very thin arch dam and steep rock abutments. In contrast, the wide contact areas of concrete and rock for gravity and arch-gravity dams constitute a substantial margin of safety against development of dangerous water pressures at critical locations in the rock downstream of the dam. Even if a fall-out of rock should occur on a steep abutment slope due to excessive water pressures, this would not necessarily endanger a concrete dam with a wide base. However, for a thin-arch dam the concrete-rock contact area is not wide enough to accommodate both a reliable grout cut-off consisting of three lines of grout holes, and also a satisfactory drainage system which should be located at least 20 ft downstream from the nearest line of grout holes. The stability of the rock immediately downstream of a thin-arch dam is of critical importance to the safety of such a dam.

Grouting of steep abutment slopes poses great difficulties and may easily do more harm than good. Even if the grouting is carried out after completion of the dam, the contact area of a thin-arch dam is not wide enough to really protect the rock against displacements. The removal of all undesirable rock along the abutment slopes should be done with much greater thoroughness for a thin-arch dam than for any other type of dam; but unfortunately, blasting of rock on steep slopes, no matter how carefully done, is liable to cause a system of tight joints to open up. On one dam project with which I am well acquainted, one abutment consists of intensely jointed quartzite. Test holes sloping into the abutment at 45° were water-tested without pressure, using only gravity flow; and for that condition were found to be tight. Just as soon as the customary water pressures were applied, joints opened up and large water losses were observed. After very light blasting was started, to prepare the contact surface with a clay core, all test holes which were originally tight began to develop large water losses. After these observations all removal of rock from this abutment by blasting was prohibited.

Perhaps there is no satisfactory way of making a reliable grout cut-off in steep abutments for a thin-arch dam. In that case the second line of defence, drainage, becomes the only line of defence. How can we make certain that drainage will provide positive protection against all possible combinations of geologic details and prevent the build-up of dangerous water pressures in the abutments downstream of the dam? We can, of course, provide several lines of drainage holes downstream of the dam. But then the question arises how to prevent freezing of the outlets of the drain holes, and of the entire rock face for that matter, during cold winters? Rock-falls are a common occurrence in spring when the infiltration of thawing water builds up high pressures in joints behind the frozen zone. For protection against such conditions we would be forced to resort to a system of "internal drainage", by means of tunnels and shafts, but which would require blasting which in turn may be very harmful.

Another possibility would be to widen substantially the thickness of the thin-arch dam as it approaches the rock. This would go a long way towards improving the stability of the abutments. In any case, I believe that I am not exaggerating the difficulties of achieving positive control of the water pressures in the steep abutments for thin-arch dams. When the geologic conditions are of a character which cannot ensure positively safe control of water pressures in the rock downstream of the dam, then a thin-arch dam should not be considered for that site. Surely, if the structural designer of such a dam had to deal with similar uncertainties concerning the integrity of the arch itself, he would never dream of building such a structure.

CONCLUSIONS AND RECOMMENDATIONS

(1) The effects of seepage through rock foundations and abutments on the safety for most types of dams can be controlled reliably and economically by means of comprehensive drainage measures. For most concrete gravity and arch-gravity dams, even the usual relatively shallow line of drain holes has been reasonably effective for controlling uplift pressures. This control could be improved and made more positive, also for very unfavourable geologic conditions, by using much deeper drain holes. The effect of a deep line of drain holes on the uplift can be predicted with reasonable accuracy by means of formulas given in the Paper.

(2) Probably a great majority of the single-line grout curtains in rock foundations and abutments of dams that were carried out in the past were relatively ineffective in reducing seepage losses, and they could not be relied upon for purposes of stability analysis. There is an urgent need for comprehensive observations on the effectiveness of such grout curtains. Some of the existing concrete dams would offer an opportunity to carry out such investigations at relatively small cost, by installing numerous piezometers between the heel of the dam and the line of drain holes, both sides of the grout curtain, along the base of the dam, and in the rock at various depths below the base.

(3) There is a need for more reliable methods to determine in advance whether and where grouting is needed. The usual geological investigations and "water tests" in drill holes may be actually misleading. They are of value only in conjunction with comprehensive testing for mass permeability of the rock by pumping from or feeding water into a series of drill holes and by observing the effects in numerous observation wells. For concrete gravity and arch-gravity dams one should test in this manner systematically the upstream third of the foundation area, and to a depth at least equal to one-half the height of the dam. Excessively pervious zones for which grouting will be considered necessary or desirable, may require three rows of closely spaced grout holes, or equivalent clusters of grout holes, in order to create the necessary width of grouted rock mass. (*Note:* Depending on their location, all exploratory holes should also be utilized either as permanent observation wells, as drainage holes, or as grout holes.)

(4) On some projects the rate of seepage could be effectively reduced by more economical means than by grout curtains. For a concrete dam with a reasonably wide base and for abutments with gentle slopes, one could construct an impervious earth fill against the lower portion of the upstream face of the dam. To prevent opening up of a crack between earth and concrete, it would be helpful to slope the lower part of the upstream face of the dam such as, for example, at Shasta Dam, Fig. 13(b). If the dam is already in operation, one could try blanketing an area adjacent to the dam by hydraulic dispersion of suitable soils in the reservoir just upstream of the dam. Another possibility is to move the line of drainage holes further downstream. It is customary to locate the drains approximately 10% of the base width from the upstream face of the dam. This distance could readily be doubled. When the depth and spacing of the drain holes is so selected that the uplift will be positively controlled, the designer would be justified in reducing his assumptions for design uplift pressures below those currently assumed, so that moving the drains further downstream would not require an increase in volume of the dam.

(5) In contrast to gravity and arch-gravity dams, it is an extremely difficult problem to develop seepage control measures in steep abutments for a thin-arch dam which will ensure the safety of such a structure for the worst conceivable combination of geologic details. Of those dam sites which would be entirely satisfactory for a high gravity or arch-gravity dam, only a small percentage could be developed with the same assurance of safety for a modern thin-arch dam. The treatment of steep abutments poses special difficulties also because blasting and grouting operations can easily cause more harm than good. Even a comprehensive drainage system may provide insufficient protection against development of dangerous hydrostatic pressures in the rock downstream of a thin-arch dam.

REFERENCES

[1] U.S. BUREAU OF RECLAMATION, DECEMBER 1960. "Design criteria for concrete gravity and arch dams." *Denver, Colorado. Engng Monograph, No. 19, p. 4.*

[2] EMMONS, W. F. Chief Design Engineer, Tennessee Valley Authority, stated in a letter to the writer dated 13 January, 1961, T.V.A.'s present design assumptions as follows:
"1. The intensity of uplift pressure is assumed as full headwater pressure at the upstream face, full tailwater pressure at the downstream face, full tailwater pressure plus one-fourth the difference between headwater and tailwater pressure at the line of drains, with intensity varying uniformly between these points.
"2. The uplift pressure is assumed to act on 100% of the base area."

[3] TENNESSEE VALLEY AUTHORITY TECHNICAL REPORT No. 24 (1952). "Civil and structural design," *T.V.A., Washington,* vol. 1.

[4] BRAHTZ, J. H. A., 1936. "Pressures due to percolating water and their influence upon stresses in hydraulic structures." *Trans. 2nd Congr. Large Dams, Washington,* 5 : 43–71.

[5] TENNESSEE VALLEY AUTHORITY TECHNICAL MONOGRAPH No. 67 (1950). "Measurements of the structural behaviour of Norris and Hiawassee Dams." *T.V.A., Knoxville, Tennessee,* Fig. 36.

[6] MUSKAT, M., 1937. "The flow of homogeneous fluids through porous bodies." *McGraw-Hill, N.Y.,* Section 9.8.

[7] DACHLER, R., 1936. "Grundwasserströmung" ("The flow of water in ground"). *Springer, Vienna,* p. 82.

[8] TENNESSEE VALLEY AUTHORITY TECHNICAL MONOGRAPH No. 69 (1953). "Measurements of the structural behaviour of Fontana Dam." *T.V.A., Knoxville, Tennessee,*

[9] KEENER, K. B., 1951. "Uplift pressures in concrete dams." *Trans. Amer. Soc. civ. Engrs,* 116 : 1128.

[10] RIEGEL, R. M., 1951. Discussion of Ref. 9. *Trans. Amer. Soc. civ. Engrs,* 116 : 1239, Fig. 17.

[11] SIMONDS, A. W., 1953. "Final foundation treatment at Hoover Dam." *Trans. Amer. Soc. civ. Engrs,* 118 : 78–99.

[12] TERZAGHI, K., Discussion on paper by Julian Hinds on "Upward pressures under dams," p. 1563, 1929. *ASCE Transactions of the American Society of Civil Engineers.*

[13] TERZAGHI, K., 1929. "Effect of minor geological details on the safety of dams." *American Institute of Mining and Metallurgical Engineers.* Technical Publication 215, p. 30.

FIELD MEASUREMENTS IN SOIL MECHANICS

L. F. COOLING, D.Sc., Assoc.I.C.E.

When I was invited by the British National Committee to give this second Rankine Lecture, I must confess that my reactions were of a mixed nature. While I was naturally very gratified at the honour this invitation conferred on me, I was also conscious of the fact that the task of maintaining the standard expected in these lectures was not an easy one and would be a considerable strain on my capacities. However, I was fortified into accepting the honour by the remembrance of the many occasions in the past when this Society had shown great indulgence to honest if somewhat pedestrian endeavour.

On this occasion, I thought it would be of value to review the position in one broad aspect of the subject, to see how far we have travelled, what remains to be done, and in which direction we should go in future development. Such an exercise could usefully be carried out on many aspects of soil mechanics (all of them important), but the one I have chosen for this talk is that of field measurements on full-scale structures and its rôle in the application of soil mechanics to civil engineering problems. I have made this choice for various reasons; first, because I think it is appropriate to a Rankine Lecture, for, although in soil mechanics we tend to regard Rankine as a theorist there is no doubt that he had a full appreciation of practical considerations and the difficulties of applying theory to soil problems. In his Manual of Civil Engineering, Rankine wrote: "The properties of earth with respect to adhesion and friction are so variable, that the engineer should never trust to tables or to information obtained from books to guide him in designing earthworks, when he has it in his power to obtain the necessary data either by observation of existing earthworks in the same stratum or by experiment." Later in the same section he wrote: "There is a mathematical theory of the combined action of friction and adhesion in earth; but for want of precise experimental data, its practical utility is doubtful." If we interpret the term "precise experimental data" to include reliable field measurements on actual structures, then my theme is obviously in line with Rankine's thinking. My second reason is that the subject is of considerable importance in its own right for the future development of soil mechanics, and anyone who has made a study of Terzaghi's writings will have been struck by his insistence on the urgent need for taking reliable field observations. My third reason is that my colleagues and I at the Building Research Station have been particularly interested in this aspect of soil mechanics and have, from time to time over the past 25 years, carried out a number of investigations involving field measurements of various types on full-scale structures.

FIELD MEASUREMENTS IN SOIL MECHANICS

INTRODUCTION

The art of dealing with soils in civil engineering works resides largely in the skill, experience, and judgement of the individual engineer and in his knowledge of precedents. This is still perhaps the decisive part of practical design and construction, but as the science of soil mechanics grows the contributions it can make, particularly in adding more precision to design

methods, become more and more important.   While it would be generally agreed that substantial advances have been made, it is also necessary to appreciate the limitations of the
methods developed and it is in defining these limitations that field measurements are essential.

Many of these limitations arise from the fact that we are dealing with geological deposits,
materials which have been laid down by nature.   Individual soil strata vary in their properties
from point to point and at any given site the geological structure may be more or less complex.

As you know, the current procedure in tackling soil problems is to put down boreholes to
procure "undisturbed" samples and to gain some idea of the pattern of subsurface strata;
then by field tests or by tests on the samples in the laboratory to obtain the salient soil properties and their degree of variation.   These are then used in a design analysis appropriate
to the particular problem.   Design methods vary a good deal in their degree of reliability,
depending on the background of knowledge and on the complexity of the factors governing
the soil action involved.   In using any design method the actual boring records and test
results need to be replaced by a "simplified" profile and "average" values of the soil characteristics.   This radical simplification admits a margin for interpretation and the more complex
the geological conditions the wider the margin becomes.   The nature and importance of these
errors can only be learned by observations and measurements on full-scale structures.   For
this reason field measurements are necessary both from a practical point of view and for the
development of design techniques.   In his Opening Address to the Rotterdam Conference,
Terzaghi stated that "Further progress depends chiefly on the improvement of our methods
for measurement in the field, on the scope and quality of the field observations and on the
adaptation of our methods of subsoil exploration to practical requirements".

Field work in general is more important in soil mechanics than in other branches of civil
engineering; I had, therefore, better define more closely what I mean by field measurement.
In my talk this evening I do not propose to deal with field tests to measure the properties of
soils "in situ"; nor shall I deal with failures of engineering structures for, while these have
been extremely useful in developing design techniques that ensure stability, such studies are
of the "post-mortem" type and are of little value for assessing the forces and strains in a
stable structure.   I shall concern myself with measurements made on full-scale structures
which, by giving an insight into the behaviour of soils in practice can further the development
of what might be called "diagnostic techniques".

SCOPE AND PURPOSE

Field measurements can yield valuable information on a very wide range of problems and
the scope of such measurements needs to cover a number of different types of observation
(Cooling, 1945).   Among these may be mentioned settlement measurements on structures,
lateral movements of earthworks, observations of pore-water pressures, and measurements of
loads and pressures on earth-retaining structures.

The purpose of recording full-scale behaviour may vary according to the type of problem
and on the complexity of the site conditions.   As already mentioned, the degree of reliability
of available design methods varies a good deal with the type of problem.   For fairly simple
site conditions involving a problem for which a well-developed method of analysis exists, the
purpose of field measurements may be to check the degree of validity of the theory.   In other
problems where the present theory is rather crude or very tenuously related to practice, the
purpose of field measurements may be to develop a better working hypothesis.

Where geological site conditions are complex, it may not be possible to give, prior to construction, a good quantitative performance forecast.   In such cases a knowledge of the
behaviour of soils gained from a background of soil mechanics experience may be helpful in
determining in advance of construction, the type and location of a potential source of trouble.

If the probable mode of failure or the probable movements can be even broadly anticipated, it is often possible to arrange for observations during construction which will reveal at an early stage whether anything untoward is happening and so enable appropriate measures to be taken before it is too late. In such cases field measurements form an essential part of that powerful approach to soil mechanics problems which had been called by Terzaghi (1961) the "observational procedure".

In addition to its use in a "learn as you go" observational procedure and for the purpose of checking and improving existing theories, field measurement is also important in those problems where the behaviour of a structure is mainly determined by varying environmental conditions. They include such problems as the creep of hillsides, the seasonal shrinkage and swelling of clay soils and the effects of industrial processes on the foundations of the structure in which they are housed. In such cases field measurements are essential to discover the nature and extent of the problem, to reveal the important factors involved and so permit the formulation of a rational design approach.

When the field measurements are made for the purpose of establishing a link between theory and practice, it is important that, on the one hand, there should be an adequate exploration of the soil conditions at the site, accompanied by sufficient tests to determine the characteristics of the important soil strata for use in the theory; on the other hand, the programme of field observations must be carefully planned and made appropriate to the particular problem under consideration and the methods adopted must be sufficiently reliable to keep the margin for their interpretation reasonably small.

FIELD TECHNIQUES

The wide range of problems calls for a variety of techniques to obtain the required observational data. This has necessitated not only the adaptation of well-known methods but also the development of new techniques and specialized instrumentation. For instance, the settlement of structures can be measured by well-known methods. The measurement of pore-water pressure, though fairly simple in principle, has required the development of new techniques to overcome the difficulties met with in field application. In certain cases electrical instruments have been developed.

To measure earth pressures, both the direct approach by means of soil pressure cells and the indirect approach by measurement of strains and loads in the structure which supports the soil, have required the development of methods which can measure accurately very small strains. A variety of instruments is available for this purpose but most have been designed to function under laboratory conditions. Many do not face up to the stringent conditions met with in field work, so special techniques need to be used.

Field work requires robust, stable instruments which are not easily damaged and which can be conveniently installed and read without interfering with constructional operations. No delicate manipulations should be expected of the operator because he may have to work in awkward positions, exposed to extremes of weather and in bad light. Since repeat tests can rarely be made and a failure or inadequate functioning of the odd instrument is a hazard which must be taken into account, reliance should not be placed on too few instruments. It is often an advantage when using specialized techniques to take check readings by an independent set of observations using another form of instrumentation, even if the second method is rather crude. Such results should at least "give the street you are in" and can lend a good deal of confidence to the more accurate measurements given by the special technique.

The planning of a field programme is most important and much could be written on the subject but I will content myself with a few general comments. First, it is necessary to have clearly in mind the purpose for which the work is being carried out so that the observations can be tailored to the particular problem and purpose in mind. Plan early so that careful consideration can be given to details before the urgency of the construction period is imposed.

Do not attempt too much; an elaborate programme is not necessarily the most rewarding. The reliability of the measurements should be the overriding consideration. Since most field measurements need to be carried out over a period of time, they have to be arranged systematically so that the readings can give a sufficiently connected picture covering any critical periods and continued as long as necessary. In addition, some thought should be given to the protection of instruments exposed to the many hazards on a construction site, and in this connexion it is often an advantage to explain to site personnel the broad object of the work. Finally, the recording of the measurements is most important; they should be clearly set out and the copying of results from the field book into the record book should never be unduly delayed. Field books are apt to become difficult to decipher and their interpretation may become a source of uncertainty.

To discuss field techniques in a little more detail I propose to describe examples of field work involving three types of measurements—settlements, pore-water pressures, and earth pressures. It will only be possible to make brief reference to a few examples of each type but I hope to bring out such considerations as: (a) method; (b) purpose of work; (c) value of the information obtained; (d) the need for future work.

TYPES OF MEASUREMENT

A good deal of field work has been carried out in this country but I hope you will forgive me if I confine myself to examples with which we at the Building Research Station have been concerned; this enables me to speak, if not with first-hand experience of all the details, at least with second-hand experience of having been responsible for the work. In quoting these examples, I am of course vastly indebted to my past and present colleagues and to the many engineers and organizations who have not only afforded facilities for the work but have actively collaborated with the site work.

(a) Settlements of structures

The technique of measuring the settlements of a structure is fairly straightforward and the value of such records both from the theoretical and practical point of view is generally recognized.

The usual method of measuring settlements is by means of a precise telescopic level and it involves determining from time to time the level of observation plugs built into the structure at suitable points in relation to a reference datum. The constancy of the level of the reference datum is, of course, of fundamental importance especially if theories are to be checked. In a few cases an easily accessible datum can be placed on a rock outcrop or on deep piles or shafts. Normally, however, it needs to be specially prepared. In such a case the reference datum should be located as deep as possible away from all possible disturbances. Fig. 1 illustrates the general features of two types of datum point which are commonly used.

Two separate datum points should be installed and observations on their relative levels can then be used to check their stability. Experience has shown that there is a risk of a datum point becoming buried in the course of tidying up the site after construction or during subsequent use of the area. For this reason accurate co-ordinates should be taken of the position of these points, say, with reference to corners of the building, so that it will be possible to find them should they become covered up.

It is sometimes convenient to locate the reference datum beneath the structure and to have observation points on the building in the same vertical line. A screw micrometer or dial gauge can then be used to measure the movements directly and thereby higher accuracy of measurements can be obtained. This was used for observations on Waterloo Bridge (see Fig. 2). The top protecting tube was built into the pier, and the datum rod, the bottom end of which was located at some 40 ft below the pier bottom, came up through a sleeve pipe and the relative movements were measured with a dial micrometer. This method has also been

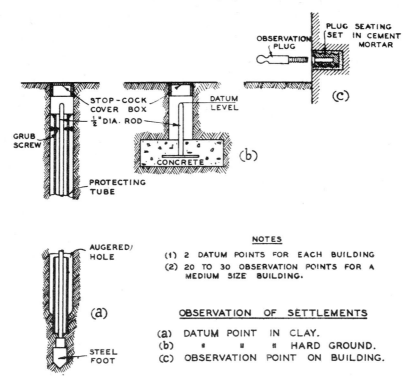

NOTES

(1) 2 DATUM POINTS FOR EACH BUILDING
(2) 20 TO 30 OBSERVATION POINTS FOR A
     MEDIUM SIZE BUILDING.

OBSERVATION OF SETTLEMENTS

(a) DATUM POINT IN CLAY.
(b)   "   "   " HARD GROUND.
(c) OBSERVATION POINT ON BUILDING.

Fig. 1. Settlement observations—typical datum points

found useful for accurate readings on small houses, when the measuring point can be located
in a cavity of the wall and a locked panel will protect it from interference. A disadvantage is
that a datum point is needed for each observation point.

The measurements at Waterloo Bridge were taken by the engineers (Buckton and Cuerel,
1943) and Fig. 2 gives the sort of information which was obtained. Apart from the datum,
it shows the sequence of soil strata, a time-loading diagram and a time-settlement record. It
also shows results of observations on the heave of the clay at formation level as the result of
excavation. This is a problem on which few observations have been taken and in view of its
importance I should perhaps emphasize the need for many more records of this kind (Serota
and Jennings, 1959).

To begin with, it may be of interest to indicate in broad outline important simple relationships which have been demonstrated by settlement observations. One example concerns the
Chelmsford Gasholder investigation described by Meyerhof (1951) and illustrated in Figs 3
and 4. This is a good example of a case where under a uniform loading of about 1 ton/sq. ft,
serious differential settlements resulted due to the variable thickness of a soft stratum underlying the structure. Another relates to a grain silo at Oxford (Cooling, 1948), illustrated in
Fig. 5. Here it will be noticed that the variations in the grain load are closely reflected in the
movements of the foundation.

The purpose for which a settlement study is carried out will, of couse, vary with the site
and problem. If site conditions are fairly straightforward, observations of settlement, apart
from confirming that the movements are within the limits that the structure can withstand,
may have their chief value as a means of checking existing theories and indicating the limits
of their application. From the time Terzaghi published his theory of consolidation of clay

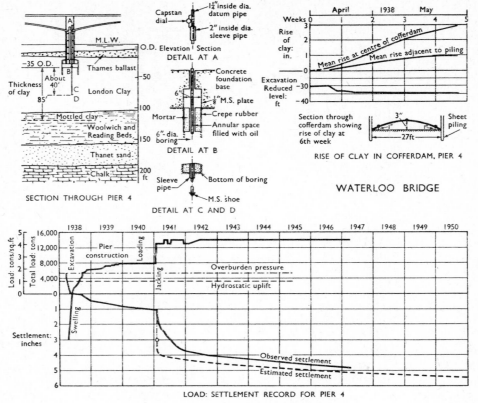

Fig. 2.   Observations on Waterloo Bridge

and demonstrated that on the basis of this theory and that using the results of tests on soil samples, a quantitative forecast of the settlements of buildings underlain by a clay layer could be made, the value of reliable records of observed settlements on actual buildings had been enhanced.   Those case records which permit a valid comparison between computed and observed settlements have played a major part in indicating the degree of applicability of theoretical methods of analysis and in pointing the way to improvements in the theoretical approach.   In recent years a number of Papers describing settlement studies on particular structures have been published and a survey of comparisons between calculated and observed settlements of structures on clay was given by MacDonald and Skempton (1955).   Fig. 6 is based on results given in this Paper and shows the agreement between calculated and observed net final settlements for eighteen case records, six of which related to measurements with which B.R.S. was concerned, most of them when Skempton was with us.   These show that current methods of calculating net final settlements give results of adequate accuracy for engineering purposes.   Other conclusions arrived at in the Paper were: (*a*) the current method of computing immediate settlement was correct in principle although attention needed to be directed towards improved determination of Young's modulus in soft clays; (*b*) the rate of settlement is usually underestimated and there was a need for further evaluation of three-dimensional consolidation theory.   Full-scale observations including pore-pressure measurements as well as settlement records would give valuable information on item (*b*).

From the point of view of structural damage, it is the differential settlement which is of

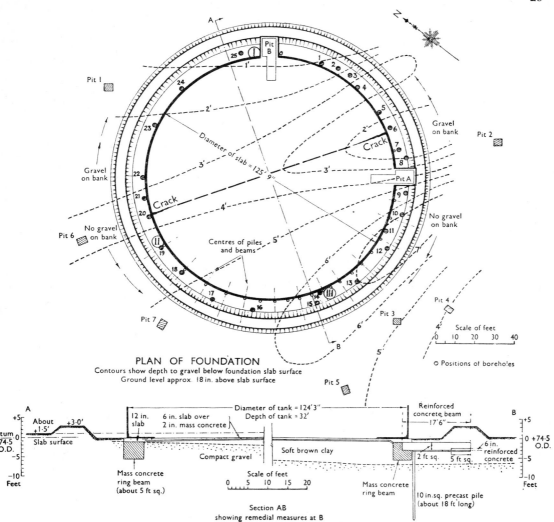

PLAN OF FOUNDATION
Contours show depth to gravel below foundation slab surface
Ground level approx. 18 in. above slab surface

Fig. 3. Chelmsford Gasholder

prime importance and consequently the general arrangement of observation points in a structure should be such as to give a fairly clear picture of the pattern and contours of differential settlements.   Skempton and MacDonald (1956) gave a comprehensive survey and analysis of existing data on the distortion of some ninety-eight buildings and established tentative values for damage limits in terms of angular distortion and in terms of maximum and differential settlements.   This permitted them to suggest allowable distortions as a basis for design for certain types of structure.

In a practical appraisal of the results of a theoretical settlement analysis it is important to be able to indicate the permissible distortion which a structure can withstand.   As is well known, the stiffness of a structure determines how, and to what extent, differential settlements can occur and important information which is required is the magnitude of the stresses occurring in the structure.   Settlement observations would, therefore, be much more valuable

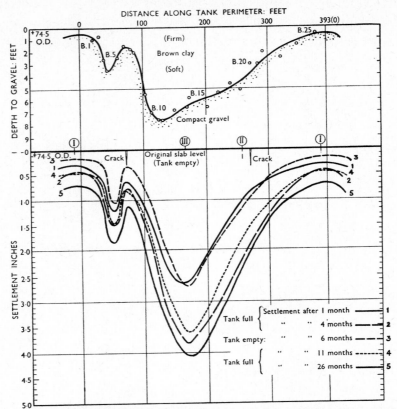

Fig. 4.   Chelmsford Gasholder—relation between settlement and depth to gravel

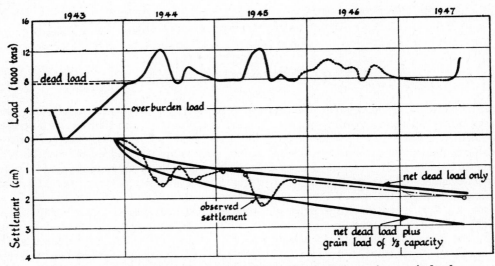

Fig. 5.   Oxford grain silo.   Response of settlement to varying grain load

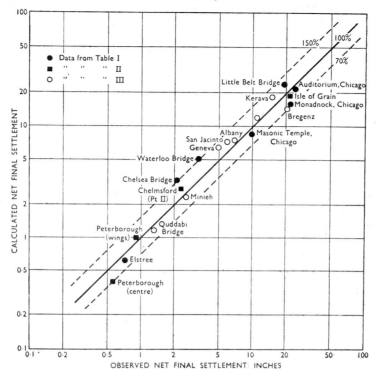

Fig. 6. **Comparison of calculated and observed net final settlements**

if they were linked with the measurement of stresses and strains in different parts of the structure. One such investigation has been carried out by B.R.S. on the Government office block in Whitehall Gardens (Wood and Mainstone, 1955), but many further comparisons between estimated and observed foundation movements and the corresponding strains and displacements in buildings are required before this difficult problem can begin to be resolved.

Incidentally, a water level system was employed for recording differential settlements in this building. This method was thought to be more convenient within the confines of the basement and although the accuracy of measurement was adequate, certain difficulties were encountered. One important source of error was found to be due to air pressure differences resulting from air conditioning in the building. For instance, near a large meeting hall, differences up to about 5 mm were observed when the doors to the hall were opened. This difficulty can be overcome by having a continuous air line connecting the tops of the wall water gauges and the reservoir.

In addition to the problems concerned with the settlement of buildings as a result of structural load there are problems, especially with clay soils, where the ground can move either as a result of seasonal change in weather conditions or due to industrial processes. A number of investigations carried out by B.R.S. on structures such as boiler houses, brick kilns, etc., founded on clay have shown the extent of settlement due to heat transmitted to the ground and have pointed the way to foundations designs which avoid this trouble (Cooling and Ward, 1948); similarly with the problem of frost-heave under cold storage rooms (Cooling and Ward, 1944). The effect of the seasonal movement of clay soils on shallow foundations is a world-wide problem which manifests itself in different ways according to the climate. Field observations in many parts of the world are helping to solve the problem. In semi-arid regions swelling of the clay under the foundations has given rise to structural damage whereas in Great Britain most trouble is experienced due to shrinkage.   The seasonal movements of both roads and houses due to the drying effect of nearby trees and vegetation has also been the subject of study at B.R.S. and at the Road Research Laboratory, and a number of Papers have been written on this subject (Ward, 1948; Croney and Ward, 1948).   However, B.R.S. have recently had occasion to make observations on two structures which exhibited long-term heave of the foundations due to wetting of desiccated clays.   These sites had previously supported the growth of large forest trees, and the time required to reach a new equilibrium has proved to be much longer than anticipated.

One was the case of a terrace block of cottages, single-storey, brick-built of 11-in. cavity wall construction.   It was built at Windsor on London Clay in 1952 and cracks had appeared after 2 years and continued to increase in size over the subsequent 4 years.   In 1958 we at the Station were asked to investigate what the architect thought was a stubborn case of settlement. A study of the site plan and aerial photographs taken before construction showed that two large elm trees had existed on the site near one end of the cottages.   Reference points were then fixed in the building and observations of movement made with reference to two datums 20 ft deep and about 50 ft from the building.   In the course of a year the observations showed that points near where the trees had been, had risen 1 cm, while points at the far end of the terrace remote from the trees had scarcely moved (Fig. 7).

The second structure was a larger one, a three-storey block 140 ft long and 37 ft wide built on a shrinkable boulder clay at Garston.   Several well-established oak trees, about 8 ft in girth, were felled and removed in November 1958.   The building was completed in July 1959 and levels have been taken since the start of the construction.   These have shown that while in other parts of the building slight settlement has occurred, in the region where the trees had been there was a rise of about 1·25 cm; this area is still rising and the movement is continuing at a rate of about 1 mm every 2 months.

In considering future work in the broad field of settlement of structures a number of problems come to mind where more full-scale observations are still urgently needed to aid their solution.   I should like to mention a few.

In the case of structures founded on deep layers of sand, reliable settlement theory is lacking and there is a need for a systematic semi-empirical approach.   To give opportunities

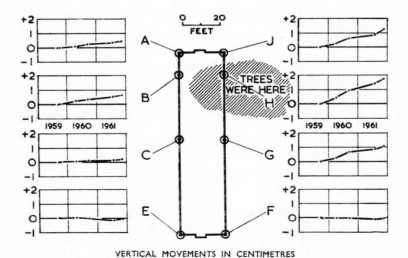

VERTICAL MOVEMENTS IN CENTIMETRES

Fig. 7.   Rise of foundations due to wetting of desiccated clay

Fig. 8.   Prototype load cell (14 in. dia.)

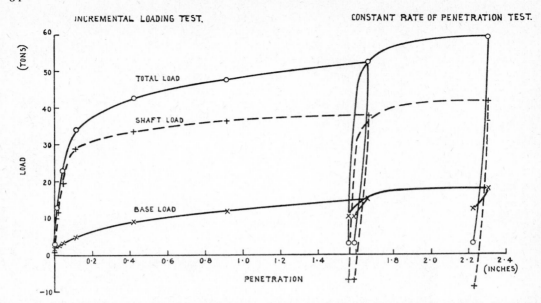

Fig. 9. Loading tests on a bored cast–in–place pile. The total load on the pile, the load on the base, and by difference the load carried by the shaft in skin friction plotted against the downward movement of the pile head in two successive loading tests

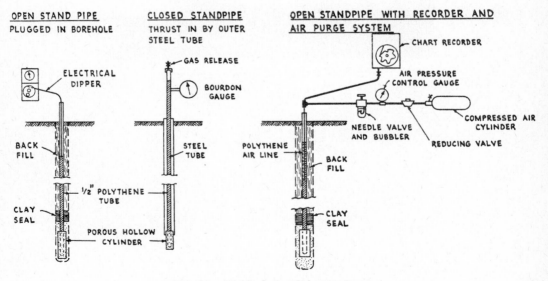

Fig. 10. Typical standpipe systems

for improvement of the design hypotheses more settlement observations on heavily loaded structures founded over sand need to be obtained.

Another problem is that of building on reclaimed land and on fills such as those resulting from open-cast mining. If measurements were taken over a period of time to record the progress of "self-consolidation" of made-ground after placing, the problem of how long it should be left before building is undertaken and the design of the proposed structures could be more confidently tackled. Mention may also be made of problems due to mining subsidence. Systematic observations of the movements of both ground and structures in mining areas are needed and the possibilities presented by the use of light flexible structures (Lacey and Swain, 1957) could be further investigated.

Another occasion when reliable full-scale measurements of settlement are likely to be useful is when a new form of foundation design is adopted; for example, the use of large

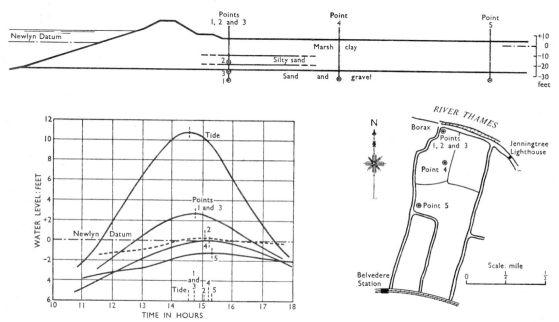

Fig. 11.   Variation of ground-water pressure in underlying gravel alongside the Thames Estuary

cylinder bored piles for the foundations of new tall buildings in London introduces many new problems. When the foundation comprises a combination of bored piles and basement raft, it is not possible to assess how much is carried by the bored piles and how much by the raft. There is, at present, no sound basis for the theoretical estimation of the probable settlement of such buildings. It is therefore very encouraging to note that in a number of these cases settlement observations have been put in train. We shall all look forward to seeing these results put on record and published. In particular I think measurements of the tilting of tall buildings would be very useful.

In this connexion I should like to mention some further work which is being carried out by the B.R.S. in conjunction with the Institution's Committee on Deep Bored Cylinder Foundations. It does not involve field measurements on a full-scale structure but is concerned with the field study of an element of the structural foundation, namely, the bored cylinder with an enlarged base. Special full-scale loading tests are to be carried out in an attempt to find what part of the load is carried by the shaft and what by the enlarged base and how the proportion varies with the settlement. Laboratory small-scale model tests have given an indication of the mechanism involved and these are being followed up by full-scale tests. A special load cell has been developed for interposing between the foot of the shaft and the base of the pile to measure the load coming on to the base. The total load is measured either by a proving ring or by special jacks. Fig. 8 shows a small prototype load cell consisting of two stiff end plates between which are placed eight small steel cylinders fitted with resistance wire gauges. These are read in groups of four to assess eccentricity of loading and the results are added arithmetically to give the aggregate load on the base of the pile. For the full-scale tests larger diameter load cells are being constructed. So far only preliminary tests for the purpose of trying out the prototype load cell have been completed and these related to a bored pile 15 in. dia., 26 ft long, with a base of the same diameter as the shaft, but it may be of interest to indicate the results obtained (Fig. 9). These show that a large proportion of the load was carried by the shaft especially at small settlements. The first part of the test was performed by incremental loading, the pile being allowed to come to virtual equilibrium before, increasing the load. At a penetration of 1·7 in. the adhesion factor α for the shaft load was 0·34 of the average shear strength and the end bearing $N_c = 7\cdot7$. The load was removed and the pile was then pushed in at a constant rate of penetration for a further 0·6 in. giving a final value for $\alpha = 0\cdot38$ and $N_c = 9\cdot2$.

(b) Pore-water pressures

One of the principal features of modern soil mechanics is the significance attached to the influence of pore-water pressure on the mechanical behaviour of soils. The recent Pore Pressure Conference held here in 1960 (Conference on pore pressure and suction in soils), in addition to discussions of a theoretical nature, included many Papers describing field measurements of pore pressure and clearly showed that many engineers appreciated the practical importance of measurements of this kind. However, a brief review of the problem may help to emphasize the value of this kind of work.

The measurement of pore-water pressures may be required for a number of purposes. First it should be emphasized that such measurements form an essential part of a site investigation since a knowledge of the pore-water pressures in the natural ground prior to construction may point to the need for special action in design or construction. This is particularly the case in relation to the excavation and installation of deep foundations when ground-water pressures are likely to be high. Appropriate measures to deal with water inflow and the avoidance of buoyancy effects and "blows" in the excavation can then be arranged. A critical situation may also arise if an impermeable stratum covers more permeable beds below holding water under artesian pressure. In such cases "relief" wells penetrating into the permeable layer to reduce the pressure have proved useful on numerous occasions (McHaffie, 1938; Ward, 1957).

Pore pressure measurements are a valuable guide in seepage problems. While theoretical flow-nets for steady flow conditions may be drawn, conditions in the practical case may be difficult to assess since these may be affected by even minor geological features and hence it is often necessary to check values of pore-water pressure by field measurements at selected points. The First Rankine Lecture, Casagrande (1961) gave many examples of the value of pore-pressure readings in seepage problems connected with dams and made a point of emphasizing the need for more observations of this type. Observations during a controlled drawdown test at Glen Shira dam were described in a Paper by Paton and Semple (1960).

Perhaps the most important use that has been made of pore-pressure measurements is in connexion with fine-pored soils, silts and clays, where they have been applied as a means of control during construction. With such soils, economic design may demand that the stability of the structure shall be dependent upon an increase in shear strength during the construction

period.   The most convenient way of inferring how the shear strength is increasing with consolidation is to measure the pore-water pressure at critical positions in the job and to follow
systematically the way the pore pressure dissipates with time.

Pore-water pressures may be determined by measuring the hydrostatic height of water
in a lined borehole or standpipe which is open at the top to the atmosphere, or by various
types of piezometer and hydrostatic pressure cells (Cooling, 1955).   The vertical standpipe
is the simplest method and three variants of the system are illustrated in Fig. 10.   In order
to ensure that a correct reading is being obtained, it is essential to stop seepage along the outside of the pipe and the space between the standpipe and the wall of the hole must be adequately sealed above the point.   Practical techniques using puddle clay, bentonite mixtures,
or sometimes cement mixtures have been developed for this purpose.   The hole is then
back-filled to the surface.   The level of the water inside the polythene tube is measured by
the means of a flexible electric cable which is lowered inside the tube until contact with the
water surface is registered by means of an ohmmeter (Casagrande, 1949).   In certain cases
it is found more convenient to push a porous cylinder into soft ground by means of a small
steel tube surrounding a polythene tube.   In some cases the open standpipe is converted into
a closed system by connecting the upper end of the polythene tube to a Bourdon gauge or
mercury manometer.   This is convenient when pore pressures are high and would need a tube
reaching well above ground surface to act as an open standpipe.   The air purge system
illustrated in Fig. 10 has also been used and is convenient for obtaining continuous records of
standpipe levels as required, for instance, in sites adjacent to tidal waters.

A typical example of results obtained is illustrated in Fig. 11 which relates to a site in
the marshland adjoining the Thames Estuary (Cooling and Marsland, 1953).   The marsh clay
was underlain by a layer of sandy gravel and measurements were taken to see how the pore
pressure in this layer responded to variations in the tidal level.   Points to be noted are that
the tidal response decreases with the distance inland; that there is a measurable response
even at $\frac{1}{2}$ mile inland; and that the time lag in the peak value of the response increases slightly
with the distance inland.

While the vertical standpipe is the simplest method to use, it is only appropriate under
conditions which permit easy access to the top of the pipe for taking observations and where
sufficient time is available for equilibrium to be established.

A closed system using twin tube piezometers is particularly useful for observations in
connexion with the construction of earth dams.   One of the first investigations in which
B.R.S. used this system was in connexion with the construction of the earth dam for the Usk
Reservoir (Sheppard and Aylen, 1957).   When the fill had reached the required level, shallow
trenches were dug across the surface and piezometers (type A, Fig. 15) placed at selected
points.   The connecting tubes were carried along the trench to a gauge house at the toe of the
dam.   One Bourdon gauge was used for each piezometer point.   This investigation was
initiated as a research project but the results turned out to be of considerable practical significance.   During the first season's construction 40 ft of boulder clay fill was placed and it was
observed that very high pore pressures were recorded.   During the winter months, the placing
of fill was stopped and although some dissipation of pore pressure occurred it was very slow
(Fig. 12).   These high pore pressures gave cause for concern.   Consideration was therefore
given to the need to modify the design of the dam, and Professor Skempton and Dr Bishop
were called in to advise.   A number of open-ended pipes were installed in other parts of the
bank, and these confirmed the gauge measurements.   However, it was interesting to note
that this simple direct method of measurement brought home the picture much more vividly
to the engineers who were most impressed to see the water rise in the pipes to a level well above
the top of the fill.   As a result of these measurements, together with laboratory tests and
analyses, a modification was made to the design by placing filter blankets consisting of a layer
of crushed rock sandwiched between two layers of sandy clay.   This enabled the rate of

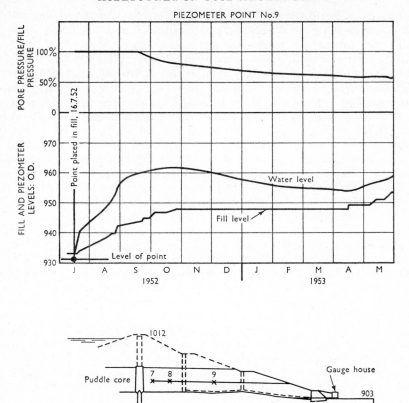

Fig. 12. Usk Dam. Pore-pressure observations in partly completed bank

dissipation of the pore pressure to be accelerated and the dam was safely completed in 1954. This investigation for the Usk Dam represents as important an example of the use of the "diagnostic technique" as the investigation for the Chingford Dam (Cooling and Golder, 1942) does of the "post-mortem" technique.

Another form of twin-tubed piezometer (type B, Fig. 15) was used in a foundation problem relating to oil tanks to be built on a deep layer of soft alluvial clay in Kent. To study this problem a number of pore-pressure measuring points were installed at selected points in the foundation soil beneath the area on which the tank was to be built (see Fig. 13). The piezo-meter in this case consisted of a fine-pored hollow cylindrical pot sealed with a rubber bung through which passed two polythene tubes. These were jacked into position by means of a steel tube, which was later withdrawn, and the hole filled with bentonite slurry. The tubes connecting the points were all led *via* a horizontal trench to a gauge house nearby. The tank, 144 ft dia., was constructed over the area and test loaded by filling with water in stages. Both pore-pressure and settlement readings were taken and the results have been discussed in detail in Papers by Cooling and Gibson (1955) and by Gibson and Marsland (1960). Fig. 14 gives an indication of the results and shows rapid response of the piezometer to changes in loading. From the rate of dissipation of pore pressure it was possible to assess the rate of increase in strength of the soil under the tank load.

Oil tanks are often built over soils which have a low bearing capacity and in these cases field measurements of pore pressure not only serve a useful purpose as a control but in addition can yield data which may have a wider value for design purposes.

Many installations using the twin-tube piezometer have been placed in earth dams in Great Britain, and at the recent Pore Pressure Conference examples were given and reference also made to developments using finer pored pots and nylon tubing (Fig. 15, type C) (Bishop, Kennard and Penman, 1960). A disadvantage of the system is that gas is apt to collect, especially when the pressure at any point falls below atmospheric, and de-airing becomes necessary. Also the response time of the system may not be short enough in certain cases. For these and other reasons, electrical instruments have been developed to follow changes in water pressure by measuring the distortion of a diaphragm which can be recorded remotely. Electric resistance strain gauges have been used in many models (Boiten and Platema, 1948; U.S. Waterways Experimental Station, 1944). At B.R.S. the vibrating-wire strain gauge has been used to measure the diaphragm deflexion. A study of the response time of various types of piezometers (see Fig. 15) has been made by Penman (1960). The advantages of the diaphragm cell type are that the volume change required to measure the pressure difference can be made extremely small so that its response is rapid; there are no connecting tubes and no trouble due to air bubbles within the system. An air tube fitted to keep the pressure on the inside of the diaphragm at atmospheric pressure (Fig. 15, type E) can also be used to calibrate the instrument when installed. The cost of the electrical equipment is higher but it has been found useful for quick spot observations for exploratory purposes to check readings given by a group of simpler type piezometers.

A new type of vibrating wire piezometer developed by my colleague, W. H. Ward, is shown in Fig. 16. This uses the distortion of a curved tube, like part of a Bourdon gauge, to actuate the vibrating wire gauge and it has been found to be very sensitive and convenient to use.

Finally, mention should also be made of work which is being carried out by Croney (Croney and Coleman, 1960) and others at the Road Research Laboratory to measure the capillary potential (negative pore pressures) of foundation soils under road slabs and to record the long-term changes that take place.

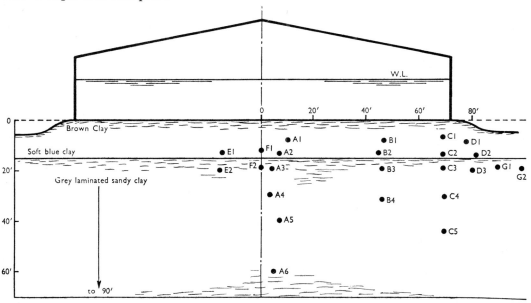

Fig. 13.   Position of pore-pressure points under oil tank

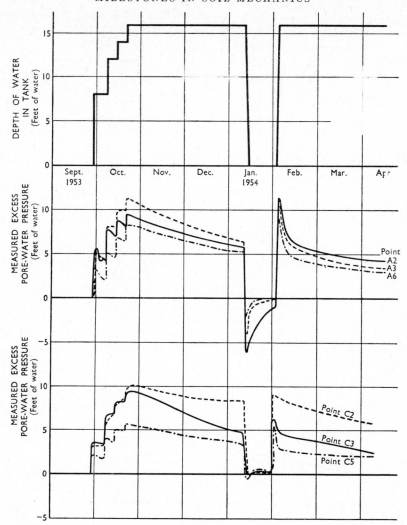

Fig. 14.   Results of pore-pressure measurements during full–scale loading tests on oil tank

As to the future, pore-pressure measurements represent such an obviously powerful new technique that there seems no doubt that all these methods will be fully exploited and developed further.

(c) *Earth pressure and related problems*

The measurement of earth pressures and the related measurements of deformation and displacement of earth-retaining structures represents a field of endeavour in which a great deal remains to be done.

Considering first the question of deformation of earth-retaining structures, much useful information can be obtained from fairly simple measurements.

It is interesting to note that Terzaghi and Peck (1948, p. 327) in considering the design of retaining walls emphasized the need for long-term observations on the movements of walls and periodic measurements of the pore-water pressure at several suitably located points in the

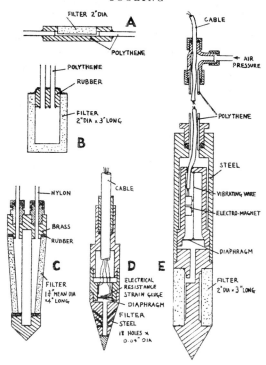

Fig. 15. Types of field piezometers

backfill as well as tests on the backfill prior to construction. They concluded with the comment: "Measurements of earth pressure against the back of the wall are desirable but not essential."

There have been very few observations of the movements of mass retaining walls, but mention may be made of the long-term observations of the old retaining wall at Kensal Green made by the London, Midland and Scottish Railway, which show the value of such measurements (Barbey, 1944).

The problem of the measurement of distortion of sheet-pile walls has received attention, mainly in the U.S.A. and in Germany, but there is still need for further full-scale observations. The Building Research Station is, at the moment, engaged in carrying out measurements on a sheet-pile wall at Avonmouth which will be referred to later.

A special case in which a small deformation assumes large importance is that of the lined tunnel. In tunnels up to about 15 ft dia. changes in distances between opposite walls can be measured by means of a metal rod or tube with a screw micrometer or dial gauge fixed at one end (Fig. 17). Thermometers must be fitted both to the measuring rod and to the reference bar and temperature corrections made in the usual way. Typical results are given in Fig. 18 which show measurements made in a small Post Office railway tunnel. The tunnel was 7 ft dia., located at a depth of 55 ft in London Clay and built of cast-iron segments which were grouted in the usual way. It will be noted that after construction the shape of the tunnel changed slowly with time, the vertical diameter decreasing slightly and the horizontal diameter increasing slightly. Similar results have also been obtained with observations on 12-ft-6-in.-dia. tunnels for the new Victoria Line and indeed all observations on tunnels in clay have shown a similar behaviour.

Brief mention may also be made of measurements to follow the distortion of the Bakerloo

Line tunnels as the result of construction work at South Bank for the new Shell building which was immediately over the tunnels. Here the removal of load by excavation caused a distortion of the tunnels in the opposite sense, the vertical diameters increasing slightly, about 0·2 in. in 12 ft, and the horizontal diameters decreasing slightly. A detailed description of this work and a discussion of the findings have been given in a recent Paper by Ward (1961).

In special cases, instruments have been constructed to measure the changes in diameter of a water tunnel when it was full with water under pressure. Such an instrument was developed at the Building Research Station in co-operation with the Metropolitan Water Board and is described in a Paper by Tattersall, Wakeling, and Ward (1955). The results of these measurements will be mentioned later.

When it comes to measuring earth pressure the question of instruments looms large. A great deal of work has been carried out in different parts of the world on the development of a suitable soil pressure cell and on the study of the important fundamental problem of the measurement of stress within a soil mass under various loading conditions. This problem is of such wide scope that I do not propose to include it.

At the B.R.S. we have been mainly concerned with the measurement of loads and pressures against earth retaining structures, or counter pressures on foundations.

As indicated by Ward (1961) the determination of loads and pressures on earth retaining structures has been based on one or other of two principles: "Advantage may be taken of the elastic nature of the structure itself and from measurements of its deformation under load, the forces causing that deformation may be arrived at by calculation. Alternatively, appropriate parts of the structure are interrupted by the insertion of load or earth pressure gauges so that the forces received by the members pass through the gauges and are measured."

The appropriate method depends on the circumstances but in most cases measurements require the use of specially designed instruments of a type not normally employed in civil engineering practice. Simple methods were tried originally. Golder (1948) carried out an investigation to measure the loads in the timber struts of an

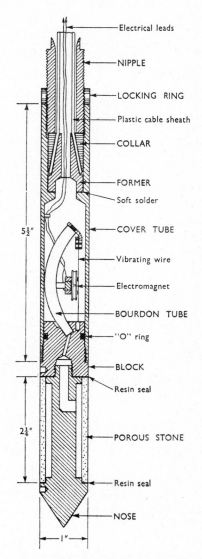

Fig. 16.   Diagram of B.R.S. vibrating-wire piezometer

Fig. 17. Measurement of changes in tunnel diameter with micrometer tube

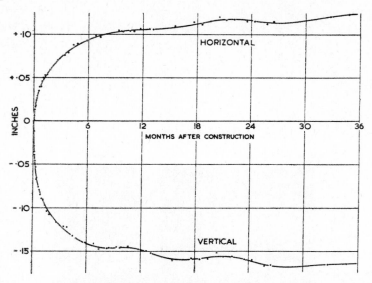

Fig. 18.   Typical measurements of diameter changes in newly constructed tunnel in London Clay

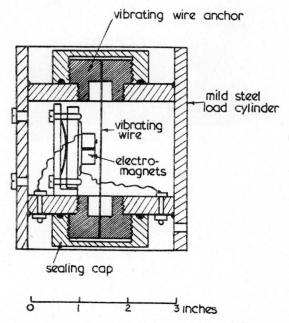

Fig. 19.   Sectional view of vibrating wire–load gauge

excavation in clay behind a wall at Park Village East, near Euston.   A simple direct method was employed by using the strut itself as the elastic member and measuring the strain by means of a gauge rod fitted with a screw micrometer; the accuracy was not high and the method was superseded.   Next a mechanical beam gauge was used as a load measuring unit placed at the end of a strut in a timbered excavation.   While this type of gauge proved reliable, the accuracy was not very high and the method still had the disadvantage that it was necessary to get down to the place where the unit was fixed before a reading could be taken.   While hydraulic gauges and proving rings have been used for short-term work, they have not been seriously considered for long-term observations owing to the possibility of breakdown due to leakage or other reasons.

A later development which has proved much more useful is that of the vibrating wire load gauge which need not be larger than 5 in. dia. and about 5 in. long and with little variation in overall size can be made to measure loads from about 1 to 100 tons.   Fig. 19 shows many features of the design of the instrument which is now being used extensively with very satisfactory results.   The stability of the gauge has proved to be very good even after being in use for a number of years and the change in zero load readings has been negligible.

The load gauge has been used in a variety of problems and a few examples will be given. An early investigation related to a deep cofferdam in soft alluvial clay at Shellhaven in the Thames Estuary.   Load gauges were used to measure the thrust transmitted from sheet piling to the walings.   A section of the sheeting comprising eleven contiguous sheet piles on one side of the cofferdam was supported against the walings at the level of each of the three frames solely by load-gauges.   Fig. 20 shows typical results of measurements on the top frame of the three: it shows the individual load gauge reading and the changes that took place as the result of various constructional operations.   A detailed account of the work has been published in a Paper by Skempton and Ward (1952) which gives the results of both soil tests and observations and also outlines an interpretation of the results in the light of the calculated earth pressures.

Another investigation which was carried out in collaboration with the Metropolitan Water Board concerned a small 9-ft-dia. water tunnel with its axis 90 ft below ground in London Clay, in which a new technique of lining was used.   The tunnel was lined with wedge-shaped concrete segments which were jacked into place.   Special segments were made to accommodate a number of radial pressure gauges comprising a load gauge bearing against a steel face plate which formed part of the earth face of the segment.   In addition, in four of the rings load gauges were installed to measure the circumferential load in the ring.   The tunnel was later filled with water under a head of about 140 ft and most of the load gauges continued to function giving results such as those indicated in Fig. 21.   These results showed that the net earth pressure on the tunnel lining decreased with increasing internal water pressure and increased again as the water pressure was reduced.   Since the net radial pressure decreased by only about two-thirds of the applied internal water pressure, none of the test rings ever became completely unstressed; also the changes in diameter of the tunnel were small.   These results provided invaluable information for the design and helped the engineers in arriving at a decision to omit a steel pipe lining, thus saving considerable cost.   A detailed account of this work is given in a Paper by Tattersall, Wakeling, and Ward (1955).

Load gauges have also been used for foundation problems.   For instance, H. B. Sutherland of Glasgow University used B.R.S. vibrating wire load gauges to measure foundation pressure distribution under two adjacent column footings in a large building (Sutherland and Lindsay, 1961).   This work enabled the pattern of load distribution found to be compared with the theoretical pattern for rigid footings on a cohesive soil.

Similar developments have occurred with strain gauges.   In 1942 the first measurements by B.R.S. were made on cast-iron linings in a tunnel being constructed at Belsize Park.   For these, Skempton used a detachable gauge of the Whittemore type, the punch marks being

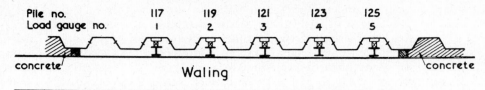

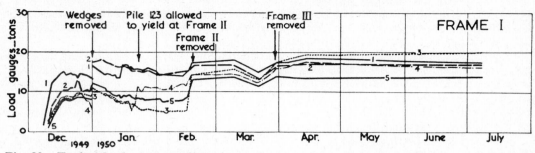

Fig. 20. Typical load gauge readings in top frame of steel sheet–pile cofferdam at Shellhaven

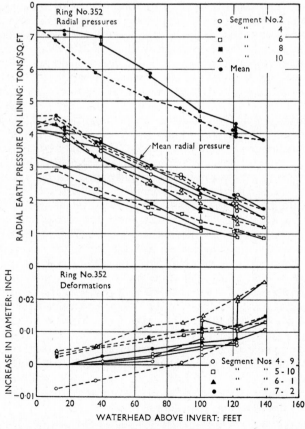

Fig. 21. Typical results of changes in radial earth pressure and in tunnel diameter with head of water in a tunnel lined with concrete segments. (Taken from Paper by Tattersall, Wakeling, and Ward, 1955)

made as soon as the segments were erected with subsequent readings taken at intervals to show the increase of stress with time (Groves, 1943). While gauges of this type can be very handy, their accuracy is not very high when used under field conditions. Attention was therefore directed to permanently attached strain gauges which would be fixed to a structure. Two types were investigated, the stick-on electrical resistance gauge and the vibrating wire gauge. The resistance type is very convenient to use under laboratory conditions where the zero drift can be checked and leads can be kept intact; however, when used in the field the method was found to be very vulnerable except when used in special field instruments where adequate protection could be provided. With the vibrating-wire gauge, a fine steel wire is clamped to two rigid posts which are screwed directly into the structure. This type of strain gauge has been used extensively for field work by B.R.S. It is fairly cheap and convenient to install and experience has proved it to be not only robust but also very stable and reliable over a period of several years. It has also been found particularly suitable for remote reading because long electrical cables can be used without difficulty, although it is necessary to ensure that there is not too much inductance between leads to different instruments; in some cases it has been found better and cheaper to use a small cable which can be switched by electro-magnetic selectors placed near the group of gauges. In fact, a very small telephone exchange is installed adjacent to each group and in this way, 200 gauges have been read using a six-core cable.

Recent developments have added to the value of the method. An electronic oscillator has been developed as a source of known frequency (Ward and Cheney, 1960) which added greatly to the accuracy and rapidity of measurement. It has also enabled shorter gauge lengths to be used as, for instance, in the pore-pressure gauge mentioned earlier. In addition, a new type of gauge has been developed using two wires mounted in the same posts and spaced one above the other (Fig. 22). From the readings of this gauge it is possible to estimate both direct and bending stress. Results from this gauge will be mentioned later.

For many years now a programme of field investigation has been in progress by B.R.S. to study stresses in linings of tunnels constructed in the London Clay. The research has required to take advantage of any constructional work that has been proceeding and much useful data have been obtained. It will not be possible to deal with this work comprehensively but a few cases will be quoted. In some cases measurements have been made of the increase in stress and the change in shape of the linings in a newly constructed grouted tunnel. Fig. 23 shows the build-up with time of the average stress at axis level of the small 7-ft-dia. tunnel for which the deformation measurements were given in Fig. 18. The shape of this curve is again typical of the behaviour of a tunnel in London Clay lined with cast-iron segments and grouted up. Measurements have also been made of the load in segmental linings which were jacked into place against the clay without the use of grout. These observations showed that the initial loads were primarily a function of the jacking pressure and that there is a slow build-up of pressure afterwards gradually approaching the full overburden pressure. In other cases, gauges have been fitted to the linings of existing tunnels, some of them 50 years old, and the stresses in them were estimated by means of strain gauges which recorded changes on the release of load when the linings were dismantled (Ward and Chaplin, 1957). Strains were measured during the process of excavating the clay around the lining and finally when the lining had been dismantled. In general, the results indicated that when the tunnel is well separated from a neighbouring tunnel, the final stresses are those attributable to the full overburden acting hydrostatically. When tunnels are spaced less than 1 diameter apart, significant bending stresses are produced in the earlier constructed tunnel by the operation involved in building another tunnel nearby.

At the present time, work is being carried out in co-operation with the Chief Civil Engineer's Department of London Transport on an experimental length of tunnel recently completed. Measurements are being made to follow the structural performance of two new types of tunnel

Fig. 22.   New type of vibrating-wire strain gauge.   Two vibrating wires fixed to a pair of posts to measure both direct and bending stresses

AVERAGE STRESS IN 7′ DIAM. C.I. TUNNEL AT AXIS LEVEL

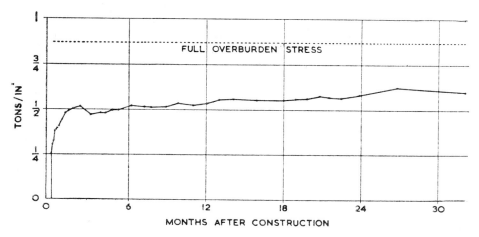

Fig. 23. Increase of average stress with time after construction of tunnel in London Clay

linings which are jacked into place directly against the clay without the use of grout. One segmental lining is made of cast-iron, and to measure stress changes an experimental ring has been equipped by fitting two of the new twin wire strain gauges mentioned above, to each of the six segments. Fig. 24 is a photograph showing the segments being instrumented and the gauges read before being built into the tunnel. The other segmental lining is made of concrete and has fourteen segments to a ring. To measure the stress changes, a series of pairs of vibrating-wire strain gauges of another new type has been cast into inner and outer faces of these segments (Fig. 25). In the concrete lining, a good proportion of the strain experienced is expected to be due to moisture movements and creep of the concrete and the experimental tunnel ring will be unloaded at some suitable time after construction in order to measure the structural stresses. Progressive changes in stress and distortion are being observed but it is too early to comment on the results.

This kind of field work is, of course, of a long-term nature and it cannot be expected to have more than a very gradual influence on design and construction methods.

Finally, a brief indication may be given of the instrumentation being used for an investigation which is at present being carried out in collaboration with the Port of Bristol Authority. A series of measurements are being made of earth pressures, forces, stresses, and displacements in a large anchored sheet-pile dock wall. The measurements are being made on a section 35 ft long anchored with six tie rods, the load in each rod being measured by vibrating-wire strain gauges (Fig. 26). The sheet piles of this wall are 65 ft long and three of them have been instrumented. The fitting of the instruments was carried out in the laboratory and the sheet piles were later transported to the site and driven into the construction (Fig. 27). Two of the piles carry a series of diaphragm-type earth pressure cells on the outside of the pile. The general features of the earth pressure cell, which is based on the vibrating-wire principle, is shown in Fig. 28. An instrument of this type was developed by the Norwegian Geotechnical Institute, after discussion with B.R.S., and its use in measurements on a sheet pile structure for the Oslo Subway was described in Papers at the Brussels Conference (Kjell, 1958). The third pile is fitted with a number of the new twin wire strain gauges. These three piles and four others have lengths of square tube welded to one side, and a remote reading inclinometer which slides inside the tubes is used to measure the deflected form of the piles. Observations

Fig. 24.   Instrumentation of new type of cast–iron tunnel lining before installation in experimental length of tunnel

Fig. 25. Vibrating-wire strain gauge recessed into surface of a precast tunnel segment

Fig. 26. Avonmouth. Vibrating-wire strain gauges fitted on either side of tie-rod to measure
load in the rod

Fig. 27. A steel sheet pile, 65 ft long, being equipped with twelve twin wire strain gauges in laboratory before transport and installation in dock wall

Fig. 28. Diaphragm type of earth-pressure gauge with a vibrating-wire anchored across the diaphragm for bolting to the surface of a steel pile

have been taken at various stages of the construction so far, and although there was been some flooding in the earth pressure gauges, almost all of them successfully withstood the shocks of pile driving. The work is still in progress but an indication of the type of results being obtained is given in Fig. 29. This shows the bending moments in the pile obtained from readings of the twin wire strain gauges (placed in the positions given by circles on the pile in the right-hand diagram) and resulting from the first stage of dredging.

SUMMARY AND CONCLUSIONS

To sum up the following points may be made. Fully documented case records which permit a comparison between forecast and performance are invaluable for the purpose of indicating the direction in which design procedure can be improved. Even without a quantitative forecast, field measurements are of considerable practical value in their own right, since

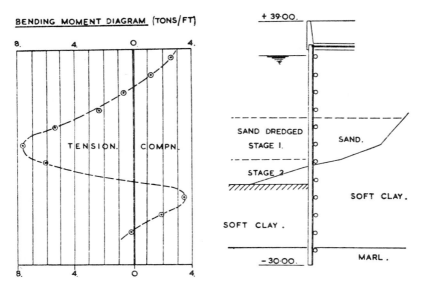

Fig. 29. Avonmouth. Typical results after first stage of dredging. Bending moments obtained from readings of twin wire strain gauges

every problem presents its own special features and quantitative data can give a sharper edge to experience. When used as part of the "observational procedure" they form the most powerful tool which soil mechanics has produced for resolving difficult soil problems.

Techniques need not be over-elaborate but the programme of field work should be carefully planned and systematically carried out. In many cases such work could be readily arranged and should become a more common feature in engineering practice. It is admitted that in some problems special equipment and techniques may be needed as, for instance, for the measurement of earth pressure. In such cases consideration should be given to providing facilities for such work when suitable opportunities come along and it is desirable that the engineer should undertake this task. He should explain to the client that while designs are based on the best advice available, it is only common prudence to provide for measurements which will confirm that the structure is behaving as expected. The words of Terzaghi when addressing the 1957 Conference should be remembered: "I have become more and more impressed by the importance of never missing an opportunity to find out by direct observation the difference between forecasts and the real developments."

REFERENCES

BARBEY, M. F., 1944. "Some soil mechanics problems on the London, Midland, and Scottish Railway." Sep. Paper No. 11, *Instn civ. Engrs*. *Discussion* by A. W. Skempton, p. 74.

BISHOP, A. W., M. F. KENNARD, *and* A. D. M. PENMAN, 1960. "Pore-pressure observations at Selset Dam." *Pore Pressure Conf.*, Paper 13, p. 91.

BOITEN, R. G., *and* G. PLANTEMA, 1948. "An electrically operating pore-water pressure cell." *Proc. 2nd Int. Conf. Soil Mech.*, 1 : 306–309. *Also* "Soil Pressure cell investigations". *U.S. Waterways Exp. Stn*, 1944, Tech. Mem., No. 210–211.

BUCKTON, E. J., *and* J. CUEREL, 1943. "The new Waterloo Bridge." *Proc. Instn civ. Engrs*, 20 : 145.

CASAGRANDE, A., 1949. "Soil mechanics in the design and construction of the Logan Airport." *J. Boston Soc. civ. Engrs*, 36 : 2. (Appendix describes piezometer.)

CASAGRANDE, A., 1961. First Rankine Lecture, "Control of seepage through foundations and abutments of dams". *Géotechnique*, 9 : 3 : 159–182.

"Conference on pore pressure and suction in soils," 1960. Conference by *Brit. Nat. Soc. Int. Soc. Soil Mech.*, *London, Butterworths*, 1961.

COOLING, L. F., 1945. "The principles and application of soil mechanics." *Instn civ. Engrs, Lecture* 1; Development and scope of soil mechanics; Fig. 31.

COOLING, L. F., 1948. "Settlement observations on four grain silos." *Proc. 2nd Int. Conf. Soil Mech.*, 2 : 135.

COOLING, L. F., 1955. "The measurement of pore-water pressure and its application to some engineering and soil problems." RILEM *Symp.* 18, *Theme* (1a), *Lisbon*.

COOLING, L. F., *and* R. E. GIBSON, 1955. "Settlement studies on structures in England." *Conf. Corr. Stresses. Instn civ. Engrs*. *Prelim. vol.*, Paper No. 18, p. 295.

COOLING, L. F., *and* H. Q. GOLDER, 1942. "The analysis of the failure of an earth dam construction." *Instn civ. Engrs*, 19 : 38.

COOLING, L. F., *and* A. MARSLAND, 1953. "Soil mechanics studies of failures in the sea defence banks of Essex and Kent." *Conf. North Sea Floods*, 1 February, 1953. *Instn civ. Engrs, N.S.F.*, 1953 : 58.

COOLING, L. F., *and* W. H. WARD, 1944. "Damage to cold stores due to frost-heaving." *Proc. Inst. Refrig.*, 41 : 37.

COOLING, L. F., *and* W. H. WARD, 1948. "Some examples of foundation movements due to causes other than structural loads." *Proc. 2nd Conf. Int. Soil Mech.*, 2 : 162–167.

CRONEY, D., *and* J. D. COLEMAN, 1960. "Pore pressure and suction in soil." *Pore Pressure Conf.*, Paper No. 5, p. 31.

CRONEY, D., *and* W. A. LEWIS, 1948. "The effect of vegetation on the settlement of roads." *Conf. Biology and civ. Engng*, 195–202, *Instn civ. Engrs*.

GIBSON, R. E., *and* A. MARSLAND, 1960. "Pore-water pressure observations in a saturated alluvial deposit beneath a loaded oil tank." *Pore Pressure Conf.*, Paper No. 16, p. 112.

GOLDER, H. Q., 1948. "Measurement of pressure in timbering of a trench in clay." *2nd Int. Conf. Soil Mech.*, 2 : 76.

GROVES, G. L., 1943. "Tunnel linings with special reference to a new form of reinforced concrete lining." *J. Instn civ. Engrs*, 20 : 29.

KJELL ØIEN, 1958. "An earth pressure cell for use on sheet pile—Oslo Subway." *Brussels Conf., Earth Pressure Problems*, 2 : 118.

LACEY, W. D., *and* H. T. SWAIN. "Design for mining subsidence." *Arch. Journal*, 126 : 557–570 *and* 631–642.

MEYERHOF, G. G., 1951. "The tilting of a large tank on soft clay." *Proc. South Wales Instn of Engrs*, 67 : 2 : 53–71.

McHAFFIE, M. G., 1938. "Southampton Docks extension." *J. Instn civ. Engrs*, 9 : 184–219.

McDONALD, D. H., *and* A. W. SKEMPTON, 1955. "A survey of comparisons between calculated and observed settlements of structures on clay." *Conf. Corr. Stresses. Instn civ. Engrs, Prelim. vol.*, Paper No. 19, pp. 318–337.

PATON, J., *and* N. G. SEMPLE, 1960. "Investigation of the stability of an earth dam subject to rapid drawdown, including details of pore pressures recorded during a controlled drawdown test." *Conf. Pore Pressures. Brit. Nat. Soc.*, Paper No. 12, pp. 85.

PENMAN, A. D., 1960. "A study of the response time of various types of piezometer." *Pore Pressure Conf.*, Paper No. 8, p. 53.

SHEPPARD, G. A. R., *and* L. B. AYLEN. "The Usk Scheme for the water supply of Swansea." *Proc. Instn civ. Engrs*, 7 : 246–274. (See also *discussion* by A. W. Skempton, A. Bishop, and A. D. M. Penman.)

SKEMPTON, A. W., *and* W. H. WARD, 1952. "Investigations concerning a deep cofferdam in the Thames Estuary clay at Shellhaven." *Géotechnique*, 3 : 3 : 119.

SEROTA, S., *and* R. A. J. JENNINGS, 1959. "The elastic heave of the bottom of excavations." *Géotechnique*, 9 : 62–70.

SKEMPTON, A. W., *and* D. H. MacDONALD, 1956. "The allowable settlement of buildings." *Proc. Instn civ. Engrs*, 5 : 727. Discussion 768.

SUTHERLAND, H. B., *and* J. A. LINDSAY, 1961. "The measurement of load distribution under two adjacent column footings." *Proc. 5th Inst. Conf. Soil Mech.*, 1 : 829.

TATTERSALL, F., T. R. M. WAKELING, *and* W. H. WARD, 1955. "Investigations in the designs of pressure tunnels in London Clay." *Proc. Instn civ. Engrs*, 1 : 4 : 400.

TERZAGHI, K., 1961. "Past and future of applied soil mechanics." *J. Boston Soc. civ. Engrs*, 48 : 97–139.

TERZAGHI, K., *and* R. PECK, 1948. "Soil mechanics in engineering practice." *Wiley, N.Y.*, p. 327.

WARD, W. H., 1948.   "The effect of vegetation on the settlement of structures."   *Proc. Conf. Biology and civ. engng*, 181–194.   *Instn civ. Engrs.*

WARD, W. H., 1957.   "The use of simple relief wells in reducing water pressure beneath a trench excavation."   *Géotechnique*, 7 : 3 : 134–139.

WARD, W. H., 1961.   "Displacements and strains in tunnels beneath a large excavation in London."   *5th Int. Conf. Soil Mech.*, 2 : 749.

WARD, W. H., 1955.   "Techniques for field measurement of deformation and earth pressure."   *Conf. Corr. Stresses*, Paper No. 3, p. 28.   *Instn civ. Engrs.*

WARD, W. H., *and* T. K. CHAPLIN, 1957.   "Existing stresses in several old London underground tunnels."   *Proc. 4th Int. Conf. Soil Mech.*, 2 : 256.

WARD, W. H., *and* J. E. CHENEY, 1960.   "Oscillator measuring equipment for vibrating-wire gauges."   *J. Scientific Instruments*, 37 : 88–92.

WOOD, R. H., *and* R. J. MAINSTONE, 1955.   "Stress measurements in the steel frame of the new Government offices, Whitehall Gardens."   *Proc. Conf. Corr. Stresses*, 1955, *Prelim. vol.*, p. 74.

RECENT WORK IN ROCK MECHANICS

A. MAYER

INTRODUCTION

When your President told me, more than a year ago, that your Institution had chosen me to give the next Rankine Lecture I felt very honoured and embarrassed—honoured because I am well aware of the degree of distinction conferred by this choice, and embarrassed because, in the words of La Bruyere, "Everything has been said, and we are here too late, for over three thousand years there have been people who can *think*." This also holds true for soil mechanics.

I was helped by Professor Skempton, who suggested I should devote this Lecture to "rock mechanics". This also is not virgin ground; in fact, I remember having had a Paper (Mayer, 1953)[1] published in *Géotechnique* in 1953, after the Zurich meeting, in which I summarized what was known at that time about rock mechanics and its applications to civil engineering. Since then the subject has developed and at present, after disasters which are still vivid in all memories, it has become even fashionable.

Let me recall that in 1957 a Symposium on Rock Mechanics was held in Paris, in which some of you present participated. In 1958 and 1961 two meetings on ground pressures took place in Leipzig and in Paris organized by mining engineers, where different Papers were also of interest to us.

Then, in 1961, at the Paris meeting on "soil mechanics", Professor Skempton in his inaugural address declared that "rock mechanics was an integral part of soil mechanics and should form a special section at our next meeting".

At the same time, the International Commission for Large Dams also decided to include in their agenda for the 1964 meeting a question on rock mechanics wide enough to allow for all developments.

In 1962 a group of Austrian, German, and Italian engineers formed at Salzburg an International Society for Rock Mechanics, centred around the research organization of Dr L. Muller. Meanwhile in France after the Symposium of 1957 the National Association for Technical Research formed an *ad hoc* commission—which included specialists in different fields, geologists, miners, civil engineers, oil engineers, and others interested in rock mechanics—for the purpose of fostering research in rock mechanics, and asked me to take the chair.

As a result, a laboratory devoted to the Mechanics of solids, aimed directly at fundamental research, was started at the École Polytechnique. This laboratory is attached to the Chair of Professor Mandel, and is under his and Mr Habib's direction. It celebrated its first anniversary in October 1962. I will refer later to some of the important work already carried out there.

In other countries there are also laboratories and scientists working in the same field, although they are perhaps more concerned with applied rock mechanics. I cannot cite them all, but I would like to mention the laboratory of Rock Mechanics Ltd, which needs no formal introduction; then there is at Bergamo (Italy) the laboratory of the Ismes, directed by Professor Oberti; there is the special section of the Building Research Laboratory in Lisbon, directed by MM. Rocha and Laginha Serafim; the studies of both these laboratories are concentrated on models.

Important work is also going on in Sweden and Norway where rock is to be found practically everywhere, as well as in Japan where seismic engineering has been developed in recent years.

Finally, in the United States of America there are several laboratories working on rock mechanics, of which I shall mention only the Bureau of Reclamation, and the Bureau of Mines. There are also a number of engineers among whom I want to cite a very prominent scientist, who has recently devoted several Papers to rock mechanics, and whom I should like to refer to at the beginning of this Paper—Professor Karl Terzaghi.

So it is safe to say that this subject happily proposed by Professor Skempton, while no novelty, is nevertheless of vivid contemporary interest.

Perhaps the best way I can project a picture of what it is today, will be by first glancing back to its state 10 years ago, and then following developments through, up to the present time, while throwing most light on the researches and applications which have been done in France.

ROCK MECHANICS IN 1953

Rock mechanics as used by the civil engineer 10 years ago was already split into two phases: first, the measurement of the mechanical characteristics of rocks and, second, the application of the knowledge gained to different practical problems.

The measures sought were:

(i) the elastic modulus of the rock, and
(ii) the stresses in the rock in situ.

The elastic modulus was generally measured in the field by the jacking method. This, to my knowledge, was used for the first time, around 1935, by the Irrigation Department in Algeria. A jack was placed across a gallery, its foot against one wall and its head thrusting against the opposite wall, where the rock surface had been carefully dressed flat and true. The thrust of the jack was increased and the rock deformation measured and expressed as a function of the applied stress.

The elastic modulus was calculated from the relationship:

$$\delta = \frac{\alpha P}{r} \frac{1-v^2}{E}$$

where E is the elastic modulus of the rock, δ is the measured deformation, P is the applied thrust, v is the Poisson coefficient of the rock, and α is a coefficient characteristic of the stiffness of the bearing effective under the foot of the jack. This coefficient is usually about 0·5.

When the results of these measurements were checked in the laboratory it was found that—in the case of homogeneous, isotropic rock, or concrete—the calculated values agreed well with those obtained by direct measurement, and roughly with those calculated from measured sound velocities in the same kind of rock, using equations of the type:

$$V = \sqrt{\frac{E}{\gamma} \frac{1-v}{(1+v)(1-2v)}}$$

where the letters have the same meaning as before, V being the velocity of the sound waves and γ the density of the rock.

In the course of the past 10 years the jack method has become quite a standard procedure and some examples of the results provided by it will be described later.

Another method, tried at that time, particularly by the Irrigation Department of Morocco, used a certain length of gallery which was put under hydraulic pressure. The length required was driven into the rock and provided with a water-tight steel bulkhead to seal it off. The gallery was then filled with water and put under pressure. The variations of the diameter with the change in pressure were measured; hence the elastic modulus was computed.

This method has the great advantage that it involves large areas and thus gives good average values, whereas by the jack method the thrust is applied only to a small and possibly not representative area. On the other hand the gallery method is far more painstaking and more expensive; therefore it has been little used since the time when M. Bernard, Ingénieur des Ponts et Chaussées, and our laboratory applied it for predicting deformations in a pressure tunnel in Morocco. Those measurements confirmed that gallery values for elastic moduli agreed well enough with the average of a sufficient number of values obtained by the jack method so that this last procedure from there on was used practically alone.

Besides the elastic modulus of the rock, the second element sought was the value of the stress acting on the rock. Two methods were used for determining it.

The first assumed that the elastic modulus of the rock was known. The method was to cut a circular groove into the wall of the gallery. This relieved the stresses acting on the core. The increase in diameter of the core was measured by means of strain gauges. Knowing the elastic modulus of the medium the value of the stress could be computed.

The stress can also be measured directly by what has been called the flat-jack method which we suggested in 1951. To measure the stresses in the wall of an underground cavity, the procedure is to stretch several vibrating strings between anchor points cemented into the wall. The tension on each acoustic string is recorded. A groove is then cut into the rock between two of these gauges and a flat jack of the Freyssinet type is placed in it.

During the process of cutting this groove the stresses on the rock are relieved and the tension on the acoustic string becomes less. When the flat jack has been placed, hydraulic pressure is supplied until the initial state of stress in the rock—as shown by the tension on the acoustic cord—has been restored to its initial value. The hydraulic pressure in the flat jack is now equal in value to the stress initially present in the rock; that is to say to the component of stress in the direction vertical to the surface of the jack.

As the flat jack is welded, it cannot take a pressure greater than about 200 kg/sq. cm, which corresponds to a depth of rock less than 1,000 m. But within this limit the method has been used with great success by M. Tincelin in the iron mines in eastern France. Here the galleries are at a depth of only 200 m and the stresses in the rock are of the order of 50 kg/sq. cm.

The flat-jack method has recently been taken up and developed by various specialists in order to measure stresses at great depths in boreholes. I will return to these developments later.

Finally, during these past 10 years model tests, taking into account the deformation of the rock, have been widely developed in order to compute the stresses in the structures.

This method has been brought to a high degree of refinement by Professor Oberti at the Ismes at Bergamo, and by M. Rocha and M. Laginha at Lisbon.

This was the state of rock mechanics in 1953 as it was known to me at the time. For the sake of completeness I would mention here the studies made at the Bureau of Reclamation, by Dr Muller of Salzburg and by Professor Hast of Stockholm, of which I had not yet heard. However, these studies did not to my knowledge involve methods other than those that have just been described.

As has been said before, during this period many different organizations have devoted large parts of their efforts to the study of rock mechanics. In describing some of their activities I will concern myself mainly with the studies made in France and with which I have myself had contact either directly or indirectly, first in the laboratory and subsequently in the field.

A. *Laboratory studies*

Before considering the mechanical properties of rocks and how these properties are modified by applied stresses, it is my object to mention recent studies on the alteration of rock; that is to say, on the changes brought about in rock by the action of water, by the variation in the water-vapour content of the atmosphere ambient to the rock, and by the changes in temperature.

(a) *The alterability of a rock.*—This property was studied, in liaison with Électricité de France, first by M. Farran and then by M. Thenot, in the mineralogical laboratory of the Faculty of Sciences at Toulouse.

The alterability of a rock is a function of its mineralogical nature and of its degree of fissuration. Both these factors were studied intensively.

In regard to fissuration, a distinction was made between different classes of cracks, according to their size, as follows:

A *macrofracture* has a width more than 0·1 mm. Sometimes it is empty, but often it is filled with alteration products.

A *microfracture* has a width less than 0·1 mm, but still of the order of the 0·01 mm. These microfractures are usually difficult to see by the naked eye. They represent schistose joints or narrow fractures but they can extend to cover major surface areas. They usually follow well-defined directions in space.

In addition to these two classes of cracks there is also the *isotropic matrix fissuration*, where the width is less than one μ and the length of the fissure of the order of the length of a crystal. This kind of microfissuration can be seen in a petrographic section cut from a piece of rock that has been suitably impregnated with coloured resins.

This kind of fissuration can be quantitatively evaluated by the fissure area per unit volume of rock, and in spite of the very small width of the fissure it strongly influences the rapidity of the alteration process; that is to say the rate at which the minerals of the rock are attacked by water.

Recent work has shown that water can travel through a soil or a rock of low porosity either in the vapour phase or, in certain cases, in the adsorbed phase (Société Hydrotèchnique de France, Compte-rendu des VIIemes Journeés de l'Hydraulique). A capillary of only a few molecules in diameter is enough to permit the flow. The walls of the fissure acquire a monomolecular skin of water and through this skin the mobile water molecules travel along in the adsorbed phase.

M. Farran and M. Thenot have shown that the alterability of a rock can be expressed as the product of two factors. The first they call the specific alterability of the rock. The second is its specific surface.

The specific alterability is an experimental quantity determined as follows: A cylindrical sample of rock is prepared, 3 cm high by 4 cm in diameter. This is mounted so that water can be applied to one end under a pressure of 250 kg/sq. cm. The water will travel along through the interior of the cylinder and issue at the other end. The barrel surface of the cylinder must be carefully sealed off here to prevent any superficial flow. The rate of flow is recorded and the rate of change with time determined. The effluent water is examined by photometric analysis.

If the rate of flow remains constant, and the removal of elements (particularly calcium ions) is small, the rock can be called of low alterability. For example, in the case of granites, which in practice are of very low alterability, calcium is removed at a rate lower than 5 mg per litre of filtrate and per hour of leaching.

But if the rate of flow is found to diminish during the run, this can be presumed to be due to blocking of the capillaries by reaction products, or to the swelling of clay minerals, both signs that the rock is alterable. To express the matter quantitatively it may be said that the rate of decrease of permeability with time is a measure of specific alterability.

The second factor is the specific surface of the rock, which is a function of its micro-fissuration. Determination takes the form of a measurement of the permeability of the rock to air. This air-permeability is a characteristic of the rock which has received great attention from the specialists in the exploration of oilfields. They have developed a variety of instruments for measuring it, all based on the simple principle that air is sucked, under a given pressure differential, through a sample of rock of standard dimensions. The volume of air passed through in unit time is a measure of the air permeability of the rock. An apparatus of this kind is in use at Toulouse (Fig. 1).

The following Table shows the results of some permeability tests on granites from different sources. The tests were made for Électricité de France by the Laboratoire de Minéralogie de Toulouse. The column on the right briefly describes the aspect and behaviour of the granite tested.

As all the samples in these tests were granites, of one sort or another, it may be assumed that the specific alterability is the same in all cases. Thus the variable that determines alterability is in each case the permeability to air of the rock.

It will be seen that there is a very good correlation between permeability to air and the condition of the rock. For a case like this, where a group of rocks all of the same nature are compared with each other, the air permeability is therefore quite a good criterion for the alterability of the rock.

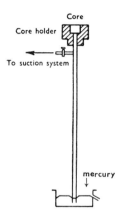

Fig. 1. Air permeability measuring device

Table 1

Sample	Permeability to air in cm/sec.	Remarks
A	$1·8 \times 10^{-12}$	Very good condition.
B	$2·5$ to $3·2 \times 10^{-12}$	Very good condition.
C	1×10^{-11}	Rock in very good condition, no alteration.
D	$1-3 \times 10^{-11}$	Rock is compact, stained with rust along large fractures but the main part of the rock is not coloured.
E	3 to 4×10^{-11}	No deep alteration. Some surface attacks.
F	1×10^{-11} to 3×10^{-10}	The quartz crystals are bared and the rock is coloured in the mass.
G	$1·2$ to 3×10^{-10}	The rock is friable and looks as though it will soon break down into sand.
H	$1·4$ to $3·2 \times 10^{-10}$	The permeability is very high, but the granite is little altered. There are vacuoles from the disappearance of feldspars.
I	$1·4$ to 5×10^{-9}	The rock crumbles easily. The increased permeability corresponds to a more advanced disintegration.
K	$1·4$ to 5×10^{-9}	The rock is obviously in a state of rapid change. Tinted with rust in the mass, crumbles easily.

These measurements provide a means for grading rocks in order of increasing alterability, but even where this property cannot be expressed with quantitative precision the observations can still reveal facts of the greatest practical importance. When the Carla pressure tunnel, for example, was being driven for the Électricité de France, the laboratory found that certain parts of the rock wall showed high alterability values. In order to obtain a practical check on the laboratory findings, some areas of this rock were left unlined and thus exposed to the action of the water, together with some less alterable areas for comparison. When the tunnel was subsequently emptied, several months later, it was indeed found, as predicted, that the alterable areas had suffered considerable attack, whereas the non-alterable areas were not affected. Thus the laboratory predictions were confirmed.

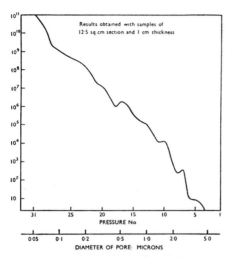

Fig. 2. Porosity tests. Samples of schist. Between diameters δ and δ+*d*, there are $\bar{N}d\delta$ pores per sq. cm

Similar practical tests were made at Bort, also with affirmative results, and since this second confirmation the Électricité de France have made it their practice to have alterability tests made on the rock surface of a tunnel before deciding whether or not to provide a protective lining. In this way alterability measurements can allow considerable economic savings to be made.

There are other types of rock where certain kinds of behaviour can be explained only in terms of the pore dimensions and the resulting permeability. This is particularly true of certain types of schist (Fig. 2).

A case of this sort occurred during the construction of the Foum el Geiss dam in Algeria. It was intended to cut an almost vertical wall in the schist and then apply a concrete lining. The terrain seemed well adapted to the procedure till somebody picked up a piece of schist which was lying on the ground and had therefore been exposed to the air for a long time, and dropped it into a bucket of water. The piece of rock had hardly touched the bottom of the bucket before it literally exploded into dust. The explanation was that in its natural state, in the body of the rock, this schist was saturated with water. The piece lying on the ground and thus exposed to the air must have dried out. When this piece of dried-out rock was immersed in water, the water penetrated into the capillaries, enclosing spaces containing dry air in which a high vapour pressure quickly developed due to the very small meniscus radii, causing in effect multiple explosions in the schist with almost instant disintegration.

The remedy was simply to prevent the newly cut surface from drying out, by applying rapidly a surface gunnite coat to hold the moisture in.

I have on occasion come across rocks with somewhat similar characteristics but not so pronounced, particularly in eastern France where there is a schist called "cardboard schist" because when a core of this material is exposed to the air it flakes off into thin, parallel disks that look like cardboard. The engineers studying a site for an excavation, to take the foundation structure of an ironworks, were not pleased to find this kind of schist there. But it was necessary merely to cover the newly bared ground with a coating of bitumen to seal in the moisture and thus avoid all difficulties. With this precaution the schist is quite capable of supporting very heavy loads. What is necessary, here again, is to prevent a desiccation of the ground, followed by re-humidification.

(*b*) *Deformation and rupture.*—On the initiative of the Institut Français du Pétrole a special study of these properties of rocks was made by the laboratory of the École Polytechnique, which acquired equipment for studying the intrinsic curves of natural rocks, and also the effect of rock flow.*

For the study of the intrinsic curve the laboratory has available a triaxial apparatus with a capacity for horizontal pressures up to 1,000 kg/sq. cm and vertical pressures up to 7,000 kg/sq. cm.   Measurements currently made include crushing of rock with lateral constraints of zero, 250, 500, and 1,000 kg/sq. cm.

The vertical pressures causing rupture at the different lateral constraints describe the intrinsic curve of the rock.   It is interesting to observe that all the rocks examined in these studies behave in the same way with changing lateral stresses.   With zero lateral constraint, that is, when only vertical pressure is applied and precautions are taken to prevent surface friction on the head and base of the sample, all the rock samples ruptured along vertical planes parallel to each other.   If some lateral stress is applied, the sample ruptures by inclined planes of failure, as would a plastic clay.   If the lateral constraint is increased sufficiently, the sample of rock first squashes out by plastic deformation into the shape of a barrel, and then ruptures by a series of planes of failure parallel to each other and symmetrical to the axis of the sample (see Figs 3 and 4).

In the presence of very high lateral constraint and consequently high friction values, the sample of rock under high vertical pressure does not rupture at all but merely becomes deformed by plastic flow, without there appearing in the rock any fissure visible to the naked eye. The samples after this test all have the same aspect, whether the rock is

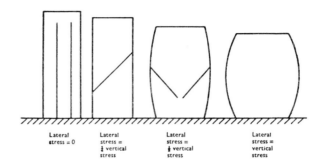

Lateral stress = 0   Lateral stress = ¼ vertical stress   Lateral stress = ½ vertical stress   Lateral stress = vertical stress

Fig. 3.   Rupture of samples under varying lateral constraint

a plastic clay, a piece of sylvinite, or gypsum, limestone, or granite.   In each case a Mohr diagram can be drawn, showing an intrinsic curve delimiting the zones of plastic deformation and of rupture.   This is not a straight line system but rather a parabola with its apex on the Ox axis at a point whose abscissa represents the tensile strength of the rock.

On the basis of these studies it is possible to predict the conditions under which a given rock will flow or rupture.   Thus when a tunnel is driven through rock it is often possible to predict how and where cracks will develop.   Knowing this, steps can be taken to prevent rock falls, by rapidly intervening before the ultimate state of stress has had time to develop in the exposed rock, and by inserting tie-bolts across the probable planes of rupture.

This method was applied on a large scale during the driving of the Mont Blanc tunnel (Renaud, 1962).   Here the rock, which was a granite, had already acquired a stratified structure from the tectonic movements that had formed the mountain chain.   It was found that there was already a preferred direction for the planes of rupture.   But the mountain load applied to the walls of the tunnel as the drilling proceeded, developed vertical stresses, and caused cracking in nearly vertical planes at the springing of the vault.   Bolts were inserted as soon as a length of gallery was opened, and although this may not have entirely prevented the development of fissures, it certainly helped to counterbalance dangerous effects.   In this way several tens of thousands of tie-bolts were inserted to act against shearing of the rock and so to prevent major rock falls (see Figs 5, 6, and 7).

* Similar studies had been made at the Engineering Laboratory of the Bureau of Reclamation at Denver and published under "physical properties of some typical foundation rocks" in 1953 (see Fig. 4).

Fig. 4.   Limestone sample before and after triaxial compression (Bureau of Reclamation, 1953)

Fig. 5.   Mont Blanc tunnel.   The Jumbo in place—In foreground, the rock bolts

Fig. 6. Mont Blanc tunnel. General view of the inlet into the Mont Blanc tunnel

Fig. 7.   Mont Blanc tunnel.   Fissured granite and rock bolts

(c) *Rock flow.*—These tests relate to a load rapidly applied to a sample of rock. A different problem is presented by deformations taking place in rock that is permanently stressed. A study of these effects is made difficult by the long periods of time during which the samples of rock have to be kept under load.

In the laboratory of the École Polytechnique there are in use twenty-four apparatuses for applying stress to rock samples. Among the many experiments begun some will continue through periods of time of up to several years.

At present it may be said that the deformations, shown after a given period by different rocks under stress, differ considerably with the nature of the rock. With certain rocks like unsaturated gneiss, up to 80% of their compressive strength, there is no noticeable delayed deformability. With others a maximum deformation is reached after a certain time. A third possibility which, until now, had not been detected, is a flow with a progressive hardening of the material. This happens for instance in the case of chalk, of potash, and of sedimentary iron ore as mined in the east of France.

The time-deformation log, after a short straight variation for low stresses, gets curved; the deformation decreases until a new ratio is reached for which the variation again is linear. This period corresponds the hardening of the material. It is followed by an increase of the deformations until the rupture occurs. In other words the material first behaves like an elastic body, then, progressively, gets more and more resistant under the load and remains so for some time. It finally gets softer, deforms and breaks down (see Fig. 8).

This observation made in the laboratory has already been checked in the field and used in mines to control the stability of different stopes. Even in cases where nothing shows that the compression on pillars increases, accurate measures indicate a slow settlement which progresses regularly. As long as the settlement varies with the time in a linear way, the risk of a rupture is still remote. But as soon as the relation is no longer linear there is a danger of collapse and either the mine must be vacuated or the pillars should be strengthened. It is interesting to note that this behaviour has already been observed both in iron ore and in chalk mines and that these experiments have shown a possibility of improving the safety in a number of cases.

At the moment this question is only making a start but it seems certain that in a relatively short time important results will be achieved in this line which shall apply not only to mines but also to civil engineering works.

As a complement to these brief observations the following are different values of the maximum flow to instantaneous deformation for particular materials:

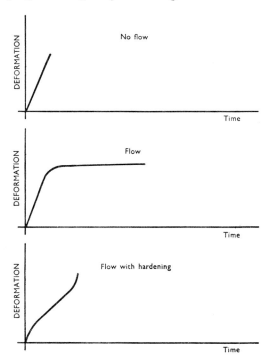

Fig. 8. **Rock flow**

	per cent
granite up to the present, less than 10	
calcareous iron ore . .	10–20
coal	30–40
chalk	100
sylvinite (potash) . .	500

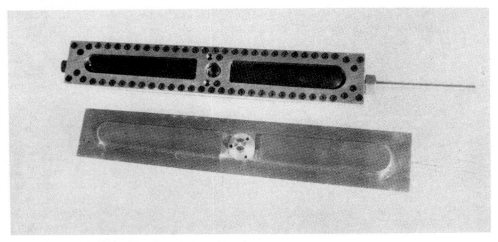

(a) Section showing the two parts of the deformation gauge

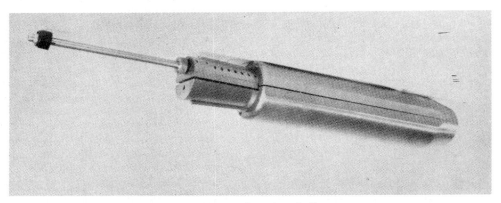

(b) Measuring device placed inside the conic outer shells

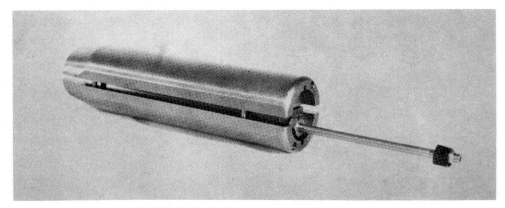

(c) Measuring device sliding between the outer conic shells

Fig. 9. Instrument devised by the C.E.B.T.P. (Paris) for the measuring of the modulus of elasticity of the rock in situ

These figures show how important it is to know the speed and the value of the rock flow for the computation of the stability of a structure set on rock, particularly in the case of hydraulic works.

(d) *Elastic moduli as found by static and by dynamic methods.*—A question that has interested research people for several years is the difference between the elastic modulus of a rock as measured by a static method, and the same quantity as obtained from the measured velocities of sound waves. In the laboratory, when a substance which is at least macro-homogeneous—for example, concrete—is tested by both methods, the values found agree quite well. In situ the results are often very different.

It has often occurred, as an example, that the static method has given moduli ranging between 4,000 and 40,000 kg/sq. cm, whereas the calculated modulus on the basis of sound velocity through the rock has ranged far above 100,000 kg/sq. cm. The explanation sometimes given is that the jack measurements are on small areas of a rock that have developed surface fissures, whereas the waves are transmitted through intact rock at a certain depth.

The problem deserved closer study, particularly in order to confirm whether the relationship understood up to the present to exist between the velocity of waves and the elastic modulus of the rock, was really valid under all circumstances, or whether it should be corrected for the effects of the applied stresses.

Measurements were therefore made in the laboratory on rock samples that had previously been subjected to high stresses. The samples were tested by both the static and the dynamic method, and the elastic modulus was calculated in each case. The stresses previously applied ranged all the way up to the beginning of plastic flow.

It was found that this previous stressing hardly affected the results of the static test, but that the velocity of sound through the rock was strongly influenced by the internal disorganization accompanying the incipient flow.

For example, tests on gypsum showed that a previous hydrostatic pressure of 500 to 1,000 kg/sq. cm caused the velocity of sound to fall from 3,600 m/sec down to 1,800 or even only 1,200 m/sec. On the other hand, if the stress/strain curve is drawn for different applied loads it is apparent that the elastic modulus calculated from the static tests remains unchanged.

From these considerations it emerges that the simple equation:

$$V = \sqrt{\frac{E}{\gamma} \frac{1-\nu}{(1+\nu)(1-2\nu)}}$$

is not adequate when applied to waves transmitted under load, but requires a further term to allow for this. This problem is the subject of research at present under way at the École Polytechnique.

Moreover, even these remarks do not entirely cover the problem of the divergencies found in the field. In the case of rock known to have suffered tectonic deformations, and which had previously been subjected to very high stresses, the elastic modulus calculated from sound velocity was much higher than the value calculated from the static test. As the result of stresses is to reduce the sound velocity, it may be supposed that if there had been no tectonic movements the two values would still be wider apart.

Such are the lines of study that this laboratory has adopted in the course of its first year of existence. But laboratory work is only part of the research and, even though the studies in the field have for a long time lacked sufficient basic support, the essential part of the research in rock mechanics must be the field work.

It is now intended to describe some of the improvements that have been made in the course of the past few years in field methods, in ways of measuring the properties of a rock in situ.

Finally, I will refer to the artificial modification of a natural terrain to improve it for the engineer.

B. *The measurement of rock characteristics in situ*

(*a*) *The modulus of deformation.*—During the past 10 years the methods already described for measuring rock characteristics in the field have been used where required by the civil engineers. But these methods have their drawbacks. The jack method for finding the elastic modulus relates to small wall areas in the gallery where the test is made. A great many measurements are required to give an average, and even this value tells nothing about the rock at depth. Velocity measurements do, of course, give average values related to certain wave paths; but the waves practically always travel in sound rock, avoiding the obstacles; that is the fissures. The values obtained are therefore generally too high. There is also the uncertainty caused by the effect on the velocity of stresses left over by ancient tectonic movements, a problem to which the laboratory has drawn attention.

It was therefore decided to examine the possibility of developing a device that would measure stresses and deformations at depth in a borehole. The Électricité de France have formed a working party whose task it is to bring together the various existing apparatus for making these measurements, to examine them, and to make comparative tests. A report on this work will be submitted to the next Congress for Large Dams in 1964.

Here it should be remembered that the requirement is merely for an apparatus capable of measuring the modulus of deformation of the rock in situ, not for making direct measurements of the ground stresses.

The following types of apparatus will now be discussed:

(1) *The C.E.B.T.P. apparatus*

This instrument has been developed by Dawance, Bonvallet, and Noel. It is based on the principle of the flat jack, but is so constructed that it can be introduced into a borehole (see Figs 9(a), (b), and (c)).

The apparatus comprises a solid steel cylinder divided by an axial cut into two halves. The two halves are partly hollowed out to receive a pair of rubber bags, which are filled with oil and so arranged that by increasing the oil pressure the bags tend to push the steel half-cylinders apart, the apparatus thus acting as a jack.

An induction extensometer sensitive to 0·01 mm is located between the two rubber bags and allows for an accurate measurement of relative movement between the two steel halves. The apparatus thus measures the stress applied and the deformations of the borehole. The figure obtained in the field is then compared to a scale drawn in the laboratory after tests on plaster, lean concrete, and hard concrete, which relates their modulus of deformation to the figures given by the instrument. The elastic modulus of the rock is thus obtained.

This jack must be set firmly in place in the drill hole. Initially this was done by casting plaster or an alloy of very low melting point around the instrument. The process was quite delicate since it is necessary to recover the apparatus after the measurement.

The method used at present is to anchor the jack in the hole by means of two conical half-shell pieces similar to those used by Professor Potts, that fit together to form a steel sleeve. In operation, the assembly forms a tight plug seal in the drill hole. After a measurement has been made, one of the conical elements is pulled out and the assembly can be withdrawn from the hole, or it can be moved to another position higher or lower in the hole. With this facility, the apparatus can be used to examine the whole length of a drill hole in quite a short time.

By this method it should be possible to make a rapid examination over the length of a borehole measuring the modulus of the rock at all depths and in different directions, and thus to obtain the data required for calculating the abutments of a dam (see Figs 10 and 11).

A further point of considerable interest has been brought out by these studies. Tests were made in the laboratory on blocks of plaster, and subsequently on blocks of concrete, to find out how the elastic modulus changed with increasing load. The block was placed between the plates of a press and stressed under controlled conditions. It was found that the stress/strain curve had a kink dividing it into two parts, each providing a distinct value of the elastic modulus. It has been found by experience that this kink corresponds to the pressure in the test block. It is therefore assumed that, in the field, the kink should occur as soon as the pressure provided by the jack becomes equal to the external pressure on the gauge. This is a method for determining this pressure. This has been checked in the field several times and allows the measurement of a pressure in the ground.

It may therefore be said that this apparatus allows complete testing over the whole length of a borehole, giving for each depth the elastic modulus of the rock and also the ground pressure at that depth.

It also has an interesting potential in that it has a very small diameter. The one now in use is of conical shape, the overall diameter being only 70–80 mm. This instrument can therefore be sent down an ordinary borehole, thus providing the most economical mode of use.

It may be felt that this description does not sufficiently refer to the formulas which have been devised in order to obtain the rock characteristics from the deformation under stress.

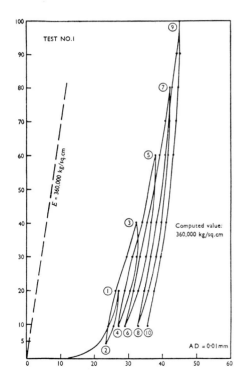

Fig. 10. Measurement of the modulus C.E.B.T.P. of elasticity in a borehole with the gauge. Test on the gneiss at La Bathie Roseland. Test 1.

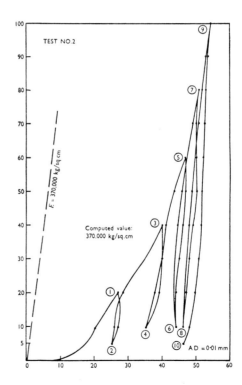

Fig. 11. Measurement of the modulus of elasticity in a borehole with the C.E.B.T.P. gauge. Test on the gneiss at La Bathie Roseland. Test 2.

They have been reviewed but as they all are based on homogeneity, isotropy, no fissuration, they really did not apply to actual field work.

(2) *The Janod–Mermin apparatus*

This apparatus was developed almost 10 years ago by Janod and Mermin, engineers on the staff of the Électricité de France, and was put into operation in 1956 to help with the study of the deformation of the rock under stress in the terrain to be passed through by the lower parts of the Roseland pressure tunnel.

It comprises a steel tube 770 mm long, 164 mm diameter, with a wall thickness of 10 mm. The steel tube is enclosed in an outer sleeve of annealed aluminium, the two tubes being joined by ring seals at either end so as to leave a hollow space between the two.

In operation, this jacket space is filled with water, which is put under pressure. The outer surface of the aluminium sleeve presses against the rock wall.

For the measurement of lateral extension there are two pairs of distance feelers arranged to measure lateral extension in two directions at right angles to each other. Each feeler passes through the wall of the steel tube by means of a pressure-tight piston bush. The outer tip of the feeler rests in contact with the inner surface of the aluminium sleeve and the inner tip touches an adjustable wedge, which transmits movement to the sensor of the instrument proper.

This apparatus, once in place, allows determination of the stress/strain curve for the rock in two directions at right angles. The assembly is extremely robust and can give readings up to about 250 kg/sq. cm, which is the limit for the joints.

(3) *The apparatus made by Mr Kujundzic, of the Cerni Institute in Belgrade (l'Institut d'Hydraulique Jaroslav Cerni)*

This apparatus is derived from the Janod–Mermin, and Mr Kujundzic has used it a great deal in Yugoslavia. Instead of the aluminium sleeve the Kujundzic apparatus uses a rubber cylinder with a wall thickness of 10 mm, which ensures good pressure distribution on the rock wall. In this case lateral extension is measured by feelers passing through pressure-tight glands in the wall of the instrument, and acting on a Huggenberger cell.

In spite of its size and the diameter of the borehole required, the Kujundzic apparatus is apparently in frequent use in Yugoslavia.

So far as is known to the Author these are the only instruments that have been developed for measuring directly the elastic modulus of rock in situ. There are quite a number of instruments for measuring stresses in boreholes. Some do this directly by simultaneous measurement of deformation in two planes at right angles, assuming that the rock is homogeneous and isotropic, and applying the corresponding formulas.

Other instruments allow indirect determination of the stresses based on the knowledge of the elastic modulus of the rock as previously measured on a core sample in the laboratory.

There are in particular the instrument developed by Professor Potts of the University of Durham, Newcastle; the apparatus of Mr Leeman of the South African Council for Scientific and Industrial Research; that of Professor Hast of Sweden; the instrument of Mr Obert of the American Bureau of Mines; the instrument of Mr May of the Department of Mines of Canada; and that of Mr Averchin of the U.S.S.R.

This long list shows how great is the interest that has developed in the course of recent years in many countries in this problem.

These instruments have all been built for mining engineers for the measurements of depth stresses.

There is not much to say about the instruments used for the dynamic measurements. These are the same as those used in geophysical work and, except for the use of transistors, no great changes in design have occurred during the past 10 years. Practically the same methods are used today in all countries.

The shear resistance of rock.—The advantage of the measurements of moduli, which have been described, is that they give values which can be used as such in the computation of structures. Other tests have been devised, particularly the measurement of the shear resistance of the rock and of the adherence at the rock-concrete contact surface. The trouble is that these tests are very costly, very difficult to carry out, and, even so, the resulting figures are nothing else but general information and not a basis for the calculation of the structures. As an example of this type of tests, the set-up adopted by Habib and Bernède for a series of tests carried out for the Cie Nationale du Bas-Rhône et du Languedoc will be described shortly.

In a gallery, a short tunnel is driven, leaving on both sides a protruding cube cut out of the rocky mass. These two protruding elements are embedded in a concrete block reaching across the tunnel and cut in two in the middle so that a flat jack can be inserted between both halves. The lower face of the block is laid on a slab coated with bitumen so as to reduce the friction. When the block has been poured the space between the block and the end of the tunnel is filled with concrete, strongly reinforced along the bottom face of the block. A slot parallel to this face and of the same length as the block is kept open while pouring the concrete so that another flat jack or better two of the same dimensions can be placed in this slot. Using these different jacks, compression and shear stresses can be applied to the rock. If the compression is kept constant, the shear stresses can be increased until rupture occurs. The shear resistance of the rock can thus be calculated. If the rock can be considered as homogeneous and isotropic and if several tests could be made with different values of the compressive strength it would be possible to draw the corresponding Mohr diagram. As the tests are costly and painstaking, one test only is generally made, so that the information obtained can only be used as a check of the values reached by other methods (see Fig. 12).

A similar set-up makes it possible to measure the adherence between the rock and the concrete. In the cases of which I have known, the plane or better the surface of rupture was entirely in the rock. This is not surprising, as generally these measurements are made only when the resistance of the rock is doubtful and because the test can only be made after high explosive has been used to drive the tunnel so that cracks have been produced near the surface.

Mr Kujundzic from Belgrade and Dr Muller from Salzburg have made similar tests with more or less expensive arrangements. The trouble with these tests is that they are much more costly and painstaking than the ordinary jack tests, and, in spite of it, they give only particulars of one location and, even so, for a superficial area of rock. The information gained can therefore not be considered as representative of the average material.

C. *An example of a study on rock in situ*

Among the many studies that I might describe I will select one, now under way for a dam in the south of France, because these studies typically show what great differences there can be between elastic moduli for the same rock, calculated on the basis of different methods of measurement.

This dam is intended as a defence against floods. The suggested site is in a gneiss massive, and seemed at first to be quite favourable, even though lying between various conspicuous surface irregularities.

The rock is rather cracked, particularly on the left bank of the river. On the other hand, there are present in the river bed large blocks of rock which seem quite sound, little fissured, and not altered, and which suggest that the fissuration on the banks is fairly superficial.

The preliminary study of the project had suggested the insertion of an arch dam, and it was to confirm this idea that a reconnaissance programme was launched, which included driving four galleries into the rock, one on each bank upstream and one on each bank downstream of the intended position for the dam.

Since the instruments for measuring elastic moduli at depth in a drill hole which have been described before are now up to experimental prototypes, jacks were used, practically of the same type as those used 10 years ago in the preliminary rock studies for the bearings of the dam at Tignes.

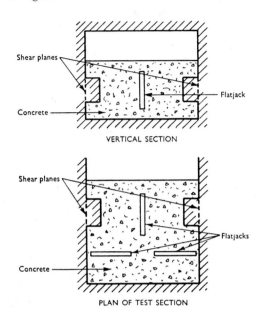

Fig. 12.   **Shear resistance of rock test in situ**

In order to compare the results with the dynamic method the propagation velocity of sound waves was also measured.   Inside the galleries it was at once apparent, merely by glancing at the exposed rock wall, that the cracks were not confined to the surface but, in fact, penetrated far into the terrain.   The engineer in charge was therefore requested to drive these galleries, which were only about 12 m deep, to greater depths.   This is at present being done and tests will be resumed shortly.

But the results of these first tests are of considerable interest in their own right.   The jacks were loaded up to as much as 100 tons thrust, corresponding to an applied pressure of 80 kg/sq. cm on the rock wall.   This is more than 50% higher than the pressure applied by an arch dam.

While the pressure in the jack was being increased, a running record was made of the elastic modulus; that is, of the slope of the tangent to the stress/strain curve.   It was found that when thrust is first applied by the jack the stress/strain curve climbs with little steepness.   If, however, the pressure is allowed to rise to a moderate value and is then taken off the jack, the return line drawn in this way is steeper and cuts the x-axis at a point determined by the residual deformations remaining at the support areas.   If the pressure is again increased the stress/strain line rises as a nearly straight line the slope of which is independent of the pressure previously applied, but can differ for different support points (Fig. 13).

Thus two slopes were obtained.   The one first recorded was called E' and that obtained in the repetition run E.   The latter corresponds a quasi-elastic deformation but whether it can be regarded as the true elastic modulus of the rock is difficult to say.

When pressure is first applied the rock gives way comparatively easily, an effect corresponding to the closing of the microfissures in the affected zone of the rock.   This zone is that for which Boussinesq, having calculated the stresses in depth on the assumption that rock is an elastic semi-solid, had found appreciable values.

Thus, even if the rock is not perfectly elastic, the physical phenomena are still the same; that is the stresses in depth resulting from a thrust applied to the surface are a function of the thrust applied and of the bearing area of the pad.   The first load on the pad gradually closes the fissures as far as a certain depth.   On the application of further loads the rock behaves as a quasi-elastic substance; for example, the initial curve for increasing pressures is not subsequently covered by the return curve for decreasing pressures, but the subsequent curves, there and back, all cover each other perfectly.

A consequence of this behaviour is that, for each position in the gallery, two values E' and E are obtained for the modulus of deformation—the first for the initial loading, the second for subsequent cycles.

If the latter is not the true elastic modulus of the rock, then at least it is a quasi-elastic modulus.

Table 2 shows the values of E' and E measured at five different places at the site in question. The Table also shows the ratio of the residual strain to the maximum measured strain, for each cycle. The final column shows, by extrapolation, the amount of flow to be expected after one year of application of the maximum stress. This figure gives an idea of the magnitude of the possible deformation after construction. In all the tests the amount of further settlement after the initial settling of the pad was very little. This could mean that the microfissuration was not extensive and was quickly closed by the first application of load to the pad of the jack. Further deformation would then be very little. Under these circumstances the value given in the Table for the elastic modulus would remain valid irrespective of the duration of the stressed condition.

It will be seen that the total elastic modulus is quite low, even along the bottom of the valley where the rock appears to be sound. These values are particularly important for the engineer designing a dam because this kind of structure always rests on decompressed rock. Actually in the case under investigation the quasi-elastic modulus E was always found to be of the same order of magnitude as the initial modulus E'.

After this first survey the engineers could not feel confident that an arch dam could be constructed in this position without expensive consolidation of the massive. The decision was taken to drive the exploratory galleries further in and to see if and where the rock might become more compact and better able to provide a good bearing.

While these static measurements were being made, the same laboratory was simultaneously making an extensive series of dynamic measurements. These dynamic tests are done much more rapidly than the static tests, and they were consequently in greater numbers. Examination of some forty separate measurements revealed the following grouping.

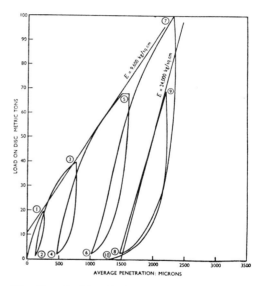

Fig. 13. **Jacking test in gneiss in a tunnel 7 m from the entrance at St Jean du Gard**

1. The measurements made near the surface on the fissured part of the massive showed propagation velocities close to the value 2,000 m/sec.
2. The measurements made on the apparently sound parts of the massive, the non-fissured part gave velocities grouped around 4,000 m/sec.

From these measurements it is clear that the results do give a general idea of the fissuration. But do they provide anything more quantitative than a general comparison?

As already mentioned the usual expression, which assumes that the medium is elastic and isotropic, takes the form:

$$V = \sqrt{\frac{E}{\gamma} \frac{1-\nu}{(1+\nu)(1-2\nu)}}$$

But if this expression is used to calculate the elastic modulus of the rock from the wave velocities measured at the positions of the three jacks 2, 3, and 5, and compare these calculated

Table 2

Results of mechanical tests in situ

Test No.	Gallery place of test	Nature and state of rock	Direction of stress	Elastic modulus: kg/sq. cm*			Rock flow after 1 year under stress of: 55 kg/sq. cm (microns)
				E' Total	E Rapid reversibility	Relative residual depth of impression: W_r/W_t %†	
1	R.D. *downstream* 7 m from the inlet (floor)	Altered gneiss Many clefts and fissures	Almost vertical dips towards South	9,600	24,000	59–50 43–40	50
2	R.D. *downstream* 7·50 m from inlet (wall on side of mountain)	Ditto.	Almost horizontal, dips towards South	28,000	42,000	40–29 17–16	15
3	R.D. *downstream* 9 m from inlet (wall on side of mountain)	Ditto.	Horizontal	18,500	30,000	50–30 16–14	—
4	R.D. *downstream* 11 m from inlet (wall away from mountain)	Mylonitized zone, vertical dip	Horizontal	6,000	17,000	60–45 31–29	40
5	In the bed of the Gardon	Apparently sound	Horizontal	50,000	96,000	50–27 14	—

* Deformation under the pad obtained by extrapolation.
† W_r (residual) W_t (total) W_r/W_t for each cycle and in chronological order.

dynamic values with the static values previously found, no agreement is reached as following Table will show.

Table 3
Elastic modulus, in bars (bar=1·02 kg/sq. cm)

Position of jack number	Total modulus E'	Quasi-elastic modulus E	Dynamic modulus E
2	28,000	42,000	290,000
3	18,500	30,000	275,000
5	50,000	96,000	620,000

Agreement is not good even between the dynamic modulus and the final static modulus E after the first settling of the pad of the jack; in fact, even there, the dynamic modulus is 6 to 10 times higher. It is evident that these dynamic values do not give a reliable picture of the mechanical quality of the rock.

Discrepancies of this kind are systematically revealed by tests carried out in the field and it was considered worth while that Habib should undertake a study of this problem and try to discover the relationship between wave velocity, as measured at the site, and elastic modulus as understood by the civil engineer.

These differences have also been evident for some time to M. Bollo of the Société de Recherches Géophysiques, who has very kindly allowed me access to his records for the preparation of the present lecture. In his reports, M. Bollo always quotes propagation velocities as measured by micro-seismograph. When he finds it necessary to quote an elastic modulus he compares the dynamic values obtained to static measures made at the site without involving theoretical expressions. It should be mentioned here that all the studies that have been referred to, were made on fissured terrains which have in the past suffered tectonic movements. What the results would be in compact, non-fissured granite, such as is found in Sweden, is not known. But in regard to all the rocks tested in France in practically no case has there ever emerged a satisfactory agreement between the dynamic and the static values for elastic moduli.

D. *The artificial improvement of rocks in situ. Treatment by grouting*

It is not my intention to end this presentation with the confession of the shortcomings of our laboratory. I prefer to mention the continued advance that has been made recently in the improvement of the mechanical properties of rock notably by means of grouts.

Before describing what is being done today, let me first go back more than 10 years, to Morocco, where a study was being made on the lining of the gallery at Im Fout.

The results have been reported by Mr Bernard (1953) to the 1953 Conference at Zurich.

In order to investigate the possibility of lining a low-pressure tunnel with unreinforced concrete, grouting tests were made so as to compare the modulus of deformation before and after, as well as the final prestress obtained. This was done in a gallery with lining in place, by injecting behind the lining a charge of cement grout to a depth of 4 m into the rock, under a driving pressure of 30 kg/sq. cm, and using 175 kg of cement per square metre of gallery wall.

In order to obtain a picture of the deformations in the lining, eleven acoustic wires were installed, each 20 cm long. These instruments indicated high compressive stresses (89 kg/sq. cm on the average) corresponding to about 2/3 of the internal pressure required in a tube of the same diameter and wall thickness to develop a uniform external pressure equal to the injection pressure. After 14 days the deformations had still a residual 2/3 of their initial values. By this time the cement had set hard and the stresses applied to the lining by the rock had become finally stabilized.

The effect of these measures is shown in Table 4 which gives the elastic modulus of the rock before and after the injection, as measured by a jack in the gallery.

It will be seen that as early as 1953 grouting was successfully used to improve artificially the mechanical qualities of a rock in situ. A second effect achieved at the same time was a substantial prestressing of the lining, in the sense of a compressive stress, with evident mechanical advantage. But the most interesting thing about this early operation is that, already then, the improvements to the characteristics of a terrain have been measured and the effect of the work strictly controlled.

To what extent the abutments of a dam can be improved by this method had been successfully demonstrated since 1947–48 at the Castillon dam, where one of the abutments was consolidated by the injection of 9,000 metric tons of ternary grout with cement.

Finally, let me describe a recent example, the dam at Avène, an arch dam that was finally constructed after extensive grouting following a careful study of the possibilities of artificially consolidating the abutments.

Table 4

Direction of measurement relative to dip of rock	Elastic modulus of rock				
	Before injection Jack test			After injection	
	Initial elastic modulus: E'	Final elastic modulus: E	Test in gallery	Jack test: E	Test in gallery: E
Perpendicular	10,000	57,000	25,000	100,000	97,000
Parallel	12,500	43,500	Not measurable	200,000	236,000

Both static and dynamic tests were made on the site. The static tests were carried out in a tunnel 2·50 m in diameter and 22 m long through quartzite rocks at a level 10 m below the position for the abutment on the right bank, the tunnel being driven to near a fault well known in this part of the site.

In the floor of the gallery, two shafts were sunk with the intention of making measurements in the direction of the abutments and in a direction at right angles to this.

Two series of measurements were made, the first before and the second after the experimental consolidation of the rock. After making the first series of measurements, with the jack thrusting against the natural rock, the gallery was lined and the shafts filled with sand. The polished places on the rock wall that had been used for applying the pad of the jack were protected by covering them with several layers of paper.

The rock was then grouted from the interior of the gallery. These injections were done in two phases. In the first phase injection under a pressure of 5 kg/sq. cm was made at the plane of contact between the concrete and the rock. A second series of injections was then made at positions forming a halo at a distance of 2 m, the pressure this time being near 50 kg/sq. cm.

That the elastic modulus of the rock was sharply increased by this treatment is evident from Table 5.

From this Table it will be seen that at the far end of the gallery, near the fault, where the

Table 5

Elastic moduli

Emplacement	Injection	Stress at right angles to dip			Stress in direction of dip		
		E' Initial elastic modulus	E Elastic modulus	Irreversible residue % of total per cycle	E' Initial deformation	E Elastic deformation	W Irreversible residue % of total per cycle
Bottom of gallery	Before	9,600	48,000	72–42–26	19,600	34,500	40–25–5
	After	54,000	93,000	42–27–12	51,000	120,000	44–34–14
Halfway along	Before	5,000	60,000	77–56–34	4,000	22,500	75–53–13
	After	65,000	170,000	83–34–11	72,000	190,000	45–13–3

rock before injection showed a very poor elastic modulus, the treatment brought a particularly great improvement (Fig. 14).

On the basis of these first tests the engineer in charge of the project requested the Société de Recherches Géophysiques to make a series of micro-seismic measurements, for correlation with the results of the static measurements. By this means it was possible to make a wider reconnaissance of the site and thus describe the borders between the cracked surface area and the zone of compact quartzites. By correlation with the static measurements it was then possible to estimate the elastic moduli for the various regions.

Moreover, this second study allowed an effective mapping of the areas that required treatment by grouting.

CONCLUSIONS

The actual possibilities of rock mechanics as seen through the eyes of a civil engineer may be summed up as follows.

The static and dynamic methods for testing rock in situ, which were developed about 10 years ago, are still applied in the field, in spite of their uncertainties. Already today micro-seismic measurements of the propagation velocities of sound waves can be correlated with direct static measurements of the elastic modulus to provide an approximate picture of the distribution of mechanical properties in a terrain. But one can with confidence predict a time when it will be routine procedure in every reconnaissance borehole to make a systematic check of the main mechanical characteristics of the rock, on the spot, just as the permeability and the percentage of recuperation are already determined now, these tests sometimes following a direct scrutiny of the drill hole by television.

But perhaps the most rapid progress is taking place today in the laboratory, particularly in two directions, the first being the very important development of methods for measuring the alterability of a rock, the second the study of how the mechanical properties of a rock are changed by applied stresses.

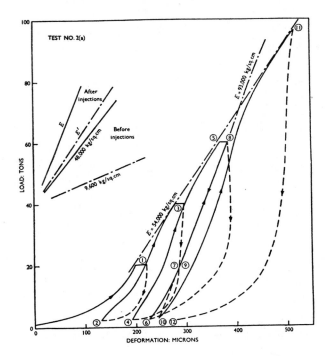

Fig. 14. Consolidation of rock by means of cement grouting. Moduli of deformation before and after grouting at Avène

These directions of advance, along which movement has already begun, will in the course of the next 10 years certainly bring us new knowledge and effective new techniques in this field.

And now I would ask the British Society for Soil Mechanics once again to accept my thanks for the great honour they have bestowed on me in inviting me to discuss these matters. I also tender my most sincere thanks to all those who by their work through the years have made this discussion possible, particularly to M. Habib who has made such valuable contributions as head of the laboratory under Professor Mandel, to M. Bernède who was in charge of all the tests reported here, to M. Bollo and to the Société de Recherches Géophysiques who placed at my disposal some of their reports, and finally to M. Bauzil, Directeur Général de la Compagnie d'Aménagement du Bas-Rhône et du Languedoc, who granted me authority to quote them.

REFERENCES

BERNARD, P., 1953. "Mesure des modules élastiques et application au calcul des galeries en charge" ("Measurement of moduli of elasticity and their application to the design of pressure tunnels"). *Proc. 3rd Int. Conf. Soil Mech., Zurich*, 2:145–156.

MAYER, A., 1953. "Les propriétés mécaniques des roches" ("The mechanical properties of rocks"). *Géotechnique*, 3:8:329–338.

RENAUD, J., 1962. "Le tunnel routier sous le Mont-Blanc" ("The tunnel under Mont Blanc"). *Travaux*, 338:835–848.

SOCIÉTÉ HYDROTECHNIQUE DE FRANCE, MEETING, 1962. "Symposium on Bulles et Gouttes" ("Symposium on drops and bubbles"). General Report on question 6, by A. Mayer, p. 415, and Special Report by Professor G. Eyraud (Lyon), p. 427.

LONG-TERM STABILITY OF CLAY SLOPES

A. W. Skempton, D.Sc., M.I.C.E., F.R.S.

I wish to thank the British Geotechnical Society for inviting me to give the fourth Rankine Lecture, and to thank Dr Cooling for his very kind remarks.

In preparing the Lecture I have received a great deal of help from various people, especially Mr John Hutchinson, Dr Laurits Bjerrum and Mr Kenneth Early, while most of the field work which I shall describe was carried out jointly with Dr David Henkel. The long-term stability of clay slopes has indeed been one of the preoccupations of Dr Henkel and myself for the past 12 years; and I would like to take this opportunity of paying tribute to the value of the contributions which he made in this particular subject, and generally to soil mechanics and engineering geology, during the time he spent in Great Britain. I am also deeply grateful to my wife for her interest, criticism, and suggestions which have been most valuable.

INTRODUCTION

When a cutting is made in clay the pore pressure at any point depends partly on the position of the ground-water level, but also, to an important extent, on the response of the clay to the changes in stress which have taken place during excavation. In the course of time, however, the pore pressures through the clay gradually adjust themselves until finally they are everywhere in hydrostatic equilibrium with the ground water. This is the stage known as the "long-term" condition, in contrast with the "short-term" or "end-of-construction" condition.

All natural slopes exist in the long-term condition, while in cuttings this stage is not reached until several months or years after excavation; the time required depending chiefly upon the permeability of the clay.

I shall be concerned only with the long-term condition. Thus in all the field cases considered, whether in cuttings or natural slopes, the pore-pressure u at any point on a potential or real slip surface can be determined from the ground-water flow net (Fig. 1). From statical considerations it is also possible to calculate with reasonable accuracy the pressure σ and shear stress τ at any point on the slip surface.

Turning now to the resistance offered by the clay to sliding along this surface, it has long been known that the shear strength of a clay may be represented by the Coulomb–Terzaghi equation:

$$s = \bar{c}' + (\sigma - u) \tan \phi'$$

where $\bar{c}'$ is the "cohesion intercept" and ϕ' is the "angle of shearing resistance"; both parameters being expressed in terms of the effective stress $\sigma' = (\sigma - u)$ acting normal to the slip surface.

In a stable slope only a part of the total available shear resistance along a potential slip surface will be mobilised to balance the total shear force. Thus, in general, we may write:

$$\sum \tau = \sum \frac{\bar{c}'}{F} + \sum (\sigma - u) \frac{\tan \phi'}{F}$$

where F is defined as the "factor of safety". For stable slopes F is greater than 1·0. But when a failure occurs the sum of all the shear stresses along the slip surface exactly equals the available strength of the clay, and $F = 1·0$.

There are several quite reliable methods for calculating F for a given slope, once the pore pressures are known and values of $\bar{c}'$ and $\bar{\phi}'$ have been obtained.* Moreover it is a relatively simple matter to carry out shear tests on undisturbed samples of clay. But, as we shall see, from the analysis of actual slips in clays, the values of the shear strength parameters as determined by conventional tests do not necessarily bear any relation to the values which must have been operative in the clay at the time of failure.

This conclusion, which has now been established beyond the slightest doubt, is obviously one of immense practical significance. We must therefore endeavour to understand why, in certain cases, there is a wide discrepancy between our ordinary laboratory test results and the actual field values of shear strength. For such cases we must also try to develop modified laboratory procedures which give results of sufficient reliability to be used with confidence in engineering design. These two objectives form the substance of my Lecture.

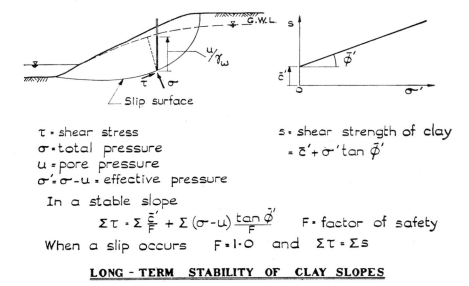

τ = shear stress

σ = total pressure

u = pore pressure

$\sigma' = \sigma - u$ = effective pressure

s = shear strength of clay

$\quad = \bar{c}' + \sigma' \tan \bar{\phi}'$

In a stable slope

$$\Sigma\tau = \Sigma\frac{\bar{c}'}{F} + \Sigma(\sigma - u)\frac{\tan\bar{\phi}'}{F}$$

F = factor of safety

When a slip occurs $F = 1.0$ and $\Sigma\tau = \Sigma s$

LONG - TERM STABILITY OF CLAY SLOPES

Fig. 1

PEAK AND RESIDUAL STRENGTHS

Frequent reference will be made to "over-consolidated" clay and it is well to be clear as to the meaning of this term. In Fig. 2, point (a) represents a clay immediately after deposition, for example on the bed of an estuary. The deposition of more clay will cause an increase in effective pressure and a decrease in water content. At a stage represented by point (b) the clay is "normally-consolidated", in the sense that it has not been subjected to a pressure greater than the present overburden. The shear strength of normally-consolidated clay is proportional to the effective pressure, and the graph expressing the relation between strength and pressure is therefore a straight line passing through the origin of axes.

Many post-glacial clays are normally-consolidated; having been deposited during the eustatic rise of sea level consequent upon the melting of the ice sheets in Late Pleistocene times. But the great majority of clays are much older, and during their geological history have been subjected to very considerable pressure, corresponding to depths of overburden of

* In the cases considered in this Lecture where the slip surface has a section approximating to a circular arc the well known method of analysis due to Dr A. W. Bishop (1954) has been used.

several hundred, or even several thousand feet of sediments, which have subsequently been removed by erosion. The clay is then left in an "over-consolidated" state represented in Fig. 2 by point (d).

The removal of pressure is accompanied by an increase in water content, but this increase is far less than the decrease in water content during consolidation. Thus although the clay at point (d) is under the same effective pressure as the clay at point (b), the water content of the over-consolidated clay is considerably smaller. The particles are therefore in a denser state of packing and, not surprisingly, the shear strength is greater than that of the normally-consolidated clay.

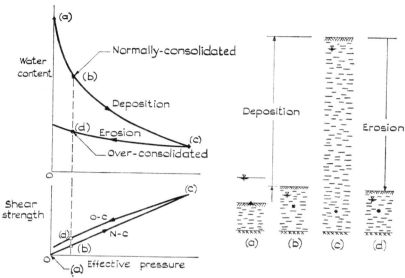

NORMALLY – AND OVER–CONSOLIDATED CLAY

Fig. 2

Examples of over-consolidated clays include the Lias, the Gault and the London Clay. These, and many other clays in this category, are fissured and jointed. They occasionally contain slickensides as well; probably as a result of tectonic movements or unequal expansion during the erosion cycle. Boulder clays are also over-consolidated, by the weight of ice rather than the weight of sediments, but they often show very little in the way of structural discontinuities; being intact, non-fissured materials without joints or slickensides. Most normally-consolidated clays are also free from such imperfections, though fissures can sometimes be seen in clays of this type.

In this Lecture I shall be concerned mainly with over-consolidated clays, since they give rise to much greater problems than the normally-consolidated clays, and they are more widespread.*

Let us, therefore, examine the shear strength characteristics of an over-consolidated clay, as shown in Fig. 3. This figure typifies the results obtained by carrying out slow drained tests in a shear box apparatus, in which the clay is subjected to displacements amounting to several inches.

As the clay is strained, so it builds up an increasing resistance. But, under a given effective pressure, there is a definite limit to the resistance the clay can offer, and this is the

* Over-consolidated clays of high sensitivity, such as the Leda clay in eastern Canada, represent a special class the properties of which may differ appreciably from those of the typical over-consolidated clays considered here.

"peak strength" s_f.   In ordinary practice the test is stopped shortly after the peak strength has been clearly defined, and s_f is referred to simply as the "shear strength" of the clay (under the given effective pressure) without further qualification except, of course, the statement that the test has been carried out under drained conditions, i.e. without the development of pore pressures.

If, however, the test is continued, then we find that as the displacement increases so the resistance or strength of the clay decreases.   But this process, which may be called "strain-softening", is not without limit, for ultimately a certain "residual strength" s_r is reached which the clay maintains even when subjected to large displacements.*   In the comparatively small number of clays so far investigated from this point of view, the strength falls to the residual value after displacements past the peak of the order of 1 in. or 2 in.   But there is field evidence that the strength is not less than this laboratory value (or only slightly less) even at displacements of many feet.

A second shear box test could now be carried out on another specimen of the same clay, but under a different effective pressure.   The results would be of the same type as those

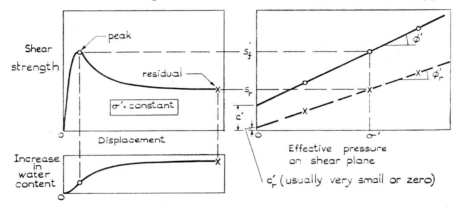

SHEAR   CHARACTERISTICS   OF   OVER-CONSOLIDATED   CLAY

Fig. 3

already described.   And if we suppose that three such tests be made, the peak and residual strengths, when plotted against effective pressure, would show a relationship approximately in accordance with the Coulomb-Terzaghi law.   The peak strengths can therefore be expressed by the equation:

$$s_f = c' + \sigma'. \tan \phi'$$

and the residual strengths by the equation:

$$s_r = c_r' + \sigma'. \tan \phi_r'$$

The test results at present available show almost invariably that c_r' is very small, and probably not significantly different from zero.   Thus I shall assume throughout the rest of the Lecture that for the residual strength we may write:

$$s_r = \sigma'. \tan \phi_r'$$

* The first determination of the residual strength of an undisturbed clay (from the Weser-Elbe canal) was published by Dr B. Tiedemann in 1937.   He carried out drained tests in a ring shear apparatus.   Tests of the same type were made by Dr M. J. Hvorslev (1937) on two clays (Wiener Tegel and Little Belt Clay) consolidated from the slurry condition.   Professor R. Haefeli introduced the term "residual" in 1938 (in German) and in 1950 (in English).   Credit is due to him for insisting on the practical importance of residual strength; at a period when scarcely anyone was interested in this aspect of the shear properties of clays. Tests leading to an approximate determination of the residual strengths of some compacted soils have been reported by Mr J. MacNeil Turnbull (1952).

In other words, in moving from the peak to the residual, the cohesion intercept c' disappears completely. During the same process the angle of shearing resistance also decreases; in some clays by only 1° or 2°, but in others by as much as 10°.

It is notable that during the shearing process over-consolidated clays tend to expand, especially after passing the peak. Part of the drop in strength from the peak value is therefore due to an increasing water content. Of comparable importance, however, is the development of thin bands or domains in which the flaky clay particles are orientated in the direction of shear. The shear strength of a mass of such particles in random orientation must be greater than when the particles are lying parallel to each other. And while it is probable that the formation of orientation domains begins at relatively small strains (Goldstein *et al.*, 1961), there is decisive evidence for the presence of continuous bands of almost perfectly orientated particles in clays subjected to large strains; both in the laboratory (Astbury, 1960) and in the field (as will be described later in this Lecture).

Irrespective of the physical explanation of the drop in strength after passing the peak, the existence of this decrease in strength (especially in over-consolidated clays) must be accepted as a fact which has been fully established. Thus, if for any reason a clay is forced to pass the peak at some particular point within its mass, the strength at that point will decrease. This action will throw additional stress on to the clay at some other point, causing the peak to be passed at that point also. In this way a progressive failure can be initiated and, in the limit, the strength along the entire length of a slip surface will fall to the residual value. Obviously, in any given case, a slip may occur before the residual strength is attained throughout the clay, but once a progressive failure has started the average strength of the clay will decrease inexorably towards the limiting residual value.

Now it is well-known that the strength of solid materials is greatly diminished by the presence of microscopic cracks, holes and other imperfections. In the simplest terms these act as stress concentrators, and they are responsible for fracture taking place at an average stress which is far less than the ideal strength of the material.* And there would seem to be no reason to suppose that the macroscopic fissures, joints and slickensides, present in so many clays, do not also act as stress concentrators in a roughly analogous manner; quite apart from the fact that they act as discontinuous planes of weakness—for it is unlikely that the strength on a fissure or joint can be appreciably higher than the residual value.

Hence we may logically expect that a fissured or jointed clay would not be able to develop its peak strength along the full length of a slip surface. Not only will the fissures and joints reduce the average strength of the clay mass, but they can cause the peak to be crossed, as a result of local over-stressing, and a progressive decrease in strength will follow.

Fissures and other physical discontinuities may not be the only explanation of landslips in clays taking place at strengths well below the conventional peak value. The peak strength as measured in laboratory tests lasting, at the most, a few weeks might be appreciably greater than the strength which could be developed in some clays when the stresses are applied over periods of years, decades or centuries. In other words the effects of shear creep have to be considered; though at present very little quantitative information is available to assess these effects so far as the peak strength is concerned.

Seasonal variations of water content and temperature will also reduce the strength of a clay, but their influence is restricted to a rather shallow depth. Thus, although perhaps of great significance in geomorphological processes, seasonal variations are unlikely to prove important in the relatively deep-seated shear failures of the type considered in this Lecture, except for the evident fact that a landslip would tend to occur at a time when the ground water level was exceptionally high. The pore pressures would then also be exceptionally high, and the effective pressure (and hence the strength) correspondingly low. Nevertheless it is with the

---

* An excellent survey of the physical processes involved in the fracture of solids will be found in the 1963 Bakerian Lecture by Professor A. H. Cottrell.

shear-strength parameters of the clay that we are concerned; not with the effects of such phenomena as pore pressures, earthquakes, lateral pressure release, and so on.

· After these generalities let us examine some actual tests.   Fig. 4 shows the results of tests carried out in the laboratory of Soil Mechanics Ltd and also at Imperial College on samples taken from clay involved in a landslide at Walton's Wood, Staffordshire.   The clay forms the weathered zone, up to 35 ft thick, of a Carboniferous mudstone and it blankets the sides of a valley eroded during a retreat phase of the Last Glaciation in that area.

A typical stress-displacement curve for an undistributed sample of the clay is shown.   In this particular test the effective pressure was held constant at 22·2 lb/sq. in.   The peak strength was found to be 10·8 lb/sq. in. and the residual strength 5·1 lb/sq. in.   These strengths are plotted in the upper diagram with an open circle and a cross respectively.   Similar tests on other specimens, at various effective pressures, show that the peak strength can be represented by the parameters $c' = 320$ lb/sq. ft and $\phi' = 21°$, while the residual strengths fall along a line passing through the origin ($c_r' = 0$) with a slope $\phi_r' = 13°$.

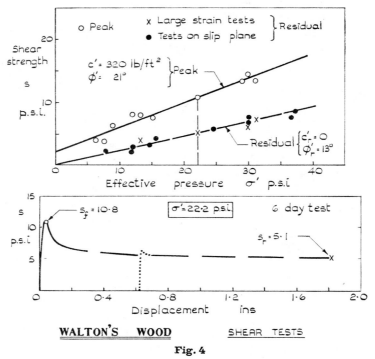

WALTON'S WOOD   SHEAR TESTS

Fig. 4

These tests were carried out in a set of Casagrande shear boxes with specimens 2·36 in. square in plan and 1 in. thick.   After completing the first traverse, with a displacement of about 0·3 in., the box was pushed back to its original position and then sheared again: the process being repeated until the strength of the clay had dropped to a steady (residual) value. Movement in both directions was slow, so that there were presumably no excess pore pressures in the clay, and the whole test took 6 days to complete.*

This technique is admittedly not perfect.   After each reversal a small peak is often observed, as indicated by the dotted line in Fig. 4, and there is some danger of slurrying the clay on the slip surface.   Ideally the displacement should be applied continuously in one

* A different type of reversal shear test, carried out rather quickly, in which the vertical load is varied to maintain a constant volume in the clay specimen during shear, has been described by Professor H. Borowicka (1963).

Fig. 5. Slickensides formed in large strain test on specimen of
undisturbed clay from Walton's Wood

direction, and, as an approach towards this ideal, Dr Alan Bishop is now designing a shear box with a length of 7 in. We are also hoping to build a large ring shear apparatus. Meanwhile, the reversal technique appears to provide a simple and reasonably satisfactory method of measuring the residual strengths of undisturbed clay samples, using equipment already available in every laboratory.*

At Walton's Wood several samples were also obtained which included the actual slip plane. Triaxial test specimens were prepared from these samples in such a way that the slip plane was inclined at about 50° to the horizontal, and the specimens were then subjected to slow drained tests. Failure took place, as expected, along the pre-existing slip surface, and the results are shown in Fig. 4 by solid black circles.† It will be seen that the strengths developed on the slip plane correspond very closely to the residual strengths obtained by subjecting specimens of originally undisturbed, unsheared clay to large displacements.

Moreover, by the time the strength of these latter specimens had fallen to the residual value, extremely well-defined slickensides had developed (Fig. 5).

Using resin and wax impregnation techniques, Mr Early and Mr W. F. Nenninger, of Soil Mechanics Ltd, have succeeded in making several thin sections of the Walton's Wood clay, showing the natural slip plane. This was seen, in fact, to consist of a continuous band within which the clay particles were so strongly orientated, in the direction of shearing, that they formed a domain exhibiting sharp extinction when viewed between crossed nicols. The domain comprising the main slip "surface" had a thickness of the order $20\,\mu$. Associated with it were several secondary slip domains, within a matrix of clay showing moderate orientation, not necessarily parallel to the slip surface, and having a thickness up to about 1 in. This is the softened zone often observed in the immediate vicinity of the slip plane. On either side of this zone the clay was found to exhibit scarcely any orientation.

Domains of strongly orientated particles have also been observed when quite soft remoulded clay is subjected to large strains (Astbury 1960). Moreover, tests by Mr Derek Petley, at Imperial College, have shown that the residual angle of shearing resistance of the Walton's Wood clay when normally-consolidated from a slurry, prepared at the liquid limit, is compatible with the value of $\phi_r' = 13°$ as measured in large strain tests on the undisturbed over-consolidated clay,‡ and in tests on the natural slip plane.

It is therefore possible to suggest, with perhaps a slight degree of over-simplification, that the residual strength of a clay, under any given effective pressure, is the same whether the clay has been normally- or over-consolidated; as indicated in Fig. 6.§ If this idea is correct then the angle ϕ_r' should be a constant for any particular clay whatever its consolidation history; depending only on the nature of the particles.

Some further support for this view is provided by the data in Fig. 7. Here the residual

---

* It is possible that the residual strength can also be measured by cutting a plane in the clay with a fine-wire saw and testing in the triaxial apparatus with this plane inclined at approximately $(45° + \phi_r'/2)$ to the horizontal. Preliminary tests, using very slow rates of strain, suggest that this technique is promising and deserves intensive study.

† If the vertical and horizontal effective stresses acting on the triaxial specimens at failure are σ_1' and σ_3', and if α is the inclination of the slip plane to the horizontal, then

$$s_r = \tfrac{1}{2}(\sigma_1' - \sigma_3'). \cos(2\alpha - 90°)$$
$$\sigma' = \tfrac{1}{2}(\sigma_1' + \sigma_3') - \tfrac{1}{2}(\sigma_1' - \sigma_3'). \sin(2\alpha - 90°)$$

Four of the ten points plotted in Fig. 4 as solid black circles are the results of tests on specimens set up in the shear box with the slip plane coincident with the plane of separation of the top and bottom halves of the box.

‡ A similar result was noted by Tiedemann (1937) who found that the residual strength of the Weser-Elbe clay, when normally-consolidated from a slurry, differed little from the residual strength of the undisturbed (over-consolidated) samples.

§ Thus, although it can be said that an over-consolidated clay at large strains behaves, in effect, as a normally-consolidated material with zero cohesion intercept, this statement is generally true only if we make the comparison with a normally-consolidated clay which has itself been brought into its residual condition.

angles of shearing resistance of a number of normally- and over-consolidated clays are plotted against the clay fraction (percentage of particles, by weight, smaller than 2 μ). No marked difference is found between the two conditions of clay, while all the points indicate a most definite tendency for ϕ_r' to decrease with increasing content of clay particles. Indeed the results suggest that if the soil consisted entirely of clay particles the angle of residual shearing resistance would be directly comparable to the angle of friction ϕ_μ as measured by Horn and Deere (1962) for various layer-lattice minerals including biotite, talc, and chlorite, the physical properties of which are possibly not very different from those of such clay minerals as illite and kaolinite.*

By contrast, the quartz grains in a sand or silt, being roughly spherical in shape, cannot orientate themselves. Thus the residual angle ϕ_r' for sands and silts always remains at a value given approximately by the relationship (Caquot, 1934) for particles in random orientation, shearing at constant volume:

$$\tan \phi_r' = \frac{\pi}{2} \tan \phi_\mu$$

Evidently, in the general case, where the soil consists of particles of clay and silt (and sand), the silt will tend to increase ϕ_r' above the value of ϕ_μ for the clay particles; by inhibiting, to some extent, the full orientation of the clay particles and, at least when there is an appreciable content of silt, by contributing some measure of its own higher angle of shearing resistance.

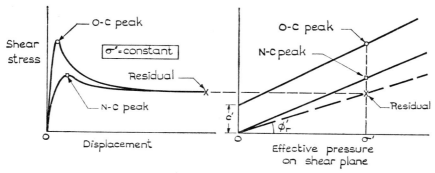

SIMPLIFIED RELATION BETWEEN NORMALLY- AND OVER-CONSOLIDATED CLAY

Fig. 6

RESIDUAL FACTOR

When confronted with the problem as to whether the peak or residual strength should be used in calculating the stability of a slope in over-consolidated clay, the designer is facing the most important question, numerically speaking, with which he will be concerned. To illustrate this point I have collected together in Fig. 8 the results of tests on four quite typical over-consolidated clays, the index properties of which are summarised in Table 1.

The boulder clay from Selset has been consolidated under a moderate thickness of ice, but it is very sandy with a clay fraction of only 17%. Consequently the cohesion intercept of the peak strength is not large and there is a drop of only 2° between the peak and residual angles of shearing resistance. Even so, in the stability analysis of a slope in this clay there is, as we

* These elegant tests by Dr H. M. Horn and Professor D. U. Deere were carried out by measuring the friction developed between the cleavage surfaces of two specimens of a layer-lattice mineral. The angle of friction obtained in such tests is therefore also the angle of shearing resistance of an assemblage of the particles in perfect orientation. The values of ϕ_μ shown in Fig. 7 are for the minerals in a saturated condition.

Table 1

Index Properties of Clays in Fig. 8

(average values)

	LL	PL	Clay fraction
Selset	26	13	17
Jari	70	27	47
London Clay	82	29	55
Walton's Wood	53	28	69

shall see, a difference of more than 30% in the factor of safety as calculated on peak or on residual strengths.

The clay from Jari, in the foothills of the Himalaya, belongs to the Upper Siwalik series and has been consolidated under at least 2,000 ft of sediments. This clay has been tested in connexion with the design of a dam forming part of the great Mangla project in West Pakistan. The samples showed no marked evidence of weathering and, as will be seen, the peak cohesion intercept is high. Indeed, the clay is very stong in its undisturbed state. Yet the residual strengths show no cohesion intercept and an angle of shearing resistance of 18°. At an

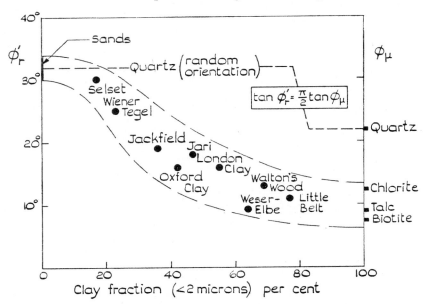

DECREASE IN ϕ'_r WITH

INCREASING CLAY FRACTION

Fig. 7

effective pressure of 1000 lb/sq. ft, for example, the peak strength is 3·6 times greater than the residual, and the practical significance of deciding which strength to use in design therefore requires no further emphasis.

The London Clay, of Eocene age, has been consolidated under a thickness of sediments, subsequently removed by erosion, varying from 500 ft in the eastern parts of Essex up to 1,000 ft in the region west of London. The test results shown in Fig. 8 apply to the zone of weathered clay, extending typically to a depth of 40 ft below the surface. Several case records

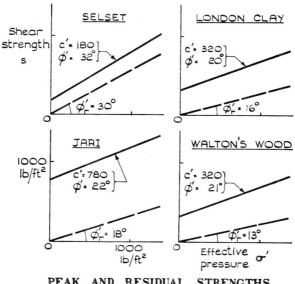

PEAK AND RESIDUAL STRENGTHS
OVER-CONSOLIDATED CLAYS

Fig. 8

of slips in this zone will be given later in the Lecture, and for these the factor of safety based on peak strengths is about 2·7 times greater than the figure based on residual strengths.

Finally, data are given in Fig. 8 for the Walton's Wood clay. Here it may be mentioned that the peak factor of safety, as calculated on the actual slip surface of this landslide, is about three times higher than the result obtained by using residual strengths.

The question as to whether peak or residuals should be used in design cannot therefore be dismissed as a matter of merely academic interest. And in the remainder of the Lecture I shall consider as briefly as possible those case records at present available which can help to throw some light on this problem.

My procedure will be, in the first place, to describe the slip and then present the results of a stability analysis of the slip. These results will be given in terms of the average effective

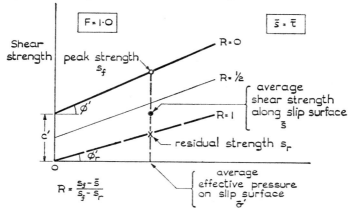

DEFINITION OF RESIDUAL FACTOR

Fig. 9

stress $\bar{\sigma}'$ and the average shear stress $\bar{\tau}$ acting on the slip surface.   In Fig. 9 these two values give the point shown by a solid black circle, and this point remains constant (after the "long-term" condition has been reached) except for the relatively small seasonal variations in pore pressure.   The actual value of $\bar{\sigma}'$ is, however, calculated using the best estimate of pore pressures existing when the slip took place.

In the second place I shall give the results of laboratory determinations of the peak and residual strengths.   With reference to Fig. 9 it is then at once possible to read off the peak strength s_f and the residual strength s_r corresponding to the average effective pressure $\bar{\sigma}'$.

Now, as in each case a slip has occurred, the factor of safety must be equal to 1·0 and the actual average shear strength of the clay at the time of the slip $\bar{s}$ must be equal to the average shear stress $\bar{\tau}$.   Thus, by comparing the value of $\bar{s}$ with the values of s_f and s_r we can see at a glance whether the strength of the clay involved in the slip was at the peak, or at the residual or, perhaps, at some intermediate value.   Indeed, if the concept of progressive failure is valid for fissured clays, we may expect to find that the average strength of these clays decreases with time; and the slip occurs when the average strength has reached a value equal to the average shear stress which, as previously mentioned, has been acting continuously since the slope came into being.

In order to have a convenient quantitative expression for the amount by which the average strength has fallen I shall introduce the "residual factor", defined by the expression:

$$R = \frac{s_f - \bar{s}}{s_f - s_r}$$

or
$$\bar{s} = Rs_r + (1 - R)s_f$$

Thus, in physical terms, R is the proportion of the total slip surface in the clay along which its strength has fallen to the residual value.

Clearly, if no reduction in strength has occurred and the whole of the clay is at the peak strength, then $R = 0$.   Conversely, if the average strength has reached the residual value, $R = 1·0$.   For the point shown in Fig. 9 the average strength has fallen rather more than halfway between the two limits and R is about 0·6; or about 60 per cent of the slip surface passes through clay having the residual strength.

The object in examining the case records is, therefore, to determine the value of R and relate this as far as possible to the type of clay.

CASE RECORDS

*Jackfield**

In 1952 a landslide occurred at the village of Jackfield, Shropshire, on the River Severn $1\frac{1}{4}$ miles downstream of Iron Bridge; destroying several houses and causing major dislocations in a railway and road (Fig. 10).   In this locality the Severn flows through a V-shaped valley (the so-called Iron Bridge gorge) which has been eroded largely, if not entirely, since the retreat of the main ice sheet of the Last Glaciation.   Erosion is indeed still continuing, and the sides of the valley are covered by a mosaic of landslides, of varying ages.

It is possible that previous landslides may have taken place along at least a part of the present slip surface, but the slope must have been more or less stable for a long time before 1950, when warnings of instability were observed in the form of a broken water main serving cottages near the river bank.   Towards the end of 1951 further movement was noted, and by February 1952 the road was becoming dangerous.   During the next month or two the landslide developed alarmingly.   Six houses were completely broken up, gas mains had to be relaid above ground, the railway could be maintained only by daily adjustments to the track and a

---

* The Jackfield landslide has been published previously (Henkel and Skempton, 1954), but I have recently made a critical re-examination of all the original data, with results that differ in some respects from those given 10 years ago.

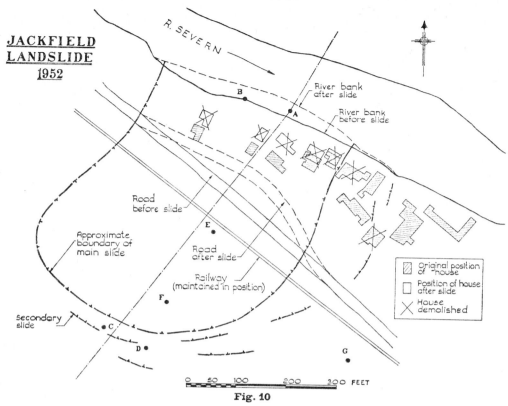

**JACKFIELD
LANDSLIDE
1952**

R. SEVERN

B

A

River bank
after slide

River bank
before slide

Road
before slide

E

Approximate
boundary of
main slide

Road
after slide

Railway
(maintained in position)

F

Secondary
slide

C

D

G

| Original position of house |
| Position of house after slide |
| House demolished |

0 50 100   200   300 FEET

Fig. 10

minor road along the river had to be closed to traffic.   By this time the maximum downhill
displacement totalled 60 ft.

In the autumn of 1952 an investigation was undertaken by Dr Henkel and myself.   Movements, which had become almost stationary during the summer, were again taking place and
we were able to observe the exact depth of the slip surface in four boreholes (Fig. 11).

JACKFIELD   LANDSLIDE   1952

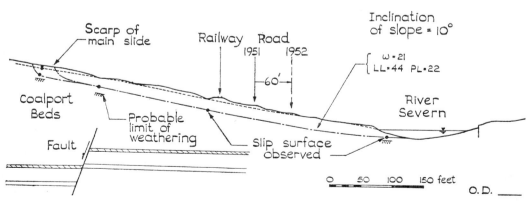

Scarp of
main slide

Railway Road
1951   1952

Inclination
of slope = 10°

$w = 21$
$LL = 44$ $PL = 22$

Coalport
Beds

Probable
limit of
weathering

River
Severn

Fault

Slip surface
observed

60'

0   50   100   150 feet

O.D.

Fig. 11

The strata, consisting of very stiff clays and mudstone, alternating with marl-breccia and occasional coal seams, dip gently in a south-easterly direction with the strike running roughly parallel to the section of the landslide.*   The slide, however, was confined wholly within the zone of weathered, fissured clay extending to a depth of 20 ft to 25 ft below the surface.†   The

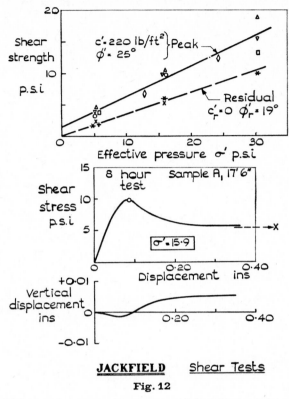

JACKFIELD   Shear Tests

Fig. 12

slip surface ran parallel to the slope (which is inclined at 10°), at an average depth of 18 ft. The length of the sliding mass, measured up the slope, amounted to about 550 ft and in the winter 1952–53 ground-water level reached the surface at a number of points, although on average it was located at a depth of 2 ft.

Analysis of the forces acting on the slip surface shows $\bar{\sigma}' = 1{,}300$ lb/sq. ft and $\bar{\tau} = 400$ lb/sq. ft.

Drained shear tests on samples taken from depths between 15 ft and 19 ft, but not in the immediate vicinity of the slip plane, showed peak strength parameters of $c' = 220$ lb/sq. ft and $\phi' = 25°$ (Fig. 12).‡   When these tests were made we had no clear idea of the significance of residual strengths.   Fortunately, however, in most cases we did at least continue the observations throughout the full travel of the shear box, and it is possible from the results to make an

* These strata comprise the Coalport Beds of the Upper Carboniferous.

† The weathered clay, though quite firm and still retaining the characteristics of an over-consolidated clay is nevertheless far less strong than the hard, almost rocklike, unweathered strata.   This explains why the slip was relatively shallow, instead of extending to the considerable depths which would be expected in a homogeneous cohesive material.

‡ As in most slides in over-consolidated clays, we found at Jackfield a zone of softened clay, not more than about 2 in. thick, containing the slip plane.   Shear tests on specimens cut from the outer edge of this zone showed $c' = 150$ lb/sq. ft. and $\phi' = 21°$.   The value of ϕ_r' on the slip plane itself was not determined experimentally.

approximate estimate of the residual angle of shearing resistance. As will be seen from Fig. 12, this estimate gives the value $\phi_r' = 19°$. Very probably a more correct value would be rather less than 19°.

Referring now to Fig. 13, the peak and residual strengths corresponding to the average effective pressure of 1,300 lb/sq. ft acting on the slip surface, are 825 and 425 lb/sq. ft respectively. But, as previously mentioned, the average shear stress (and hence the average shear strength) along the slip surface at the time of failure was 400 lb/sq. ft.

It is therefore clear that when the landslide took place the strength of the clay was closely equal to its residual value. In fact, taking $\phi_r' = 19°$, we arrive at the conclusion that the residual factor $R = 1.12$ but, when the approximate nature of ϕ_r' is taken into account, I doubt if the value of R is significantly different from 1.0.

Expressing the results in another way, had the peak strength been used in a stability analysis of the Jackfield slope, the calculated factor of safety would have been 2.06 (an error of more

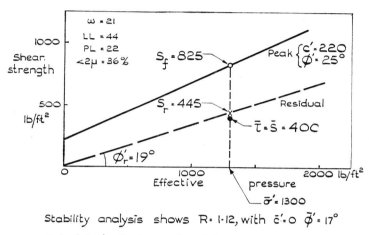

Stability analysis shows R = 1.12, with c̄' = 0 φ̄' = 17°

Calculated factors of safety :–
(i) on peak strength   F = 2.06
(ii) on residual strength F = 1.11

JACKFIELD   SUMMARY OF DATA

Fig. 13

than 100%, since the true factor of safety was 1.0). On the other hand, using even the rather crude value of $\phi_r' = 19°$, the calculated factor of safety based on residual strength would differ by only 11% from the correct result.

It may be added that the values of $\bar{\sigma}'$ and $\bar{\tau}$ calculated on the actual slip surface correspond to an average angle of shearing resistance of 17° (with $\bar{c}' = 0$). This figure, which I obtained from an approximate analysis, has been confirmed by Mr Morgenstern using a more refined method of calculation.

Selset

During an early visit to the site proposed for Selset dam in north Yorkshire, near Middleton-in-Teesdale, Dr Bishop and I found an interesting landslide which had taken place not long before in a boulder clay slope of the River Lune valley. During the years 1955–60, while work was proceeding on the dam, a short distance upstream, various opportunities were taken of investigating the slide and testing samples of the clay. The results have been published

(Skempton and Brown, 1961) and it is necessary to add very little here in order to bring this case record into the framework of our present enquiry.

The river, when in flood, is eroding the valley side and in this way is still widening its alluvial plain (Fig. 14). Nevertheless the process is not very rapid (on an historical, rather than a geological time scale) and the Ordnance Survey map of 1856 shows the river to have been at that time in just about its present position, relative to the toe of the slope. Thus there can be no doubt that we are dealing with a "long-term" condition.

The boulder clay was remarkably uniform, without fissures or joints, and it showed little if any signs of weathering except in the very shallow zone of seasonal variations.

The exact location of the slip surface was not determined, although the tension crack near the top of the slope was clearly visible, and various possible slip circles were therefore analysed. Representative values, sufficiently accurate for our purpose, of the average effective stress $\bar{\sigma}'$ and the average shear stress $\bar{\tau}$ are 760 lb/sq. ft and 640 lb/sq. ft. respectively.

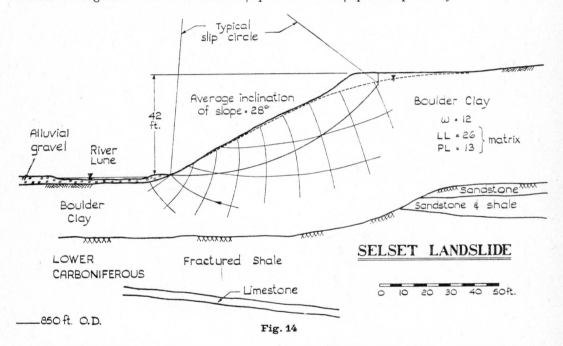

Fig. 14

Triaxial and shear box tests on eight samples of the boulder clay gave a consistent set of results, showing that the peak strength could be expressed by the parameters $c' = 180$ lb/sq. ft and $\phi' = 32°$. The tests were not carried to strains which, in the light of subsequent experience, we know to be necessary if the residual strength is to be accurately defined, but even so it is possible to estimate the parameters $c_r' = 0$ and $\phi_r' = 30°$ with reasonable certainty (Fig. 15).

Corresponding to the average effective pressure $\bar{\sigma}' = 760$ lb/sq. ft, the peak strength is therefore $s_f = 660$ lb/sq. ft and the residual strength $s_r = 440$ lb/sq. ft (Fig. 16). But the average shear stress, and hence the average shear strength, at the time of the slip, is 640 lb/sq. ft. This is scarcely less than the peak strength; and the residual factor $R = 0.08$.

Thus, if the slip had been analysed using $c' = 180$ lb/sq. ft and $\phi' = 32°$, the calculated factor of safety would have been very close to the correct value of 1·0. By contrast, using $c_r' = 0$ and $\phi_r' = 30°$ the calculated factor of safety is 0·69, a result which is about 30% in error.

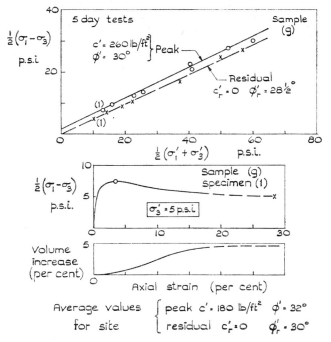

Average values { peak c' = 180 lb/ft² φ' = 32°
for site { residual c'ᵣ = 0 φ'ᵣ = 30°

SELSET   SHEAR TESTS

Fig. 15

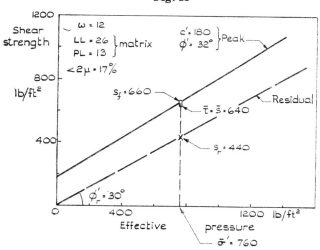

Stability analysis shows R = 0.08, with c̄' = 160 φ̄' = 32°

Calculated factors of safety:-

(i) on peak strength   F = 1.03
(ii) on residual strength   F = 0.69

SELSET   SUMMARY OF DATA

Fig. 16

It is notable that the peak strength appears to have been almost fully mobilized simultaneously along the entire length of the slip surface. Even in this intact, non-fissured clay one might perhaps expect to find a rather more pronounced indication of progressive failure than that corresponding to a residual factor of only 8%. Nevertheless the fact remains that an analysis based on peak strengths leads to a result which is quite satisfactory from a practical point of view.*

London Clay

Data are available for a number of slips which have occurred in the weathered zone of the London Clay. Fissures and joints and occasional slickensides can be seen throughout the full depth of the London Clay, but such features are far more conspicuous in the weathered zone, which is typically about 30 ft to 40 ft deep (Fig. 17). An obvious sign of weathering is the brown colour of the clay, in contrast to the "blue" (actually a slaty grey) colour of the unweathered material. A more sensitive indication of weathering, however, is the presence of thin films of minerals such as goethite and limonite in some of the fissures and joints. These alteration products are frequently found at depths well below the base of the "brown" clay.

The peak strength parameters of the weathered clay naturally vary to some extent from site to site, but representative values can be taken as $c' = 320$ lb/sq. ft. and $\phi' = 20°$ (Fig. 18).† So far as residual strengths are concerned, Mr William Watson of Soil Mechanics Ltd has carried out a shear test on a sample including the existing slip plane, taken from the site of a landslide at Dedham, Essex; and Mr Petley at Imperial College has measured the residual strength of three specimens of undisturbed clay, using the reversal shear box technique. The results indicate that ϕ_r' is about 16° (Fig. 18).

One of the large-strain reversal tests is plotted in Fig. 19, and the slickensides in the specimen at the completion of the test are shown in Fig. 20, facing p. 83. Examination under the microscope of a thin section prepared by Mr Early from a specimen of clay containing the Dedham slip plane showed a domain of strongly orientated particles, similar to that observed in the Walton's Wood clay, with a thickness of approximately 10 μ.

A zone of softened clay extending for roughly an inch on either side of the slip plane is characteristic of London Clay, and three representative examples are shown in Fig. 21. The water contents immediately adjacent to the slip plane will be seen to be about 35, as compared with water contents of around 30 in the unsoftened clay.

Turning now to the case records of slips in the London Clay, the first refers to the failure of a retaining wall at Kensal Green, which took place in 1941 (Fig. 22).‡ The wall has a considerable length. It was built in 1912, and at its highest section, about 250 ft from the

---

* A similar conclusion can be derived from the investigations of a slip which occurred on 6 October 1954 in a deep cutting at Lodalen, near Oslo (Sevaldson, 1956). Here the clay, of marine origin, was lightly overconsolidated and non-fissured with $c' = 210$ lb/sq. ft and $\phi' = 27°$; $w = 29$, LL $= 35$, PL $= 19$ and clay fraction $= 46\%$.

The case records of Selset and Lodalen may further be interpreted as indicating that shear creep has little effect on peak strength in the clays at these sites.

† Tests on block samples taken from a deep shaft at Ashford Common, near Staines, show that the values of c' and ϕ' in the unweathered London Clay are considerably greater than those in the weathered zone. The tests have been carried out at Imperial College and at the Building Research Station, and will be published in a paper to Géotechnique by Dr A. W. Bishop, Mr D. L. Webb, and Mr P. I. Lewin.

Peak strength parameters as quoted for the London Clay and other fissured clays (unweathered or weathered) are measured on comparatively small specimens and relate essentially to the intact material. Tests on large specimens show lower strengths due to the inclusion of fissures. The residual strength, however, should be independent of sample size.

‡ A cutting at Kensal Green was excavated in 1835 for the London–Birmingham Railway. Widening took place in 1875 and again in 1912, when the present wall was built. It seems unlikely that the 1875 cutting had any significant effect on the clay involved in the 1941 failure. As a member of the Building Research Station staff, under Dr Cooling, I had the good fortune to be given the job of investigating this failure.

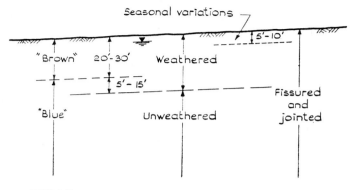

500'-1000' removed by erosion
since Eocene times

TYPICAL PROFILE OF LONDON CLAY

Fig. 17

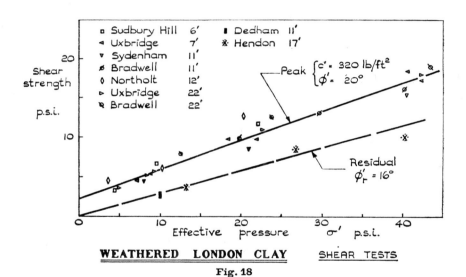

WEATHERED LONDON CLAY   SHEAR TESTS

Fig. 18

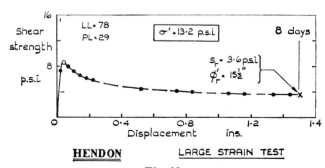

HENDON   LARGE STRAIN TEST

Fig. 19

Fig. 20. Slickensides formed in large strain test on specimen of
London Clay from Hendon motorway

1941 slip, a failure occurred in 1929.   After repairs had been carried out observation points were established at various places along the whole length of the wall.   As it happens, one of these survey sections was located only a few feet from the position of maximum movement in 1941.   Therefore we are fortunate enough to have a continuous record of displacements over a period of 12 years preceding failure (Fig. 22).   For several years after observations started, when the wall had already been in existence for 17 years, the rate of movement was small (about $\frac{1}{4}$ in./year).   But gradually the rate increased, and finally the movement amounted to 18 in.

It would be difficult to imagine a better demonstration of progressive failure.   Looking at the time-displacement curve in Fig. 22 one can sense that the average strength of the clay is decreasing and approaching the existing shear stress, with correspondingly larger and larger movements as more of the clay is brought to its residual strength.

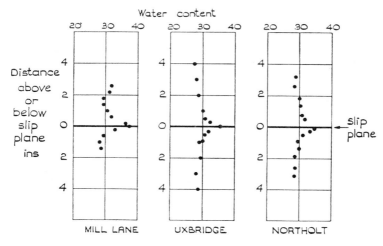

LONDON   CLAY

Distribution of water content near slip plane

Fig. 21

An analysis of the forces acting on the slip surface shows that $\bar{\sigma}' = 800$ lb/sq. ft.   The average peak and residual strengths are therefore 610 lb/sq. ft and 230 lb/sq. ft respectively (Fig. 23).   But the average shear stress along the slip surface is 380 lb/sq. ft, and this is also the shear strength at the time of failure.   Thus the residual factor can be immediately calculated, since:

$$R = \frac{610-380}{610-230} = 0\cdot61$$

Hence, after a period of 29 years, the average strength has fallen about 60% of the way from the peak to the residual.   Or, in other words, the strength has fallen to the residual value along 60% of the slip surface, whilst remaining at the peak value over the other 40%.

Looking at the problem from another point of view, if the peak strengths had been used throughout, the calculated factor of safety would have been 1·6; while, using the residual strengths, the figure would have been 0·6.   The correct factor of safety is 1·0, and the strength parameters required to give this result in a stability analysis are $\bar{c}' = 125$ lb/sq. ft and $\phi' = 17\frac{1}{2}°$, corresponding to $R = 0\cdot61$.

Very similar data have been derived from the analysis of a slip in a cutting at Northolt

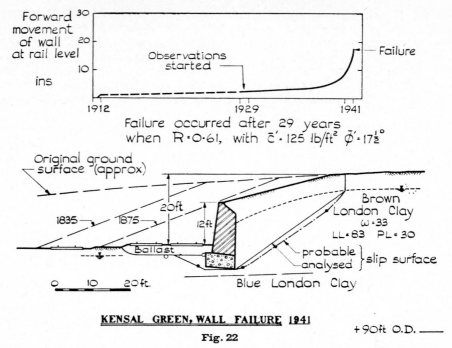

KENSAL GREEN, WALL FAILURE 1941

Fig. 22

(Fig. 24).*   Here the excavation was made in 1936, and the failure occurred 19 years later in 1955. A site investigation was carried out shortly after the slip had taken place. The investigation included the installation of piezometers, taking samples for test and surveying considerable portions of the slip surface exposed in trenches which were later cut in the slope for counterfort drains.

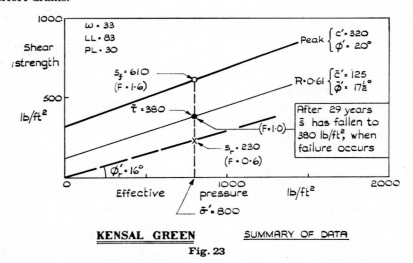

KENSAL GREEN   SUMMARY OF DATA

Fig. 23

* The investigations at Northolt, as also at Sudbury Hill and various natural slopes in London Clay, described later in this Lecture, were carried out by Dr Henkel and myself with the able assistance of Dr F. A. DeLory. Papers dealing with Northolt (Henkel, 1957) and with the natural slopes (Skempton and DeLory, 1957) have been published. In recent months I have re-examined the data and made new stability calculations with the help of Mr Noel Simons.

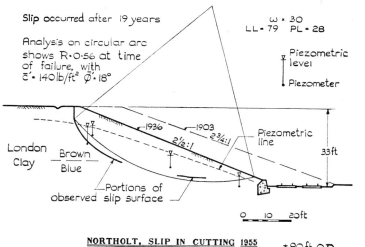

NORTHOLT, SLIP IN CUTTING 1955   +90 ft. O.D. ____

Fig. 24

The analysis, made on a circular arc approximating to the observed slip surface, shows that $\bar{\sigma}' = 750$ lb/sq. ft. The corresponding average values of peak and residual strength are 595 lb/sq. ft and 215 lb/sq. ft respectively. The average shear stress, and hence the average shear strength acting along the slip surface at the time of failure, is 380 lb/sq. ft. Consequently $R = 0.56$, and the strength parameters consistent with a factor of safety of 1·0 are $\bar{c}' = 140$ lb/sq. ft and $\phi' = 18°$.

The third slip in weathered London Clay which I shall consider took place in 1949, in a cutting excavated at Sudbury Hill in 1900 (Fig. 25). Apart from trimming the toe of the slip where it impinged on the railway, no remedial measures were undertaken. The profile of the slope after the slip is shown by the dashed line in Fig. 25, and it will be seen that there has been a displacement of several feet along the slip surface.

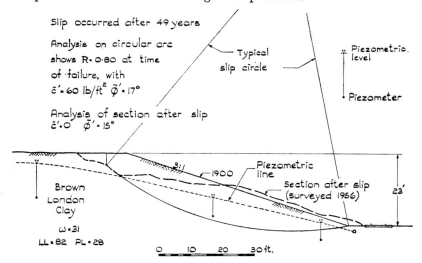

SUDBURY HILL (2ʍ 44c) SLIP IN CUTTING 1949   +80 ft. O.D. ____

Fig. 25

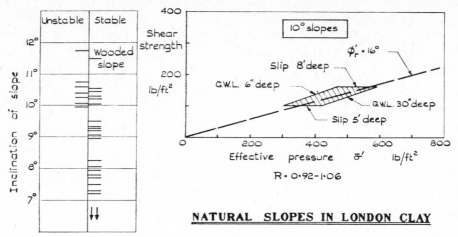

NATURAL SLOPES IN LONDON CLAY

Fig. 26

Between 1949 and 1956, when this slip was investigated, small intermittent movements had occurred. Therefore the slope was standing in a condition of limiting equilibrium, and an analysis of the forces should lead to an estimate of the residual strength.

Three piezometers were installed, and the water levels plotted in Fig. 25 are the highest recorded during a period of 20 months. Using these water levels and the slip circle as shown, the average effective pressure is found to be $\bar{\sigma}' = 650$ lb/sq. ft with a corresponding shear stress of $\bar{\tau} = 170$ lb/sq. ft. Thus, if we take $c_r' = 0$, the residual angle of shearing resistance can at once be calculated, since in this case:

$$\tan \phi_r' = \bar{\tau}/\bar{\sigma}'$$

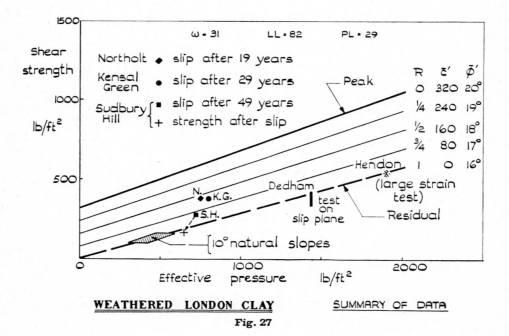

WEATHERED LONDON CLAY   SUMMARY OF DATA

Fig. 27

and we find that $\phi_r' = 15°$. This value is in reasonable agreement with the test results previously mentioned.*

The conditions obtaining just before the slip can also be investigated, assuming that the piezometer levels observed in 1956–57 are sufficiently representative of those in 1949. The results of this analysis may be summarised by saying that $R = 0.80$, with $\bar{c}' = 60$ lb/sq. ft and $\bar{\phi}' = 17°$.

These figures must be regarded as approximate, since they depend to some extent on rather uncertain knowledge of piezometric levels. Nevertheless, when considered in relation to the results from Kensal Green and Northolt, they show an unmistakable tendency for the strength to decrease with time; as would be expected in a material susceptible to progressive failure.†

In natural slopes the time scale is so great that we may anticipate that the strength of a fissured clay has fallen to the residual value. Observations of natural slopes in London Clay, where the water-table is close to the surface, have shown that an inclination of 10° marks approximately the division between stable and unstable conditions (Fig. 26). Values of $\bar{\sigma}'$ and $\bar{\tau}$ have been calculated for slip surfaces at depths between 5 ft and 8 ft, and for water levels between 6 in. and 30 in. below the surface.‡ The results are plotted in Fig. 26, from which it will be seen that a limiting slope of 10° is compatible with a residual angle of shearing resistance equal to about 16°.

All the foregoing data on London Clay are assembled in Fig. 27, and the pattern which emerges is so consistent that I feel encouraged to think we are working along the right lines in this problem.

SUMMARY

Residual factors for the various slips which have been considered in this Lecture are summarised in Table 2. The Selset boulder clay, without fissures or joints, develops its peak strength along very nearly the entire length of the slip surface. The weathered London Clay is heavily fissured and jointed. In such a material there will be some decrease in the shear strength parameters, below the peak values, even during the process of excavation; and there is definite evidence from the investigations at Northolt and Kensal Green that in slips which have taken place after 20 or 30 years the average strength of the clay has fallen about 60% of the way from the peak to the residual. At Sudbury Hill, where the slip occurred after nearly 50 years, the factor has increased to 80%, while in natural slopes in the London Clay the strength appears to be close to the residual. The Jackfield landslide, which also occurred in a natural slope in weathered, fissured clay, similarly shows a strength approximately equal to the residual value.

It would therefore seem that the presence of fissures and joints can indeed lead to progressive failure in a clay slope and, in the limit, this process can continue until the residual strength is reached. But in clays which are not fissured or jointed the decrease in strength from

---

* The rather close correlations between laboratory and field values of ϕ_r' as found at Sudbury Hill and Jackfield (and also in the investigations now being made at Walton's Wood) suggest that the residual strength of clays is virtually time-independent for failure times ranging from about one week, as in the laboratory tests, to periods of several years.

It should be noted that in some landslips the kinetic energy of the movement, after the initial failure, may be sufficient to cause appreciable "over-riding". In such cases the sliding mass will come to rest in a position corresponding to a strength lower than the true residual value.

† As previously mentioned, the existence of fissures implies that the average strength is less than the peak even if no progressive failure has occurred. It is, for example, quite possible that the London Clay might have a value of R in the region of 0.25 immediately after excavation, simply by virtue of the fissures and joints. With time, progressive failure leads to the higher values of R as found at Kensal Green, Northolt and Sudbury Hill, and in the natural slopes.

‡ Details of the field observations and the method of stability analysis will be found in a paper by Skempton and DeLory (1957). In that Paper, ground-water level was taken as coincident with the surface. I now realize that this is too great an over-simplification.

Table 2
Values of *R*

Condition of clay	Stratigraphy	Location	Natural slope N cutting C (time to failure)	Residual factor: R
No fissures or joints Unweathered	Boulder clay	Selset	N	0·08
Fissures and joints Weathered	London Clay	Northolt Kensal Green Sudbury Hill	C (19 yrs) C (29 yrs) C (49 yrs)	0·56 0·61 0·80
		Sudbury Hill 10° slopes	C (after slip) N	1·04 0·92–1·06
	Coalport Beds	Jackfield	N	1·12
Movement on existing slip surface in *any* type of clay				*c.* 1·0

the peak value is small, or even negligible. Compacted clay fills, as used in embankments and earth dams, may well fall into this latter category.*

Finally, if a failure has already occurred, any subsequent movements on the existing slip surface will be controlled by the residual strength, no matter what type of clay is involved. It is probable that this is the main reason for the exceptionally low angles of shearing resistance (compared with conventional peak values) deduced from landslides such as those, for example, in the Bearpaw clay-shale in south Saskatchewan (Ringheim, 1964); and the analysis of the slope at Sudbury Hill, after the initial slip, provides supporting evidence for this interpretation. It is also probable that in shear zones, caused by tectonic movements, the strength will be at the residual value.

The case records from which these conclusions have been derived are still few in number. But they are perhaps sufficient to justify the belief that a more logical basis than existed hitherto is now available for analysing the long-term stability of clay slopes.

REFERENCES

ASTBURY, N. F., 1960. "Science in the ceramic industry". *Proc. Roy. Soc. A.*, 258:27–46.
BISHOP, A. W., 1954. "The use of the slip circle in the stability analysis of slopes". *Proc. European Conf. Stability of Earth Slopes*, 1:13, Stockholm; reprinted in *Géotechnique*, 5:1:7–17.
BOROWICKA, H., 1963. "Der Wiener Routine-Scherversuch". *Mitt. Inst. Grundbau u. Bodenmech. Vienna*, 5:7–13. This paper will be published in English under the title "The Vienna method of shear testing" in the A.S.T.M. Symposium on *Laboratory Shear Testing of Soils* (Ottawa 1963).
CAQUOT, A., 1934. "Equilibre des massifs à frottement interne". *Gauthier-Villars, Paris.*
COTTRELL, A. H., 1963. "Fracture". *Proc. Roy. Soc. A.*, 276:1–18.
GOLDSTEIN, M. N., V. A. MISUMSKY *and* L. S. LAPIDUS, 1961. "The theory of probability and statistics in relation to the rheology of soils". *Proc. 5th Int. Conf. Soil Mech., Paris*, 1:123–126.
HAEFELI, R., 1938. "Mechanische Eigenschaften von Lockergesteinen". *Schweiz. Bauzeitung*, 111:321–325.
HAEFELI, R., 1950. "Investigation and measurements of the shear strengths of saturated cohesive soils". *Géotechnique*, 2:3:186–208.
HENKEL, D. J., 1957. "Investigations of two long-term failures in London Clay slopes at Wood Green and Northolt". *Proc. 4th Int. Conf. Soil Mech., London*, 2:315–20.

* The three conclusions stated in this paragraph were first put forward in a discussion at the 5th International Conference on Soil Mechanics (Skempton, 1961).

HENKEL, D. J. *and* A. W. SKEMPTON, 1954. "A landslide at Jackfield, Shropshire, in an over-consolidated clay". *Proc. European Conf. Stability of Earth Slopes, Stockholm,* 1:90–101. See also *Géotechnique,* 5:2:131–137.

HORN, H. M. *and* D. U. DEERE, 1962. "Frictional characteristics of minerals". *Géotechnique,* 12:4:319–335.

HVORSLEV, M. J., 1937. "Uber die Festigkeitseigenschaften gestörter bindiger Böden". *Ingenior. Skrifter A., Copenhagen,* No. 45.

RINGHEIM, A. S., 1964. "Experiences with the Bearpaw shale at the South Saskatchewan River dam". *Trans. 8th Int. Cong. Large Dams, Edinburgh,* 1:529–550.

SEVALDSON, R. A., 1956. "The slide in Lodalen, October 6th, 1954". *Géotechnique,* 6:4:167–182.

SKEMPTON, A. W., 1961. *Discussion* on Section 6 (Earth Dams, Slopes and Open Excavations). *Proc. 5th Int. Conf. Soil Mech., Paris,* 3:349–350.

SKEMPTON, A. W., *and* J. D. BROWN, 1961. "A landslide in boulder clay at Selset, Yorkshire". *Géotechnique,* 11:4:280–293.

SKEMPTON, A. W., *and* F. A. DELORY, 1957. "Stability of natural slopes in London Clay". *Proc. 4th Int. Conf. Soil Mech., London,* 2:378–381.

TIEDEMANN, B, 1937. "Uber die Schubfestigkeit bindiger Böden". *Bautechnik,* 15:433–435.

TURNBULL, J. McN., 1952. "Shearing resistance of soils". *Proc. 1st Aust.-N.Z. Conf. Soil Mech., Melbourne,* pp. 48–81.

EFFECTS OF EARTHQUAKES ON DAMS AND EMBANKMENTS

N. M. Newmark, D.Sc., Ph.D., M.S., M.I.C.E.

I wish to thank the British Geotechnical Society for the opportunity of visiting London again and for the honour of appearing before you in the home of the Institution of Civil Engineers, of which I am so proud to be a member.

Several years ago I transmitted some preliminary notes on the topic of earthquake effects on dams to the late Karl Terzaghi, whose invaluable advice and suggestions regarding those notes were freely used in the preparation of this Paper. I wish also to acknowledge the comments and suggestions I have had from time to time concerning the subject from my colleague at the University of Illinois, Dr Ralph B. Peck; from my associate in several consulting assignments, Dr Laurits Bjerrum; and from my colleague for several months, while he was visiting the University of Illinois, Dr N. N. Ambraseys.

Finally, I should like to acknowledge the assistance on some of the calculations for this lecture that were made by two of my associates at the University of Illinois, Dr John W. Melin, and Mr Mohammad Amin.

INTRODUCTION

General description of earthquake motions

In an earthquake, the earth moves in a nearly random fashion in all directions, both horizontally and vertically. Measurements have been made of earthquake motions in a number of instances. In general, those measurements which are of greatest interest are the records of 'strong motion' earthquake accelerations, measured by the U.S. Coast and Geodetic Survey for a number of earthquakes in California in the past three decades. These accelerations, as a function of time, are available for motion in two horizontal directions as well as in the vertical direction, at a number of locations for several earthquakes. From the time-record of the acceleration, the velocities and displacements can be computed by integration.

One of the most intense strong motion records available is that for the El Centro, California earthquake of 18 May, 1940. The record for the north–south component of acceleration of this earthquake is shown in Fig. 1, which also shows the values computed for velocity and displacement in the same direction. From the figure it can be observed that the maximum ground acceleration in the direction of this measurement is about 0·32 g, the maximum ground velocity 13·7 in/sec, and the maximum ground displacement 8·3 in.

The general nature of earthquake motions is indicated by this figure. It can be noted that the highest intensity peaks of acceleration have a relatively short period or a relatively high frequency; the most important peaks in the velocity, however, have a longer period which corresponds to a lower frequency; and the important peaks in the ground displacement have a much longer period still. For the ground conditions at El Centro the length of single loops of the highest intensities, in the various records, have durations of the order of the following: for acceleration, about 0·1 to 0·5 sec; for velocity, about 0·3 to 2 sec; and for displacement

109

about 1 to 4 sec.   In other types of soil, the relative durations may differ, with softer soils in general showing lower magnitudes of acceleration, but longer durations and much larger displacements, than in Fig. 1.

It must be remembered that the El Centro earthquake is not the largest earthquake which has been experienced, even in California.   It happened only to yield the most intense record at a point where a strong motion accelerograph was located.

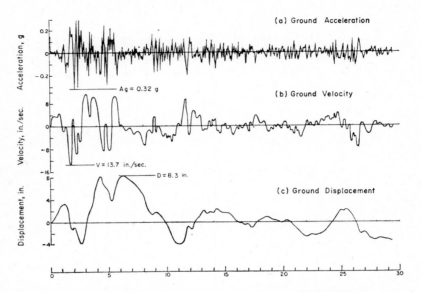

Fig. 1.   El Centro, California, earthquake of 18 May, 1940, N–S component

Significant factors of earthquake motion

In considering the effect of an earthquake on a structure such as an earth or rock-fill dam, it is necessary to consider all of the aspects of the motion.   In other words, the peak acceleration may not be significant in determining the response of the dam.   The effects of the velocities and of the ground displacement, and of the differential displacement of the ground leading to fissures in the ground surface, may be of equal or of even greater importance.   It will be shown later that the most important measure of the intensity of an earthquake is the maximum ground velocity reached at any time during the earthquake.

Records of the same general nature as those in Fig. 1 have been obtained for other earthquakes.   Some major differences exist in the records, which show distinctive situations: in some cases an earthquake may correspond only to one short series of major pulses, with essentially only one major loop of displacement; and in other cases it may show an almost periodic displacement response for a large portion of time.   The El Centro record is typical of a nearly periodic response of moderately low intensity combined with one very large displacement peak.

The durations of large motion in earthquakes vary from less than 10 seconds to as long as several minutes.   The total duration and the total number of 'spikes' or peaks of velocity, and the reversals of velocity, are of importance in determining the response of a structure such as an earth or rock-fill dam, or embankment.

In the studies made for this Paper, earthquakes have been considered patterned after those for which records are available in California, but which differ in some respects in terms of the significant frequencies of the various kinds of motion, and in the total duration of motion or number of spikes.

One of the most important special conditions existing at some sites is a relatively soft sedimental deposit of fairly great depth and wide extent. When such a soil deposit is set in to motion at its contact with the bed rock, there is a tendency for the resultant motions of the soil to reflect the natural frequency of the bowl of soil. This has the effect of increasing the magnitude of surface displacements and velocities, but it also causes the resultant motion to be more periodic in character, with many loops of successive displacement or velocity nearly in resonance, that is, having nearly the same period and with successive positive and negative peaks. A structure built on such material and hence subjected to such a motion will generally have a larger response than it would have if it were subjected to the motions of the bed rock.

Intensities of maximum motion for major earthquakes

Although earthquakes in many parts of the world may be less intense than the maximum recorded earthquake in California, in regions in which major seismic activity must be expected one should consider the probability of even larger motions. In any location, it is desirable to design for the maximum probable earthquake, that is, an earthquake that has a reasonable probability of occurring within the lifetime of the structure, with a sufficiently large factor of safety to preclude the necessity for major repairs. One should also consider an extreme earthquake, of about the maximum intensity that might be expected at the site, and for which some damage might be permissible, but collapse or failure should be prevented. Estimates of the maximum probable earthquake that might occur once in a hundred years in California, and an extreme earthquake with only a relatively small chance of occurrence, are given in Table 1, for comparison with the maximum recorded earthquake in California. It is not considered likely that the extreme earthquake indicated in Table 1 would be exceeded anywhere in the world. The parameters indicated in Table 1 describing the intensity of possible earthquakes, are intended to apply to the general motions of the soil or rock away from the regions where the major fault motions occur. Although even at such fault motions, the accelerations and velocities are not likely to exceed the values tabulated, the displacements might be considerably greater, and the relative displacement at a fault may be of such a magnitude that it would cause damage or serious difficulty in a structure or a dam at the fault.

Table 1

Probable intensities of maximum motion for major earthquakes

Condition	Maximum acceleration g	Maximum velocity: in/sec	Maximum displacement: in.	Duration of major motion: sec.
1. Maximum recorded EQ. in California — —	0·32	14	12	30
2. Maximum probable EQ. in California — —	0·50	24 to 30	24	90 to 120
3. Extreme values considered	0·50 to 0·60	30 to 36	36 to 48	120 to 240

Note: Lower values of motions apply to rock, in general.

OBSERVED EFFECTS OF EARTHQUAKES

Ambraseys (1962) points out that no major earth dam has been damaged by an earthquake during the last 25 years. However, he also points out that this argument can not be used as a proof for the adequacy of modern design methods, since no major dam built after the late thirties has been subjected to a severe earthquake. There have been a number of dams that have been damaged, or even destroyed, in earthquakes (Ambraseys, 1960, 1962). Moreover, it is generally true that in all compacted dam-construction materials, and in many natural soil strata, the dynamic shearing resistance is about the same as the static shearing resistance, or slightly greater, and the usual factor of safety is sufficiently large to prevent catastrophic motions. However, at some localities, natural soil strata are encountered which can lose part or almost all of their shearing resistance under shock conditions, either because of increased hydrostatic pressure or owing to loss in shearing strength from even slight remoulding. Under such conditions, major failures can occur, and have occurred, in embankments or under the foundations of dams which otherwise would not have suffered difficulties.

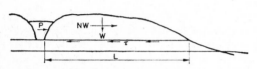

Fig. 2. Sliding of block in Anchorage (after Wilson)

In the recent Anchorage earthquake, large motions and catastrophic failures occurred in natural embankments which slid major distances on sensitive clay strata or on loose, low relative density sand layers. A typical example of the type of failure which occurred is shown in Fig. 2, taken from Shannon and Wilson (1964). The entire block of material of the order of 1000 ft in length and 60 to 100 ft in height, moved bodily tens of feet in an earthquake the maximum acceleration of which has been variously estimated as about 0·15 to 0·18 g.

Motions along a sliding surface may occur in a dam, under certain conditions, and a succession of slides of limited displacement on the upstream and downstream faces of a dam are indicated schematically in Fig. 3, taken from Ambraseys (1958). The successive motions coming from the several shocks in different directions produce slides along different surfaces, with the net results shown at the bottom of the figure. The major settlement at the crest and the pattern of the deformations are similar to those which have been observed in several older dams which may not have been designed to have adequate earthquake resistance.

Tests of models of earth or rock-fill dams have been made by Davis and his associates at Berkeley (Davis *et al.*, 1960; Clough and Pirtz, 1958), by Seed and his associates, also at Berkeley (Seed and Clough, 1963; Seed and Goodman, 1964), and by Bustamante (1964) at the University of Mexico. In granular material the patterns of slip are similar to those shown in Fig. 4. The outline marked 1 shows the original slope, that marked 2 shows the deformation after a re-

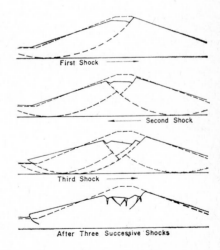

Fig. 3. Major deformation pattern (after Ambraseys)

latively small shock, and the outline marked 3 shows the deformation after major motions have occurred. Similar motions have been observed when the base of the model was tipped, to simulate a constant acceleration field.

Fig. 4.   Patterns of slip in
granular embankment

General concepts of behaviour

The types of motion of earth or rock-fill dams, or of an embankment, subjected to an earth-quake can be considered to be of the following forms:

(*a*) motion of a block or wedge or slice of the upstream or the downstream slope, generally out and downhill, as indicated in Fig. 5, arcs 'a' or 'b';

(*b*) motion of the dam as a whole block, as in Fig. 5, line 'c';

(*c*) relative motions in either the dam or the foundation, of such a nature as to cause fissures to open, generally vertical, caused either by relative shearing motions or tensile strains in the earth crust, corresponding to differential movements arising from the wave characteristics of the surface motion of the earth, or from stresses arising when parts of the mass of the dam and foundation are accelerated in one direction and other parts in other directions. This type of effect is illustrated in Fig. 5, by the fissures marked 'd' and 'e'.

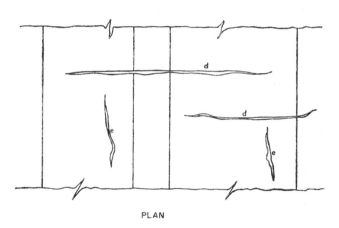

PLAN

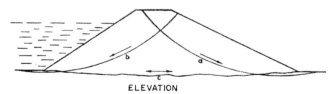

ELEVATION

Fig. 5.   Possible motions and deformations of an earth
dam in an earthquake

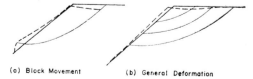

(a) Block Movement   (b) General Deformation

Fig. 6.   Comparison of two types of
gross-motions

The characters of the motions in different types of materials are somewhat different. In general, for non-cohesive materials, and for cohesive materials where a well-defined plane of weakness can develop, the motion occurs along arcs or planes, and is similar to that assumed in the usual static analysis of stability of an embankment, as indicated in Fig. 6(a). However, in highly cohesive materials, the motion is more nearly general and elastic or nearly elastic in character, and a well defined sliding surface may not be formed. This is illustrated in Fig. 6(b). Where movements such as those in Fig. 6(a) occur, a relatively simple analysis can be used to compute the magnitude of dynamic motions produced by earthquake or other shocks. However, where motions such as those in Fig. 6(b) occur, the situation is much more complex, and the analysis cannot be made so readily or so accurately. For this case, the methods described herein can only be used as a crude approximation. In general, we shall devote our further attention in detail to situations of the type illustrated in Fig. 6(a).

Resistance to sliding motion

The resistance to earthquake shock motion of a block of soil or rock that slides on a surface is a function of the shearing resistance of the material under the conditions applicable in the earthquake. Although the magnitude of the resistance depends on the amount of displacement, the displacement necessary to mobilize the average 'yielding' resistance, normally considered in a stability analysis, is not large. For the purpose of simplifying the calculations the resistance which we shall use is measured by (and in fact equal and opposite to) that steady force acting at the centre of gravity of the sliding mass, in the direction in which the force can have its lowest value, which will just overcome the stabilizing forces and will barely keep the mass moving, after it has started to move, or after several pulsations (or reversals) of motion have occurred.

It is convenient to state this resistance in terms of a coefficient N multiplied by the weight of the sliding mass. Then the quantity Ng, where g is the acceleration of gravity, corresponds to that steady acceleration, acting in the proper direction, which would just overcome the resistance to sliding of the element, in the direction indicated, as defined above.

The resistance to sliding downhill, as on lines 'a' or 'b' of Fig. 5, is much lower than the resistance to sliding uphill on the same lines. The uphill resistance, without serious error in the calculations, may be taken as infinitely large. On the other hand, the type of motion characterized in line 'c' of Fig. 5 may have nearly the same resistance in either direction of relative motion of the mass compared with its foundation. This resistance may change as a function of displacement, and with reversal of displacement, but it is not generally greatly affected by the direction of motion other than in these ways.

We are not limited in the argument which follows by the use of a constant or steady-state value of N. We can consider the quantity n to be a coefficient, multiplied by the weight of the sliding material, which is used as a measure of the resistance to sliding, and which can be a function of the amount of deformation, or of time, or of any other parameters which it is desirable to consider. It is convenient to use the single parameter n as a measure of resistance, and to compare it with a single parameter a, as a measure of the acceleration driving the element. In other words, the quantity nW is a measure of the resistance as a generalized force, and the quantity aW, where the transient ground acceleration is ag, is a measure of the disturbing force as a generalized force, which varies with time. For further simplicity, we may use $n = N$, the steady-state resistance; and $a = A$, as a measure of the maximum ground acceleration, in developing approximate relationships.

Dynamic properties of soil and rock

In the determination of the value of sliding resistance, the dynamic properties of the material must be considered. This involves also the dynamic effects on the pore-water pressure, and the effects of the motion or shearing strain itself on the volume change and the pore pressure change. In general, it is the undrained shearing resistance that is of importance. For highly permeable materials, the drained shearing resistance may be appropriate. Because of the fact that our primary concern is with the resistance of the soil or rock and its strength under dynamic conditions, although the dynamic resistance is used in a sort of static analysis, we shall refer to the resistance as the 'pseudostatic' resistance. In other words, the calculation of stability which leads to the determination of the steady-state sliding resistance N is made for properties of the material that are related to the dynamic situation.

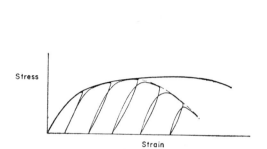

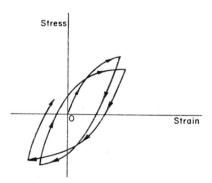

Fig. 7. Stress–strain relations for pulsating loads

Fig. 8. Stress–strain relations for reversed loading

Effect of pulsation or reversal of stress

Because of the vibratory character of earthquake shock motions, the direction of stresses and of deformations may reverse, or at least pulsate with relatively rapid fluctuations. In Fig. 7 is shown the relation between stress and strain for a load applied and released successively. So long as the strains are relatively small, for many soils the bounding curve to the pulsating stress–strain relation is the same as for a single application of stress. However, for some soils after a certain strain has been reached the stress may drop from the original virgin curve, as indicated by the dashed line on the right-hand side of the figure. The situation shown, with a diminishing resistance beyond the maximum, is not untypical of many sensitive soils. Where the stress is reversed, or where motions can take place in both directions, the reduction may be even greater, and the change in shape of the stress–strain relationship is very marked, possibly even more than is indicated in Fig. 8. Under these conditions a change in the resistance function N, with number of reversals or with time, is necessary if one is to account properly for the behaviour of the embankment.

DYNAMIC RESPONSE THEORY

The dynamic response of a deformable body can be computed by the direct application of Newton's laws of motion. However, in many cases this application is extremely tedious or involved. Some basic concepts and principles are available to permit a relatively simple summary of the responses to earthquake motions to be developed. These are described in some detail by Blume *et al.* (1961).

The maximum responses of a simple system such as that shown in Fig. 9, consisting of a single mass connected by an elastic spring to a movable base, are best described by the so-called 'response spectrum', which is a plot against frequency of one of several measures of the stress or deformation in the system. One of the most convenient ways of indicating the response for a variety of conditions is the tripartite logarithmic plot indicated in Fig. 10. The frequency f of the mass-spring system is the abscissa. For a particular motion of the base, the maximum strain in the spring or relative displacement of the mass with reference to the base D_f, is plotted along the axis sloping up to the left. A quantity from which the maximum energy absorbed in this system may be readily computed, the pseudo-velocity V_f is plotted as the ordinate, vertically, and the maximum acceleration of the mass A_f is plotted along the axis sloping up to the right. For damping other than zero, the quantity that is plotted is not exactly equal to the acceleration but is the 'pseudo-acceleration'. The relations among the pseudo-velocity, the pseudo-acceleration, and the relative displacement, are indicated in Fig. 10. The spectrum shown in Fig. 10 is plotted against frequency rather than against period, as are those in Blume *et al.* (1961).

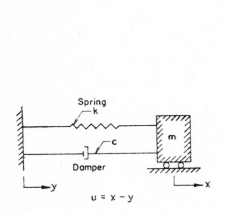

Fig. 9.   System considered

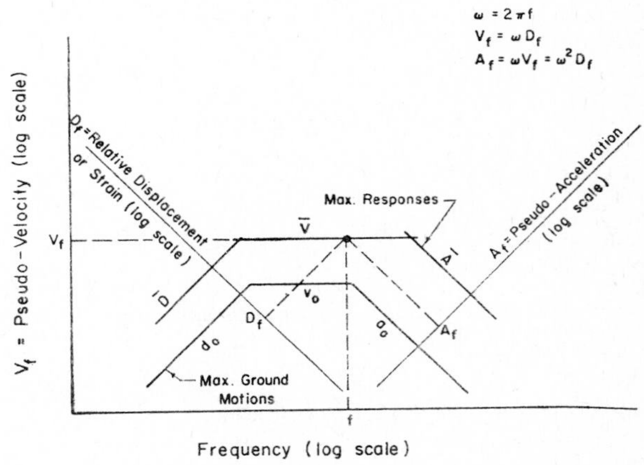

Fig. 10.   Tripartite logarithmic response spectrum plot

For a base motion corresponding to the El Centro earthquake described in Fig. 1, the response spectra for several different values of the damping factor β, the proportion of critical damping for the system, are shown in Fig. 11.

The general characteristics of the response spectrum, as summarized from a great many studies of different input motions, are indicated in Fig. 10, where the quantities representing the maximum ground displacement d_0 the maximum ground velocity v_0, and the maximum ground acceleration a_0, are indicated schematically in the lower part of the figure by straight lines. Then the response spectrum has the shape shown roughly by the upper series of three straight lines parallel to the lines just described, fairing in at the high and low frequency ends to the ground motion lines. The bounds to the response spectrum for displacement $\bar{D}$, pseudo-velocity, $\bar{V}$, and pseudo-acceleration, $\bar{A}$, are for moderate amounts of damping, of the order of 5 to 10%, given by the relations

$$\bar{D} = d_0, \ \bar{V} = 1\cdot5\,v_0, \ \bar{A} = 2\,a_0 \qquad . \quad . \quad . \quad . \quad . \quad (1)$$

Multi-degree-of-freedom system

The simplicity inherent in the description of the response of a single-degree-of-freedom system is not possible in describing the multi-degree-of-freedom system. A typical multi-

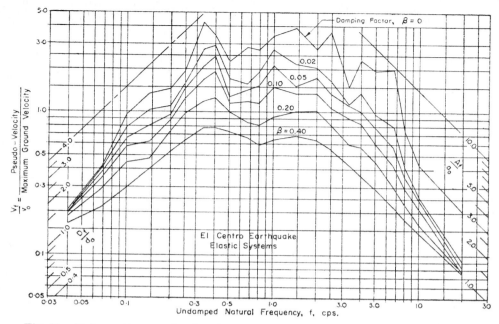

Fig. 11.   Deformation spectra for elastic systems subjected to the El Centro quake

degree-of-freedom system having the characteristics of a so-called 'shear beam' is shown in Fig. 12.   A shear beam is a system made up of masses which can move horizontally with respect to one another.   This is not untypical of the type of motion that occurs in a dam or embankment.   Sketches of the modes of vibration of a typical shear beam are also shown in Fig. 12.   Each of these modes has a frequency, with the fundamental mode having the lowest frequency, the second mode the next higher frequency, etc.

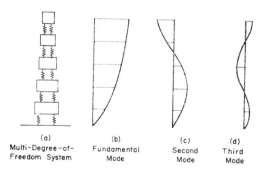

Fig. 12.   Modes of vibration of shear beam

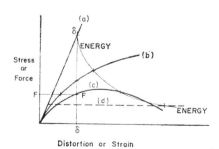

Fig. 13.   Comparison of strains for equal displacement, energy, or force

The maximum strains or distortions in the springs, or the maximum stresses at any elevation, in a multi-degree-of-freedom system, can be stated in terms of the corresponding quantities for a set of single-degree-of-freedom systems corresponding to each of the modes of vibration. For a particular system, a plot similar to that in Fig. 10 can be drawn, as a function of the fundamental frequency.

Inelastic relations between stress and strain

The spectra indicated previously in Figs 10 and 11, for an elastic system, correspond to elastic behaviour, which is represented by the upper inclined straight line (a) in Fig. 13. There are also shown in Fig. 13 several inelastic relations between stress and strain, or between force and deformation. For an inelastic relation between stress and strain, corresponding to one of the curved lines such as (b) or (c) in Fig. 13, the spectrum as described previously cannot be used directly. Curve (b) corresponds to a strain hardening situation, and curve (c) to an unstable one. An elasto–plastic resistance is indicated by the dashed line (d), in Fig. 13.

Spectrum bounds for the distortion or strain can be derived from Fig. 10, as indicated by the schematic plot in Fig. 14. Here three different regimes are considered. At the left, for a frequency f, the inelastic spectrum bound $\bar{D}_1$ is the same as $\bar{D}$. At the right, the inelastic spectrum gives the displacement bound $\bar{A}_1$ corresponding to the same force as the elastic spectrum bound $\bar{A}$. Where we have an elasto–plastic resistance, the bound $\bar{A}_1$ may be infinitely far above $\bar{A}$.

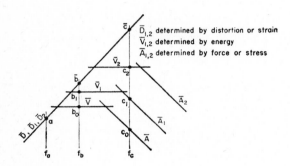

$\bar{D}_{1,2}$ determined by distortion or strain
$\bar{V}_{1,2}$ determined by energy
$\bar{A}_{1,2}$ determined by force or stress

Fig. 14. Response spectrum displacement limits

In the intermediate range of frequencies, the spectrum bound $\bar{V}_1$ corresponds to the same total energy or area under the stress–strain curve as $\bar{V}$. These three conditions are illustrated in Fig. 13 by the lines marked FF at a constant force level, which intersects three of the curves but not the elasto–plastic curve; the line marked δδ which intersects all of the curves at the same displacement, and the line marked 'energy' which intersects all of the curves at such a point that the area up to that displacement is the same. In Fig. 14 two different levels of inelastic displacement are considered, corresponding to $\bar{V}_1$ and $\bar{V}_2$, or $\bar{A}_1$ and $\bar{A}_2$.

Results of a number of studies, still under way, indicate that in general the displacement for an inelastic system is bounded by the *least* of the following three quantities:

(1) a displacement corresponding to the same force as for the elastic spectrum bound $\bar{A}$;

(2) a displacement corresponding to the same energy as for the elastic spectrum bound $\bar{V}$;

(3) a displacement corresponding to the elastic spectrum bound $\bar{D}$. In other words, one can compute the displacement of the inelastic system by taking the smallest of the displacements that correspond to force, energy or maximum ground displacement, as indicated in Fig. 14.

For very large amounts of plastic deformation, the acceleration bound for the inelastic spectrum lies so high that the energy bound is the only one of importance other than the displacement bound. Consequently, for large amounts of plastic deformation, it is appropriate to consider the preservation of energy, and to neglect the preservation of force, provided the stipulation is made that the displacement does not exceed the maximum ground displacement. Actually the displacement bound that should be considered is the maximum elastic spectrum displacement which may be slightly greater than the maximum ground displacement.

The methods described heuristically in the foregoing can be used for the analysis of systems in which the resistance varies with displacement. However, when the resistance is essentially rigid-plastic, corresponding to no displacement until the yield point is reached, after which the displacement may have any value, the analysis is particularly simple. In the remainder of the analytical discussion herein, this is the type of resistance that is considered. We shall simplify the cases of motion to that of a rigid block of weight W, supported on a base which moves as a function of time. We are concerned with the motion u of the block relative to the base. This model will be used for all of the cases of sliding that we have defined for a dam or embankment.

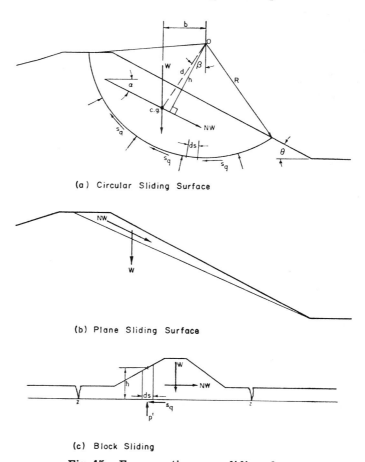

(a) Circular Sliding Surface

(b) Plane Sliding Surface

(c) Block Sliding

Fig. 15. Forces acting on a sliding element

The three important cases of sliding for a dam, on a circular sliding surface, on a plane sliding surface, or block sliding horizontally, are shown in Fig. 15. Of course, one might consider even more complex sliding surfaces if one can make the appropriate analysis for the resistance. For a general non-circular sliding surface the distortions within the sliding mass must be taken into account in arriving at the value of N for the entire mass.

Measures of dynamic resistance to sliding

In order that a dam or embankment have any dynamic resistance to sliding in an earthquake, it must have a margin of safety against static failure. Values of the static factor of safety against sliding are determined by conventional analysis with no consideration of horizontal or inclined accelerations. Values of the dynamic factor of safety against sliding may be determined in a similar manner, but one must use in such an analysis the appropriate properties of the materials, which may involve considerably reduced shearing strengths owing to the dynamic effects on the pore pressures.

The method of analysis described here is a simplified approach permitting a rapid estimate to be made of the order of magnitude of the displacement or deformation in an earthquake.

Circular cylindrical sliding surface

Consider the sliding element of the dam shown in Fig. 15(a), where a circular arc of radius R defines the sliding surface. The weight of the element W has a lever arm b about the centre of rotation O. Consider a force NW which corresponds to a constant acceleration N times that of gravity, acting along the line shown making an angle α with the horizontal, which may be different from the angle θ of the surface slope of the element. For constant values of acceleration less than Ng, no sliding occurs, but for greater values, sliding of the element will take place. For any arbitrary acceleration $N'g$, we may define a dynamic factor of safety $\overline{FS'}$, which becomes unity if $N'=N$.

Now, when N' is taken as zero, the dynamic factor of safety, $\overline{FS'}$ for this definition becomes equal to $\overline{FS}$, defined as the ratio of moment of the resisting forces on the sliding surface to the disturbing moment Wb. This dynamic factor of safety is defined differently from the usual static factor of safety. Drawdown seepage forces, etc. should be taken into account, also, in defining the factor of safety.

The shearing stresses τ for static conditions are to some extent indeterminate, but their total or their average value can be determined from the relation between the disturbing moment Wb and the restoring moment $R \sum \tau \, ds$, when $N'=0$:

$$Wb = R \sum \tau \, ds. \qquad . \qquad . \qquad . \qquad . \qquad . \qquad . \qquad (2)$$

The moment of the resisting forces on the arc is $R \sum s_q ds$. Hence the dynamic factor of safety is:

$$\overline{FS} = R \sum s_q ds / R \sum \tau \, ds = \sum s_q ds / \sum \tau \, ds.$$

An approximate value of N which will just cause sliding is obtained by equating disturbing and resisting moments as follows:

$$Wb + NWh = R \sum s_q ds. \qquad . \qquad . \qquad . \qquad . \qquad . \qquad (3)$$

Therefore, by subtracting equation (2) from equation (3), one obtains:

$$NWh = R \sum s_q ds - R \sum \tau \, ds.$$

On dividing this equation by equation (2), and multiplying through by b/h, one obtains the result:

$$N = \frac{b}{h} \left(\frac{\sum s_q ds}{\sum \tau \, ds} - 1 \right)$$

which can be written:

$$N = \frac{b}{h} \left(\frac{\bar{s}_q}{\bar{\tau}} - 1 \right) \qquad . \qquad . \qquad . \qquad . \qquad . \qquad . \qquad (4)$$

if $\bar{s}_q$ and $\bar{\tau}$ are considered as average values. This expression is valid for any case such as steady seepage or after rapid drawdown, but the value of $\bar{\tau}$ and $\bar{s}_q$ have to be determined separately for each case. Equation (4) can also be written as:

$$N = (\overline{FS} - 1) \frac{b}{h} \qquad . \qquad . \qquad . \qquad . \qquad . \qquad . \qquad (5)$$

Since the maximum value of h for a given sliding surface occurs when h equals d, the distance from O to the c.g. of the element, the minimum value of N occurs for a slope perpendicular to d, and one finds for this:

$$N = (\overline{FS} - 1) \, b/d = (\overline{FS} - 1) \sin \beta \qquad . \quad . \quad . \quad . \quad . \quad (6)$$

where β is the angle between d and the vertical, and $\overline{FS} = \bar{s}_q/\bar{\tau}$.

For N horizontal, the result would be:

$$N = (\overline{FS} - 1) \tan \beta. \qquad . \quad . \quad . \quad . \quad . \quad . \quad (7)$$

In the calculations, N is taken as inclined rather than horizontal, in order to be conservative, and also because the earth moves vertically as well as horizontally in an earthquake.

For soils which have nearly the same static and dynamic shear resistance, equation (5) may be approximated as:

$$N = (FS - 1) \sin \beta \qquad . \quad . \quad . \quad . \quad . \quad . \quad (8)$$

in which FS is the conventional static safety factor. This equation will hold good for free-draining materials and can also be used for dilatant soils in which only small or negative pore pressures will be developed.

When N' is different from zero, the same type of derivation leads to the relation:

$$R \sum s_q ds = \overline{FS'} \, (Wb + N'Wh) \qquad . \quad . \quad . \quad . \quad . \quad (9)$$

By equating equation (9) with (3), one obtains

$$N = N'(\overline{FS'}) + (\overline{FS'} - 1)b/h \qquad . \quad . \quad . \quad . \quad (10)$$

which reduces to equation (5) when $N' = 0$ and $\overline{FS'} = \overline{FS}$. Note, however, that equation (10) is valid even if $\overline{FS'}$ is less than unity.

Because we are concerned with the minimum value of N for all of the possible sliding surfaces, and because the minimum value does not necessarily occur for the sliding surface for which $\overline{FS}$ has a minimum value, use of equation (10), involving a trial value of N', will lead to more accurate results than use of equations (4) and (5) in which no assumed value of accelerating force is included in the basic computation. The most accurate results are obtained when $\overline{FS'}$ is nearly equal to unity. The poorest results are obtained from the static factor of safety computed for the case of zero lateral force.

For completeness, the relations corresponding to (6) and (7) are given, for the case in which N' is different from zero:
for N perpendicular to d,

$$N = N'(\overline{FS'}) + (\overline{FS'} - 1) \sin \beta \qquad . \quad . \quad . \quad . \quad . \quad (11)$$

for N horizontal,

$$N = N'(\overline{FS'}) + (\overline{FS'} - 1) \tan \beta. \qquad . \quad . \quad . \quad . \quad (12)$$

Block sliding

For block sliding of the entire dam along a surface such as z–z in Fig. 15(c), between fissures or embankment surfaces, the relationships to be used involve summation of forces rather than summation of moments. For the static condition of equilibrium it can be assumed without significant error that the average static shear stress along the horizontal surface is zero and the only disturbing force is thus the effect of the horizontal constant acceleration. The maximum shear strength which can be mobilized for earthquake conditions is the undrained shear strength s_q.

Since the sum of the disturbing forces NW per unit of width of dam must equal the sum of the shearing resistances per unit of width,

$$NW = \sum s_q ds \qquad \ldots \ldots \ldots \quad (13)$$

where ds is the length of the element on which the resistances act. Hence N is the ratio of the total horizontal resistance to the weight of the dam.

The effective overburden pressure p' is equal to the weight of the material above minus the pore pressure; hence

$$p' = \gamma h - u_p \qquad \ldots \ldots \ldots \quad (14)$$

where γ is the bulk density of the soil, h the height of the element, and u_p the pore pressure.

However,

$$W = \sum \gamma h\, ds. \qquad \ldots \ldots \ldots \quad (15)$$

In general the undrained shear strength is a function of the effective overburden pressure. For the special case of a normally consolidated soil the ratio of s_q to p' is a constant.

From equations (13) and (14), for a normally consolidated soil, one can determine N as follows:

$$N = \frac{1}{W} \sum s_q ds = \frac{1}{W} \sum \frac{s_q}{p'} p'\, ds$$

$$= \frac{1}{W}\left(\frac{s_q}{p'}\right) \sum p'\, ds$$

$$= \frac{s_q}{p'} \frac{\sum \gamma h\, ds - \sum u_p\, ds}{\sum \gamma h\, ds}$$

$$= \frac{s_q}{p'}\left(1 - \frac{\sum u_p\, ds}{\sum \gamma h\, ds}\right) \qquad \ldots \ldots \ldots \quad (16)$$

This equation can be written as

$$N = \frac{s_q}{p'}(1 - r_u) \qquad \ldots \ldots \ldots \quad (17)$$

where

$$r_u = \frac{\sum u_p\, ds}{\sum \gamma h\, ds}. \qquad \ldots \ldots \ldots \quad (18)$$

The quantity r_u is in general not a constant and has to be determined in each case as an average value. It should be taken at a conservative value to provide for pore pressure increase in an earthquake.

Plane sliding surface

For cohesionless and free-draining materials, with a plane sliding surface, as in Fig. 15(b), it is found that the most dangerous sliding plane is the upper slope, making an angle θ with the horizontal. Under these conditions, for a material with an angle of internal friction ϕ when sliding is taking place, the value of factor of safety against sliding is

$$\overline{FS} = \frac{\tan \phi}{\tan \theta} \qquad \ldots \ldots \ldots \quad (19)$$

It can be determined under these conditions that the minimum value of N is

$$N = (\overline{FS} - 1) \sin \theta. \qquad \ldots \ldots \ldots \quad (20)$$

Sliding of a rigid–plastic mass

A simple derivation for a rigid–plastic resistance is developed to give a quick estimate of the magnitude of the motions to be expected in a sliding wedge of rock or earth in a dam, when it is subjected to the influence of dynamic forces from an earthquake. The calculation is based on the assumptions that the whole moving mass moves as a single rigid body with resistance mobilized along the sliding surface.

Consider the rigid body having a weight W, and a mass M, shown in Fig. 16, having a motion x. The motion of the ground on which the mass rests is designated by $y(t)$, where y is a function of time t. The relative motion of the mass, compared with the ground, is designated by u, where

$$u = x - y. \qquad \ldots \qquad \ldots \qquad \ldots \qquad (21)$$

The resistance to motion is accounted for by a shearing resistance, which can be expressed as being proportional to the weight W, of magnitude NW. This corresponds to an acceleration of the ground of magnitude Ng that would cause the mass to move relative to the ground.

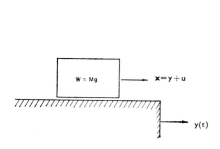

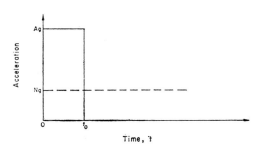

Fig. 16. **Rigid block on a moving support**   Fig. 17. **Rectangular block acceleration pulse**

In Fig. 17, the accelerating forces acting on the mass M are shown. The acceleration considered is a single pulse of magnitude Ag, lasting for a time interval t_0. It would be possible to consider a sinusoidal pulse, but this complicates the expressions unnecessarily. The resisting acceleration, Ng, is shown by the dashed line in Fig. 17. The accelerating force lasts only for the short time interval indicated, but the decelerating force lasts until the direction of motion changes.

In Fig. 18, the velocities are shown as a function of time for both the accelerating force and the resisting force. The maximum velocity for the accelerating force has a magnitude V given by the expression

$$V = Agt_0.$$

After the time t_0 is reached, the velocity due to the accelerating force remains constant. The velocity due to the resisting acceleration has the magnitude Ngt. At a time t_m, the two

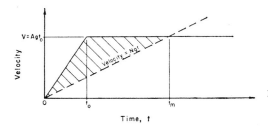

Fig. 18. **Velocity response to rectangular block acceleration**

velocities are equal and the net velocity becomes zero, or the body comes to rest relative to the ground.   The formulation for t_m is obtained by equating the velocity V to the quantity Ngt, giving as a result the expression

$$t_m = \frac{V}{Ng} \qquad \cdot \quad \cdot \quad \cdot \quad \cdot \quad \cdot \quad \cdot \quad \cdot \quad (22)$$

The maximum displacement of the mass relative to the ground u_m is obtained by computing the shaded triangular area in Fig. 18.   The calculation is made as follows:

$$u_m = \tfrac{1}{2} Vt_m - \tfrac{1}{2} Vt_0$$

or

$$u_m = \frac{1}{2}\frac{V^2}{Ng} - \frac{1}{2}\frac{V^2}{Ag}$$

whence

$$u_m = \frac{V^2}{2gN}\left(1 - \frac{N}{A}\right) \qquad \cdot \quad \cdot \quad \cdot \quad \cdot \quad \cdot \quad \cdot \quad (23)$$

The acceleration pulse shown in Fig. 17 corresponds to an infinite ground displacement. The actual situation corresponds to a number of pulses in random order, some positive and some negative.   If we consider a second pulse, of a negative magnitude, to bring the velocity to zero even without the resisting force, it can be shown that the net displacement with the resistance generally cannot exceed that which would occur without resistance.

The result given in equation (23) generally overestimates the relative displacement for an earthquake because it does not take into account the pulses in opposite directions.   However, it should give a reasonable order of magnitude for the relative displacement.   It does indicate that the displacement is proportional to the square of the maximum ground velocity.

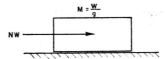

Fig. 19.   Mass sliding under constant force

The result derived above is applicable also for a group of pulses when the resistance in either direction of possible motion is the same.   For a situation in which the body has a resistance to motion greater in one direction than in another, one must take into account the cumulative effect of the displacements.   A simple example where this must be considered would be found if Fig. 16 were rotated clockwise, as in Fig. 19, so that the body has a tendency to slide downhill.   In this situation, ground motions in the direction of the downward slope tend to move the mass downhill, but ground motions in the upward direction along the slope leave the mass without relative additional motion except where these are extremely large in magnitude.   One may consider that this case is applicable to the dam.

Energy concepts

Another interpretation of equation (23) may be useful.   Consider the situation where the sliding mass of material acquires somehow a velocity V relative to the ground or foundation. This velocity may be imparted by motion of the foundation and that part of the dam which presses against the sliding wedge, but in any event, it is the velocity of the mass, relative to the ground or foundation on which it slides, that is needed.   This is not necessarily the same as the maximum ground velocity.

The kinetic energy of the moving mass, with this velocity, then is given by the relation $WV^2/2g$.   The resistance to sliding is given by the quantity NW and the energy absorbed in the sliding resistance is NW times the displacement.   It follows, therefore, that the displacement required to absorb the kinetic energy is given by the first term on the right of equation

(23), namely, $V^2/2gN$. The solidus term takes into account to some extent the manner by which the mass acquires its velocity.

We may extend the energy concept to other types of force displacement relationships such as shown in Fig. 13 or even more complex relations. It is of particular interest to compute the relative displacement for an elasto–plastic resistance as compared with a purely elastic resistance. To do so one can compare the two types of resistance shown in Fig. 20 and note that areas 1 plus 2 plus 3, for the elastic resistance energy, must be equal to areas 1 plus 2 plus 4 for the elasto–plastic resistance energy.

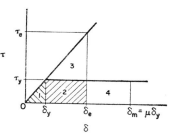

Fig. 20.   Conventionalized elastic and elasto–plastic stress–strain diagrams

From this relation, taking note of the fact that

one derives the result

$$\tau_e/\tau_y = \delta_e/\delta_y \qquad \qquad (24)$$

$$\frac{\delta_y}{\delta_e} = \frac{1}{\sqrt{(2\mu-1)}} \qquad \qquad (25)$$

$$\frac{\delta_m}{\delta_e} = \frac{\mu}{\sqrt{(2\mu-1)}}. \qquad \qquad (26)$$

In these equations, as indicated in Fig. 20, μ is the ratio of the maximum total displacement to the elastic component of displacement. For purely elastic conditions, $\mu=1$.

For a rigid–plastic resistance, the energy absorbed at a maximum displacement δ_{mp} is $\delta_{mp}\tau_y$, whereas for the elasto–plastic resistance, the energy absorbed at a maximum displacement δ_m is

$$\delta_m\tau_y(1-1/2\mu). \qquad \qquad (27)$$

Then, for the same energy the relative value of maximum displacement is:

$$\delta_m/\delta_{mp} = 1/(1-1/2\mu). \qquad \qquad (28)$$

The maximum value of this ratio is 2·0. For even moderate values of μ, however, the ratio is close to unity.

Number of effective shocks in an earthquake

Since the sliding of either the upstream or downstream slopes in an earthquake can only occur downhill, if sliding occurs at all there will be a lowering of the crest of the dam caused by a cumulative slip on both slopes, always downhill. The net motions of either slope can be determined only after assumptions are made of: (a) the input motions of the ground; (b) the effective number of spikes of accelerations similar to one of the single spikes considered in Fig. 17 and in the derivation of equation (23); and (c) the resistance of the sliding elements.

The effective number of pulses in an actual earthquake can be determined by an analysis of the response of simple systems to the earthquake motion. This has been done for four of the West Coast United States earthquakes for which strong motion records are available. These four are described in Table 2.

For convenience in interpreting the results the four earthquakes were normalized to a maximum acceleration of $0.5\,g$ and a maximum ground velocity of 30 in/sec, by modifying the acceleration and time scales appropriately. Normalized displacements are given in Table 2 for each of the earthquakes.

The analysis was made on the high-speed digital computer at the University of Illinois Digital Computer Laboratory for the normalized accelerograms for the earthquakes. The results are plotted in Fig. 21 for a symmetrical resistance function, in which the resistance is rigid–plastic but having the same value in each direction of motion. It appears from Fig. 21 that the results are bounded by the expression for energy $V^2/2gN$, and also by the maximum displacement y_0 of the ground. Where the value of N approaches the maximum earthquake acceleration, there is a reduction in response from that given by the energy expression, as shown by the equation in the lower right-hand part of the figure, in which the correction factor derived in equation (23) appears to be applicable. Apparently this is important only beyond a value of N/A greater than 0.5.

Table 2

Earthquakes considered in analysis

Earthquake	Maximum ground motions				Normalized* displacement: in.
	Acceleration g	Velocity in/sec	Displacement: in.	Duration: sec.	
1. Ferndale, 21 Dec., 1954, N45E —	0.205	10.5	8.26	20	27.7
2. Eureka, 21 Dec., 1954, S11W —	0.178	12.5	10.0	26	51.2
3. Olympia, 13 April, 1949, S40W —	0.210	8.28	9.29	26	20.5
4. El Centro, 18 May, 1940, N–S —	0.32	13.7	8.28	30	25.5

* Normalized to give acceleration = $0.50\,g$
and velocity = 30 in/sec.

Unsymmetrical resistance

When the motion takes place with a different resistance in the two directions, corresponding to a mass sliding downhill, as in Fig. 19, the displacement is increased greatly. Although there is a smooth transition between the value given in Fig. 21 and the greatly increased value corresponding to completely unsymmetrical resistance, the results approach very rapidly those corresponding to an infinite resistance in one direction. The results of calculations for this case are summarized on Fig. 22. A conservative upper bound to the computed values of displacement is given by the relation

$$\frac{V^2}{2gN}\cdot\frac{A}{N} \quad \cdot \quad \cdot \quad \cdot \quad \cdot \quad \cdot \quad \cdot \quad \cdot \quad \cdot \quad \cdot \quad (29)$$

This appears to indicate that the effective number of pulses in the earthquakes considered is equal to the quantity A/N. If one multiplies equation (23) by A/N, one obtains a bound which is somewhat closer in the region where N/A is larger than about 0.5, but is not conservative for somewhat smaller values. For very low values of N/A, the number of effective pulses in the earthquake apparently is no greater than 6 for the earthquakes considered. This, however, may be considered a peculiarity of the particular earthquakes examined. It would be undoubtedly true that for earthquakes lasting for a longer time the number of effective pulses would be greater. Preliminary studies indicate a relative value for longer durations roughly proportional to the square root of the duration.

Comparisons with model tests

The theoretical procedures described herein have been applied to tests of a model of a rock-fill dam, described by Davis *et al.* (1960). The scale of the model was 1/300 of the prototype. The dynamic tests of the model were made by striking a shaking table with a heavy pendulum. A rebound of the pendulum caused a second input at a lower acceleration. Hence, data could be obtained both for the initial strike and for the first rebound.

On the whole, the model tests indicated a fair agreement with the calculations, for comparable conditions. Within the accuracy of the records obtained in the tests, the measured motions were in fairly good agreement with the results computed by means of equation (23) and Fig. 21.

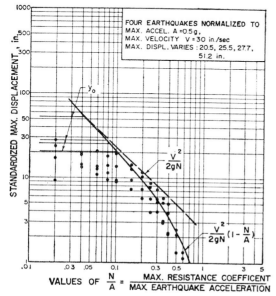

Fig. 21. Standardized displacement for normalized earthquakes (symmetrical resistance)

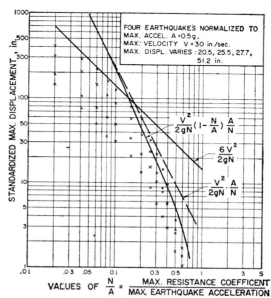

Fig. 22. Standardized displacement for normalized earthquakes (unsymmetrical resistance)

Comments and conclusions

For the maximum probable earthquake in California, which is a reasonable maximum earthquake for many other areas of the world, Fig. 22 may be used directly to obtain a measure of the maximum displacement for unsymmetrical sliding. If the maximum resistance coefficient is about 0·16, or about one-third the maximum earthquake acceleration, the net displacement will be about 1 ft. If the maximum resistance coefficient N is about 0·20 times the maximum earthquake acceleration, or N equals 0·1, the maximum displacement is about 5 ft. The maximum displacement increases rapidly as N decreases. Values of N in the range of 0·1 to 0·15 are not uncommon for earth dams designed for earthquake resistance. Of course, a design with a somewhat smaller value of N would have a smaller displacement if the earthquake were less intense. For an earthquake with a maximum acceleration of 0·25 g, and a maximum velocity of 15 in/sec, the displacements computed would be one-fourth those quoted, if the value of the ratio of N to A were the same. In other words, for the same relative value of resistance coefficient, the displacement varies as the square of the ground velocity. This displacement lowers the crest of the dam.

Another factor that must be considered in the design of a dam is overtopping caused by wave action. Such wave action can be initiated by slumping of the dam but it is more likely to be caused by slides from unstable natural areas in the reservoir. Slides of this sort caused failure of the Vaiont Reservoir in Italy; the dam itself did not fail structurally.

Faulting or sudden settlement may also cause wave action. Such a settlement that took place very rapidly at the dam itself caused the large waves at Hegben Lake (Anon, 1964).

Damage and serious danger may occur if an earth dam is in the neighbourhood of the fault where the fault may intersect the dam and cause a break or fissure through it. When an earth dam is founded on rock or a firm soil stratum, and is made of well compacted material, the danger in an earthquake may be minimal. However, if the dam is located above a stratum which can liquefy or lose its shearing strength an earthquake may cause a failure by spreading of the dam even though the dam itself may have an ample factor of safety with respect to failure in the material of the dam itself. In general, sites underlain by strata which may suffer a major reduction in shearing resistance should be considered unsuitable unless the sensitive strata can be removed.

Open cracks across the impervious section of an earth dam can form as a result of differential settlement of the base of the dam, or as a result of differential movements within the body of the dam, as well as a result of earthquakes. Transverse cracks may develop even in earthquake-free regions. Because an earthquake with even moderately large motions may introduce fissures and cracking which may lead to piping, provisions should be made to induce self-healing of open cracks. Dr Terzaghi has suggested that such provisions might consist of establishing the impervious section of the dam, or core, between two layers of properly graded cohesionless material. These layers should be only moderately compacted, and in each layer the grain size should increase with increasing distance from the contact surface with the impervious core. A method of this sort was adopted by Terzaghi for Mission Dam.

In arriving at the design of a dam which is required to resist earthquake motions one may either adopt a procedure in which the static resistance of the dam is greater than the maximum earthquake acceleration likely to be encountered, or one can make the dam capable of resisting displacements corresponding to those computed by the methods described herein. The former approach gives a misleading sense of security because of the fact that there are small displacements that take place even when N equals A or exceeds it, owing to the fact that resisting forces are developed even by elastic displacements less than the yield point. Hence the motions can be of such a nature as to cause a reduction in shearing stress and a consequent amplified displacement.

It may be required, to avoid permanent displacements altogether, that the value of N be well in excess of the maximum earthquake acceleration. This appears to be too uneconomical a procedure for general use.

For years engineers were convinced that foundations did not settle if they were adequately designed. The methods introduced by Terzaghi concentrated attention on methods by which the settlements could be determined and subsequent measurements indicated that almost all foundations settle. One might expect that the same situation applies to earth and rock-fill dams and embankments. When one concentrates attention only on the strengths and neglects the displacements or motions, one is not likely to realize that these motions will take place. It is desirable to try to keep them at a level such that they can cause no danger.

REFERENCES

AMBRASEYS, N. N., 1958. 'The seismic stability of earth dams.' *Ph.D. dissertation, University of London.*
AMBRASEYS, N. N., 1960. 'On the seismic behaviour of earth dams.' *Proc. 2nd World Conf. on Earthquake Engng, Tokyo,* vol. 1, p. 331.
AMBRASEYS, N. N., 1962. 'The seismic stability analysis of earth dams.' *Second Symposium on Earthquake Engineering, University of Roorkee, Roorkee, India.*

ANON, 1964. 'The Hegben Lake, Montana, earthquake of August 17, 1959.' Geological Survey Professional Paper 435. *U.S. Government Printing Office, Washington, D.C.*

BLUME, J. A., N. M. NEWMARK, *and* L. H. CORNING, 1961. 'Design of multi-storey reinforced concrete buildings for earthquake motions.' *Portland Cement Association, Chicago.*

BUSTAMANTE, J. I., 1964. 'Dynamic behaviour of non-cohesive embankment models.' *Ph.D. dissertation, University of Illinois.*

CLOUGH, R. W. *and* D. PIRTZ, 1958. 'Earthquake resistance of rock-fill dams.' *Trans. Amer. Soc. civ. Engrs,* 123 : 792–810.

DAVIS, R. E. *and associates,* 1960. 'Model study of stability of Portage Mountain Dam during earthquakes. Berkeley, California, November 1960. (Report to International Power and Engineering Consultants Ltd, Vancouver, Canada.)

SEED, H. B. *and* R. W. CLOUGH, 1963. 'Earthquake resistance of sloping core dams.' *Proc. Amer. Soc. civ. Engrs,* 89 (SM1) : 209–242.

SEED, H. B. *and* R. E. GOODMAN, 1964. 'Earthquake stability of slopes of cohesionless soils.' *Proc. Amer. Soc. civ. Engrs,* 90 (SM6) : 43–73.

SHANNON *and* WILSON, Inc., 1964. Report on Anchorage area soil studies, Alaska, to U.S. Army Engineer District at Anchorage, Alaska, 28 August, 1964.

THE STRENGTH OF SOILS AS ENGINEERING MATERIALS

A. W. BISHOP, M.A., D.Sc.(Eng.), Ph.D., M.I.C.E.

INTRODUCTION

Of the Rankine Lecturers so far appointed from the United Kingdom I am the first to have spent the early years of my professional life working on the design and construction of civil engineering works. Although I became deeply involved in soil testing during this period, and spent more than a year working at the Building Research Station with Dr Cooling and Professor Skempton, the tests which I performed were carried out primarily for the solution of immediate engineering problems and only secondarily as a fundamental study of soil properties.

This period no doubt left its mark, because I find that I have retained a preference for investigating naturally occurring soils, either in their undisturbed state or in the state in which they would be used for constructing the embankments of earth or rockfill dams, or other engineering works. As a consequence, I would like to direct attention to the following four aspects of the study of the strength of soils which are not only of fundamental significance, but also of immediate practical importance to the engineer:

(1) the failure criteria which are used to express the results of strength tests and which reflect the influence, if any, of the intermediate principal stress;
(2) the behaviour of soils under the high stresses implied by the greatly increased height of earth and rockfill dams now under construction;
(3) the difficulty of determining what is the in-situ undrained strength of a soil, due to the influence both of anisotropy and of unrepresentative sampling;
(4) the influence of time on the drained strength of soils.

(1) FAILURE CRITERIA

A satisfactory failure criterion should express with reasonable accuracy the relationship between the principal stresses when the soil is in limiting equilibrium. To be of practical use it should express this relationship in terms of parameters which can be used in the solution of problems of stability, bearing capacity, active and passive pressure, etc, and which can form the currency for the exchange of information about soil properties.

If we consider soil properties in terms of effective stress (Fig. 1), the most marked feature of which the failure criterion must take account is the increase in strength as the average effective stress increases. But we will wish to apply the information obtained from testing samples in axial compression in the triaxial cell (Fig. 2) (where the intermediate principal stress σ_2' is equal to the minor principal stress σ_3') to practical problems where σ_2' is greater than

131

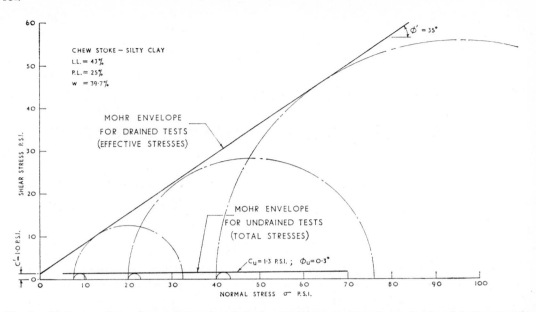

Fig. 1.   Mohr envelopes for undrained and drained tests on a saturated soil, showing increase in strength with increase in effective stress

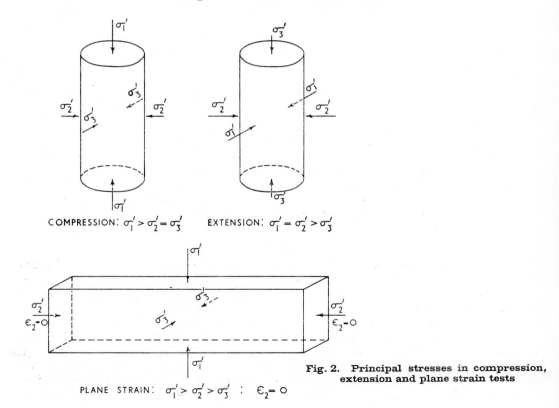

COMPRESSION: $\sigma_1' > \sigma_2' = \sigma_3'$ EXTENSION: $\sigma_1' = \sigma_2' > \sigma_3'$

PLANE STRAIN: $\sigma_1' > \sigma_2' > \sigma_3'$: $\epsilon_2 = 0$

Fig. 2.   Principal stresses in compression, extension and plane strain tests

σ_3' and may in the limit equal σ_1' (as in the centre of an excavation about to fail by heaving). A common special case is that of plane strain, where there is no change in length along the axis of the structure (Fig. 2). Most problems of slope stability fall into this category, and it is here that low factors of safety are most often encountered. The failure criterion should therefore also reflect the influence on the strength of the soil of the variation of σ_2' between the limiting values of σ_3' and σ_1'.

The principal failure criteria currently under discussion (see, for example, Kirkpatrick (1957), Hvorslev (1960), Scott (1963a), Roscoe et al (1963)) are given below. For simplicity they are given for cohesionless soils (or soils in which the cohesion intercept c' is zero). Also for simplicity σ_1', σ_2', σ_3' are chosen to denote the major, intermediate and minor effective principal stresses respectively.

The failure criteria may then be written:

Mohr–Coulomb:

$$\sigma_1' - \sigma_3' = \sin\phi' . (\sigma_1' + \sigma_3') \qquad . \quad . \quad . \quad . \quad . \quad . \quad (1)$$

Extended Tresca:[1]

$$\sigma_1' - \sigma_3' = \alpha\left(\frac{\sigma_1' + \sigma_2' + \sigma_3'}{3}\right) \qquad . \quad . \quad . \quad . \quad . \quad . \quad (2)$$

Extended von Mises:[2]

$$(\sigma_1' - \sigma_2')^2 + (\sigma_2' - \sigma_3')^2 + (\sigma_3' - \sigma_1')^2 = 2\alpha^2\left(\frac{\sigma_1' + \sigma_2' + \sigma_3'}{3}\right)^2 \qquad . \quad . \quad . \quad (3)$$

For the present discussion we are concerned with two points:

(1) that for a given stress system the strength should be proportional to the normal stress, and

(2) that the influence of the intermediate principal stress should be correctly indicated.

The first requirement is clearly satisfied by all three criteria. The second can be examined only on the basis of experimental evidence. It should be pointed out that whether or not yield takes place at constant volume is irrelevant to the present stage of the discussion, though it is relevant to any examination of the physical components of shear strength.

It will be noted that in the Mohr–Coulomb criterion the value of σ_2' has no influence on the strength, and the same principal stress ratio at failure would be expected for both compression and extension tests. This is in contrast to the extended Tresca and extended von Mises criteria, which both show an important difference between the stress ratios and angles of friction in compression and extension.

In *axial compression* $\sigma_2' = \sigma_3'$ and the extended Tresca (equation 2) and the extended von Mises (equation 3) both reduce to:

$$\sigma_1' - \sigma_3' = \alpha\left(\frac{\sigma_1' + 2\sigma_3'}{3}\right) \qquad . \quad . \quad . \quad . \quad . \quad . \quad (4)$$

In *axial extension* $\sigma_2' = \sigma_1'$ and the extended Tresca and the extended von Mises both reduce to:

$$\sigma_1' - \sigma_3' = \alpha\left(\frac{2\sigma_1' + \sigma_3'}{3}\right) \qquad . \quad . \quad . \quad . \quad . \quad . \quad (5)$$

---

[1] This is attributed by Johansen (1958) to Sandels. Roscoe et al (1958 and 1963) denote $\sigma_1' - \sigma_3' = q$ and $(\sigma_1' + \sigma_2' + \sigma_3')/3 = p$ and take $q = \alpha p$ as the failure criterion.

[2] This is attributed to Schleicher (1925, 1926).

The influence of the intermediate principal stress on strength may be more readily appreciated in terms of the variation in ϕ' which is implied by the different failure criteria as σ'_2 varies between the limits σ'_3 and σ'_1.

The Mohr–Coulomb criterion (equation 1) may be written:

$$\frac{\sigma'_1 - \sigma'_3}{\sigma'_1 + \sigma'_3} = \sin \phi' \qquad . \quad . \quad . \quad . \quad . \quad . \quad . \quad (6)$$

The relative position of σ'_2 between σ'_3 and σ'_1 may be denoted by the parameter b, where:

$$\frac{\sigma'_2 - \sigma'_3}{\sigma'_1 - \sigma'_3} = b \qquad . \quad . \quad . \quad . \quad . \quad . \quad . \quad (7)$$

and b varies between 0 and 1.

The extended Tresca criterion then becomes:

$$\frac{\sigma'_1 - \sigma'_3}{\sigma'_1 + \sigma'_3} = \frac{1}{\dfrac{1}{3} + \dfrac{2}{\alpha} - \dfrac{2}{3}b} \qquad . \quad . \quad . \quad . \quad . \quad (8)$$

and the extended von Mises criterion becomes:

$$\frac{\sigma'_1 - \sigma'_3}{\sigma'_1 + \sigma'_3} = \frac{1}{\dfrac{1}{3} + \dfrac{2}{\alpha} \cdot \sqrt{1 - b + b^2} - \dfrac{2}{3}b} \qquad . \quad . \quad . \quad . \quad (9)$$

The variation of ϕ' (as defined by equation 6) with b (as defined by equation 7) corresponding to the two failure criteria expressed in equations 8 and 9 is illustrated in Fig. 12 and will be compared with observed values in a later section. It will be seen that the predicted ϕ' varies between $\sin^{-1}\dfrac{1}{\frac{2}{\alpha} + \frac{1}{3}}$ in the compression test, and $\sin^{-1}\dfrac{1}{\frac{2}{\alpha} - \frac{1}{3}}$ in the extension test, which is a very marked difference since the value of α at failure is typically more than 0·8.

A great many tests have been carried out, at Imperial College and elsewhere, to examine the influence of the intermediate principal stress, and some of the principal results are illustrated below.

As the accuracy of the tests is usually called in question when they fail to fit whichever theory is in vogue, it is of interest to note several points. The error in the determination of the principal stress ratio due to the distortion of the sample *at failure* has often been considerably over-exaggerated. The strain at failure in the test series to be quoted below (Cornforth, 1961) varied in compression, from $3\frac{1}{2}\%$ for dense sand to 6% for the middle of the range and 12% for loose sand. A sample which reached its peak stress at $6·3\%$ axial strain is illustrated in Fig. 3. A detailed study of 4-in. diameter samples having different heights and degrees of end restraint (Fig. 4) suggests that measurement of peak strength in compression need be subject to little ambiguity (Bishop and Green, 1965).

In plane strain the failure strain ϵ_1 varied from $1·3\%$ for dense sand to 2% in the middle of the range and 4% for loose sand. Rupture in a thin zone then occurred (Fig. 5). With these very small failure strains little uncertainty again arises in the stress calculations.

In extension the axial strain ϵ_3 at failure varied from -4% to -5% for dense and medium dense sand and rose to -9% for loose sand. In drained tests a neck begins to form at about the peak stress ratio, though it may not be very apparent to the eye (Fig. 6). If the test is stopped as soon as the peak is defined and the actual shape of the sample determined, the computed[3] value of ϕ' may be $\frac{1}{2}°$ to $1°$ higher at the dense end and about $2°$ higher at the loose end than the value based on average cross-sectional area. This correction has been made by Cornforth (1961) in the tests quoted.

---

[3] Based on the average cross section of a zone capable of containing a plane inclined at $45° - \phi'/2$.

Fig. 3. 4-in. dia. × 8-in. high compression test: Ham River sand: porous disc at each end: $n_i = 40 \cdot 2\%$, $\phi'_{max} = 37 \cdot 4°$, $\epsilon_{1f} = 6 \cdot 3\%$, test stopped at $\epsilon_1 = 7 \cdot 5\%$. (Test by Green, 1966)

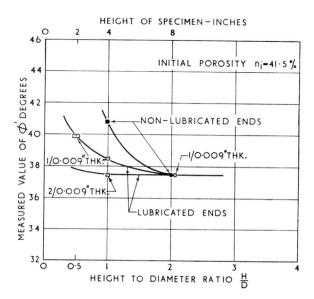

Fig. 4. Effect of sample height and degree of end restraint on measured peak ϕ' (number and thickness of lubricated membranes on end plattens indicated)

Fig. 5a.   Plane strain test apparatus (with cell body removed).
(Wood, 1958)

Fig. 5b. Plane strain compression test sample (4 in. × 2 in. × 16 in.) of Brasted sand after failure $n_i = 35 \cdot 6\%$, $\epsilon_{1f} = 1 \cdot 7\%$, test stopped at $\epsilon_1 = 15 \cdot 0\%$. (Test run with end plattens removed) (Cornforth, 1961)

A comparison between the peak strength values, expressed in terms of ϕ' as defined above, of plane strain and axial compression tests is given in Fig. 7. This indicates values of ϕ' in plane strain higher by 4° at the dense end of the range and by $\frac{1}{2}$° in loose sand. A subsequent series of tests at Imperial College on Mol sand by Wade (1963) shows similar results. Tests on sand by Kummeneje (1957) in a vacuum triaxial apparatus and also by Leussink (1965) are in general agreement, but show less tendency to converge at higher porosities.

The comparison between compression and extension tests is shown in Fig. 8 and it is apparent that the difference in the value of ϕ' is not significant over the range of porosities investigated. The same general conclusion is indicated by a subsequent series of tests by Green on Ham River sand,[4] using lubricated end plattens in both compression and extension tests (Fig. 9).

To examine the failure criteria a knowledge of σ_2' is required. In the compression and extension tests σ_2' is equal to the fluid pressure in the triaxial cell less the pore pressure in the sample. In the plane strain test σ_2' is determined from the load on the lubricated plattens maintaining zero strain in the σ_2' direction (Wood, 1958).

---

[4] Due to the variation in ϕ' with normal stress, the cell pressures in the extension tests have been selected so that the minor principal stress at failure approximates to the minor principal stress used in the compression tests.

Fig. 6a. 4–in. dia. × 7–in. high extension test; Ham River sand: porous discs at each end. $n_i = 39.2\%$, $\phi'_{max} = 40.5°$, $\epsilon_{3f} = -7.4\%$, test stopped at $\epsilon_3 = -8.4\%$

Fig. 6b. 4–in. dia. × 4–in. high extension test; Ham River sand: 2/0·010–in. thick lubricated membranes at each end. $n_i = 45.8\%$, $\phi'_{max} = 32.6°$, $\epsilon_{3f} = -9.5\%$, test stopped at $\epsilon_3 = -9.8\%$

(Tests by Green, 1965)

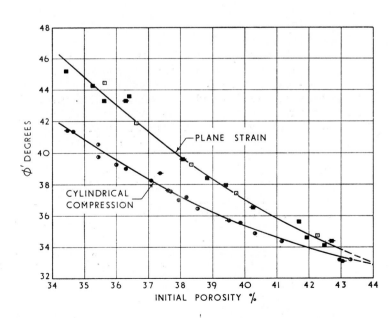

Fig. 7. Comparison of results of drained plane strain and cylindrical compression tests on Brasted sand (Cornforth, 1961)

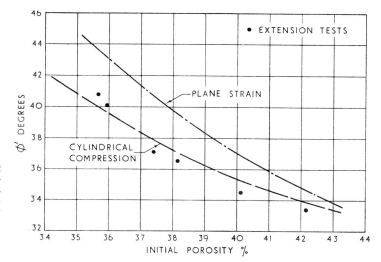

Fig. 8. Comparison of results of drained extension, compression and plane strain tests on Brasted sand (Cornforth, 1961)

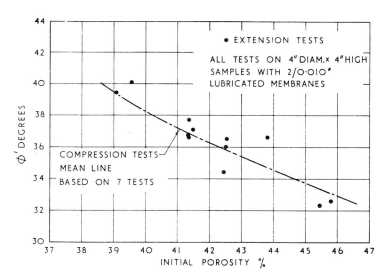

Fig. 9. Comparison of results of drained extension and compression tests on saturated Ham River sand: cylindrical samples with lubricated ends, $\dfrac{H}{D} = 1$ (Tests by Green, 1965)

The observed values of the ratio $\dfrac{\sigma_2'}{\sigma_1'+\sigma_3'}$ show a close correlation with the peak value of ϕ'

(Fig. 10), over a wide range of values. The empirical expression $\dfrac{\sigma_2'}{\sigma_1'+\sigma_3'} = \tfrac{1}{2}\cos^2\phi'$ is in good

agreement with the general trend, but slightly underestimates σ_2'. The expression may be derived by combining two earlier empirical relationships. Wood (1958) noted that for tests on compacted moraine carried out in the plane strain apparatus at Imperial College, the relationship between σ_2' and σ_1' at failure approximated to the expression:

$$\sigma_2' = K_0\sigma_1' \qquad\qquad\qquad (10)$$

where K_0 was the coefficient of earth pressure at rest measured with zero strain in both lateral directions (i.e. when both $\epsilon_2=0$ and $\epsilon_3=0$). Tests reported by Bishop (1958) and Simons (1958) had shown that there was an empirical relationship between K_0 and ϕ' which could be represented with reasonable accuracy by an expression due to Jaky (1944 and 1948):

$$K_0 = 1 - \sin\phi' \qquad\qquad\qquad (11)$$

Combining these expressions and putting

$$\frac{\sigma_1'-\sigma_3'}{\sigma_1'+\sigma_3'} = \sin\phi' \quad \text{(from equation 6)}$$

we obtain

$$\frac{\sigma_2'}{\sigma_1'+\sigma_3'} = \tfrac{1}{2}\cos^2\phi' \qquad\qquad\qquad (12)$$

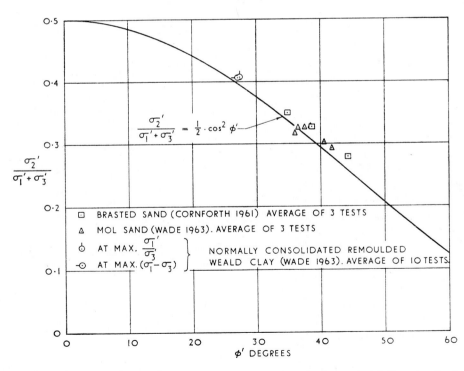

Fig. 10.   **Correlation with ϕ' of value of intermediate principal stress σ_2' at failure in plane strain**

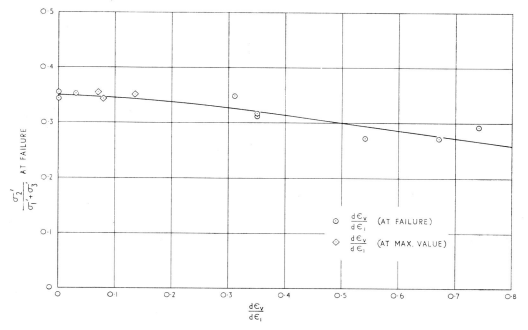

Fig. 11. Variation of $\dfrac{\sigma_2'}{\sigma_1'+\sigma_3'}$ **with rate of volume change** $\dfrac{d\epsilon_v}{d\epsilon_1}$ **for drained tests on Brasted sand**

It is of interest to note that samples which were deforming at constant volume when the peak stress ratio was reached[5] conformed to this relationship and the ratio $\dfrac{\sigma_2'}{\sigma_1'+\sigma_3'}$ showed no indication of being equal to $\frac{1}{2}$ as might have been expected (Fig. 11). What occurs to this ratio at strains beyond those corresponding to the maximum stress cannot be determined in the present apparatus, as zone failure always follows closely after the peak and the localized value of σ_2' cannot be measured.

With the knowledge of σ_2' we can now compare the observed values of ϕ' $\Bigg($defined by $\sin\phi'=\dfrac{\sigma_1'-\sigma_3'}{\sigma_1'+\sigma_3'}\Bigg)$ with those predicted by the various failure criteria as b $\left(=\dfrac{\sigma_2'-\sigma_3'}{\sigma_1'+\sigma_3'}\right)$ varies between 0 and 1. Fig. 12(a) shows this comparison for loose Brasted sand, which is shearing almost at constant volume at the peak stress ratio. It will be seen that the results fit well with the Mohr–Coulomb failure criterion, whereas the extended von Mises and extended

[5] In a plane strain compression test on loose sand constant volume shear may occur firstly at the peak stress ratio, when the condition of pure shear is approximated to, and then subsequently at a lower stress ratio, when strains are largely confined to a thin slip zone in which simple shear is approximated to. In the tests on Brasted sand performed by Cornforth (1961) the peak value of ϕ' corresponding to zero rate of volume change is 34·3°. If the direction of the thin slip zone is taken to correspond to a Mohr–Coulomb slip plane a residual ϕ' of 32·3° is obtained. If, alternatively, the shear stress acting along the boundary of this zone is taken (following Hill, 1950) to be equal to the maximum shear stress within the zone, the residual value of ϕ' would be 39·2°, which is clearly unreasonable. These differences suggest that constant volume yield in pure shear may involve a failure mechanism significantly different from that associated with constant volume yield in simple shear.

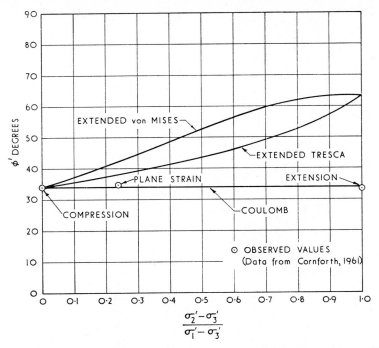

Fig. 12a.   Observed and predicted values of ϕ'.   Loose sand; ϕ' in compression $=34°$ and $\alpha=1\cdot375$

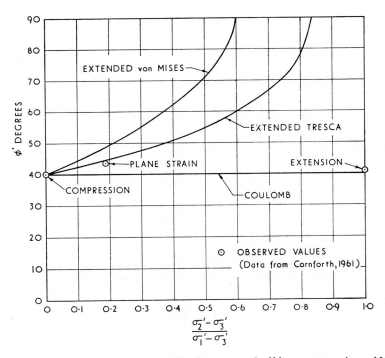

Fig. 12b.   Observed and predicted values of ϕ'.   Dense sand; ϕ' in compression $=40°$ and $\alpha=1\cdot636$

Tresca criteria predict values which differ from the observed values by more than the most pessimistic estimate of experimental error.

Fig. 12(b) shows that for dense sand, which is dilating at failure, the Mohr–Coulomb criterion again gives the best over-all fit, though for a comparison of the compression test and the plane strain case only the extended Tresca is in better agreement.[6] However, for the extension tests the extended Tresca and the extended von Mises both fail to predict meaningful results. The reason for this is of considerable interest.

In Fig. 13 the values of ϕ' in compression predicted by the two failure criteria are plotted against the value of the parameter α which is used in both expressions to indicate the increase in strength with normal stress. This α is the same as that used by Roscoe *et al* (1958). It will be seen that for the compression test the relationship between ϕ' and α is almost linear and in fact approximates to $\phi' = 25\alpha$ over the range $\phi' = 20°$ to $40°$. However, the value of ϕ' in extension predicted by both failure criteria rapidly diverges from that in compression as α increases, and becomes equal to $90°$ (i.e. $\sigma_1'/\sigma_3' = \infty$) when $\alpha = 1.5$. At this value of α the compression value of $\phi' = 36.9°$, which is well within the range of values encountered in dense sand.

The physical explanation can be seen from the representation of the failure criteria in a three-dimensional stress space (Fig. 14). If the axes σ_1', σ_2', σ_3' represent the magnitudes of the principal effective stresses in those three directions, we can select a plane on which $\sigma_1' + \sigma_2' + \sigma_3' = \text{constant}$, and a diagonal $00'$ (normal to it) for which $\sigma_1' = \sigma_2' = \sigma_3'$ (i.e., no shear

---

[6] If the value of $\sigma_2'/(\sigma_1' + \sigma_3')$ in the failure zone exceeds the average value recorded in the plane strain apparatus and approaches $\frac{1}{2}$ the apparent agreement with the extended Tresca criterion no longer obtains.

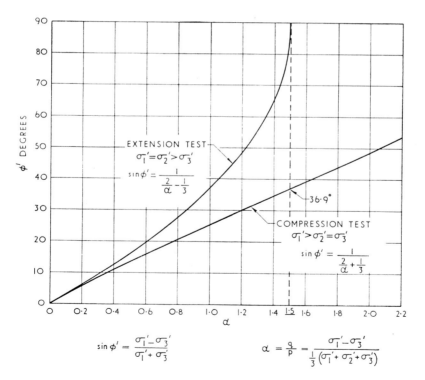

Fig. 13. Relationship between parameters used in failure criteria

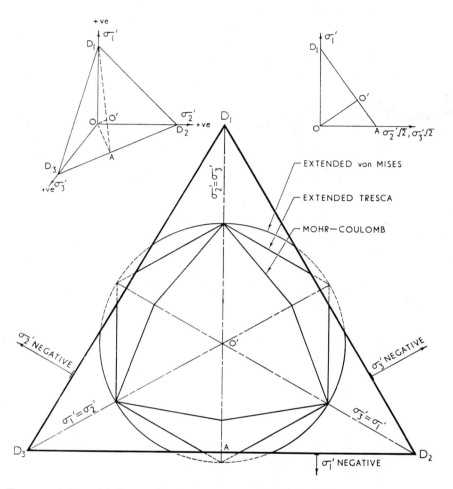

Fig. 14. Representation of failure criteria in principal effective stress space, showing boundaries of positive stress field. Sections of failure surface shown for $\phi'=40°$ in axial compression

stress).   States of limiting equilibrium expressed by the various failure criteria are then represented by pyramid shaped surfaces having their apex at 0 and showing characteristic sections on the plane $D_1D_2D_3$.   These are an irregular hexagon for the Mohr–Coulomb criterion; a circle with centre 0' for the extended von Mises criterion and the regular hexagon inscribed in this circle for the extended Tresca criterion.

In Fig. 14 these sections are plotted for $\phi'=40°$ in axially symmetrical compression (i.e. $\alpha=1·636$), and it will be seen that as σ_2' moves from σ_3' to σ_1' the circle and hexagon representing the extended von Mises and Tresca criteria respectively go outside the lines D_1D_2 etc., into negative effective stress space.   For a cohesionless soil (or $c'=0$ material) this is meaningless.   These failure criteria are therefore in principle unable to represent the behaviour of the denser frictional materials having a compression ϕ' of more than 36·9° (i.e. $\alpha=1·5$) for which the extended von Mises circle is tangential to D_1D_2, D_2D_3 and D_3D_1.

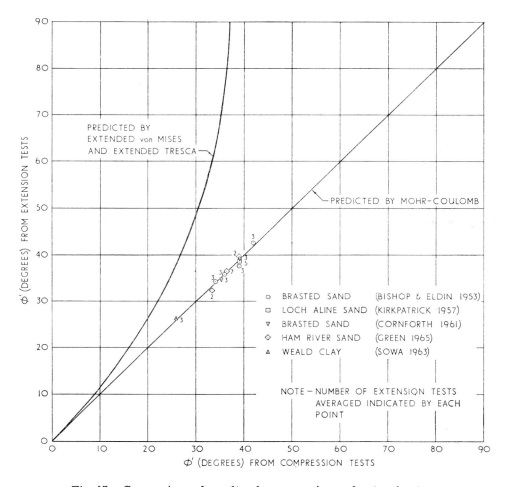

Fig. 15. Comparison of results of compression and extension tests

Even within this range the two criteria predict values of ϕ' in extension (Fig. 15), which differ from the experimental results by an amount which cannot be attributed to experimental error. The experimental results, however, strongly support the Mohr–Coulomb criterion,[7] and we must, I feel, accept the Mohr–Coulomb criterion as being the only simple criterion of

---

[7] This applies to all the data illustrated in Fig. 15, to tests reported by the Norwegian Geotechnical Institute (1958), and by Wade (1963). The tests illustrated in Fig. 15 were drained tests on saturated samples consolidated under equal all round pressure, with the exception of the series by Cornforth (1961), where consolidation with zero radial strain was used. Unpublished tests at Imperial College by Walker on dry sand consolidated under equal all round pressure agree with the tests described above. In contrast early tests by Habib (1953) and Peltier (1957) show lower values of ϕ' in extension. No obvious explanation for this difference is apparent. Tests by Haythornthwaite (1960) also show a difference, but are based on a different definition of the point of failure. On the other hand undrained tests on undisturbed clays or clays initially anisotropically consolidated from a slurry (Ladd and Bailey, 1964; Smotrych, unpublished data) show higher values of ϕ' in extension. The interpretation of the test data is, however, subject to more uncertainty. The influence of undrained stress path on the value of ϕ', which is of greater importance in clays, and the anisotropy of the soil structure, are likely to play a more significant part in the behaviour of clays and more experimental data is required before general conclusions can be drawn.

reasonable generality.[8,9]   It does, however, underestimate the value of ϕ' for plane strain in dense sands by up to 4° (from tests on Brasted sand by Cornforth and Mol sand by Wade). Tests representing the actual state of stress or strain to be encountered in practice are obviously best for precise work in this case.   The present data can be expressed in terms of an extended Mohr–Coulomb criterion involving two parameters:

$$\frac{\sigma_1' - \sigma_3'}{\sigma_1' + \sigma_3'} = \frac{K_1}{1 - K_2\sqrt{b(1-b)}} \qquad \cdots \cdots \cdots \quad (13)$$

where $b = \dfrac{\sigma_2' - \sigma_3'}{\sigma_1' - \sigma_3'}$

and K_1 and K_2 are parameters determined from compression and plane strain tests (K_1 being equal to sin ϕ' in the compression and extension test).

Further studies of the variation of ϕ' with b for dense frictional materials now being carried out at Imperial College may, however, suggest a more elaborate expression.

It is clear, however, from Fig. 12 that from an engineering point of view the use of the extended von Mises or Tresca criteria would lead to a very substantial overestimate of strength for a wide range of b values.

(2) THE BEHAVIOUR OF SOILS UNDER HIGH STRESSES

There is one limitation, which is of considerable engineering significance, common to all the failure criteria so far discussed.   The constant of proportionality between strength and normal stress, either ϕ' or α, is not really a constant when a wide range of stress is under consideration.   This is of particular importance when drawing conclusions from tests on models on the one hand, where unpublished tests at Imperial College by Dr Ambraseys and Mr Sarma have shown that values of ϕ' may rise by up to 8° at stresses represented by a fraction of an inch of sand, and on the other hand in the design of high dams (Fig. 16) which are now reaching 1000 ft in height and imply considerably reduced values of ϕ'.   The major principal stress in such a dam could approach 900 lb/sq. in.

Typical Mohr envelopes for various soils tested under a wide range of pressures are illustrated in Fig. 17.   The marked curvature of many of the failure envelopes will be seen. It is of interest to note that the uppermost envelope[10] represents tests on one of the fill materials of the Oroville dam shown in the previous figure.   The other materials include rockfill from the Infiernillo dam,[11] compacted glacial till, two dense sands, and one loose sand (Ham River), and undisturbed silt and two undisturbed clays, as well as one clay consolidated from a slurry. There is some indication that the curvature is most marked for soils which

(a) are initially dense or heavily compacted,
(b) are initially of relatively uniform grain size,
(c) if undisturbed, have been heavily over-consolidated.

In the coarser granular materials (the sands, gravels, and rockfills) the curvature is clearly associated with crushing of the particles, initially local crushing at interparticle contacts, and ultimately shattering of complete particles.   This in turn is associated, in dense materials,

---

[8] This conclusion was reached by Kirkpatrick (1957).   However, from thick cylinder tests on dense sand he obtained an increase in ϕ' of only 2° for $b = \frac{1}{2}$.
[9] The method proposed by Johansen (1958) reduces to the Mohr–Coulomb criterion for the case when the value of ϕ' in extension is equal to that in compression.
[10] The minimum ratio of sample diameter to maximum particle size which may be used without an overestimate of the strength resulting has not been fully investigated.   The ratio of only 4 was used in the tests by Hall and Gordon (1963) quoted above.
[11] Details of the special triaxial cell for samples 113 cm. diameter are given by Marsal et al (1965).

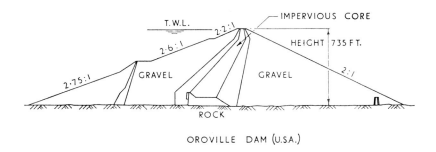

OROVILLE DAM (U.S.A.)

Fig. 16. Two high dams now under construction. (USCOLD Newsletter, Jan. 1963; Nitchiporovitch, 1964)

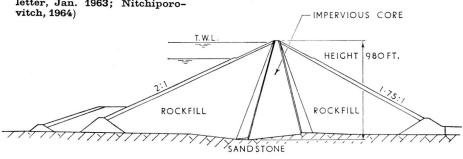

NUREK DAM (U.S.S.R.)

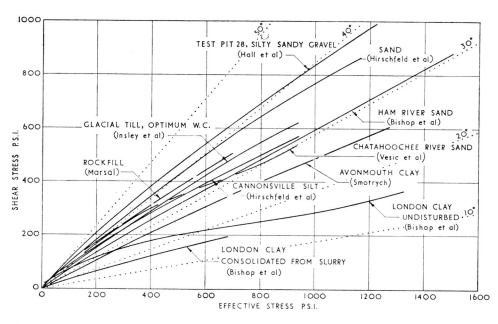

Fig. 17. Mohr envelopes for various soils under high confining pressures (all tests drained except London Clay consolidated from slurry)

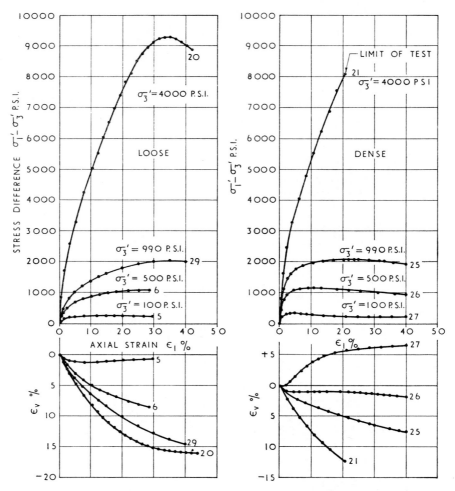

Fig. 18.   Results of drained tests on saturated Ham River sand.   (Tests by Skinner 1964–66)

with a greatly reduced rate of volume increase at failure, and this leads to a marked reduction in the overall value of ϕ' at failure.   The dependence of ϕ' on rate of volume change was demonstrated by Taylor (1948), Bishop (1950), Hafiz (1950), and Bishop and Eldin (1953). A discussion of the various mathematical approaches to the problem is outside the scope of the present paper, particularly as the work done in crushing the particles is usually omitted from the calculations.   From a practical point of view it should be noted that only London Clay and Avonmouth Clay gave ϕ' values significantly below 30°.

Typical stress, strain and volume change curves for drained tests on saturated Ham River sand are given in Fig. 18.   The marked effect of pressure on the volume change during shear can be clearly seen.   For loose sand the reduction in volume during shear rises rapidly with increase in σ_3' up to about 1000 lb/sq. in., and then more gradually as σ_3' is increased to 4000 lb/sq. in.   Dense sand, which is strongly dilatant at low confining pressures, shows almost zero rate of volume change at failure when σ_3' reaches 500 lb/sq. in.   At higher values of σ_3'

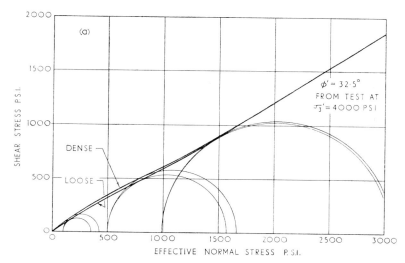

Fig. 19a. Mohr envelopes for drained tests on loose and dense Ham River sand (data from Skinner, 1964–66)

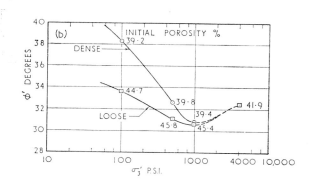

Fig. 19b. Variation of ϕ' with σ_3' (data from Skinner, 1964–66)

dense sand shows an increasingly marked reduction in volume during shear and at $\sigma_3' = 4000$ lb/sq. in., its behaviour approximated to that of loose sand. For loose sand the stress difference at failure when $\sigma_3' = 4000$ lb/sq. in. exceeds 9000 lb/sq. in.

The Mohr envelopes for loose and dense sand are given in Fig. 19(a). The marked curvature of the envelope for the dense samples and its convergence at high stresses with that for loose samples can be seen. Fig. 19(b) shows that the difference between ϕ' for dense sand and ϕ' for loose sand drops from nearly 5° at $\sigma_3' = 100$ lb/sq. in. to only 0·2° when σ_3' is 1000 lb/sq. in.[12] It is also apparent that even for sand placed in a very loose state ϕ' is not independent of effective stress, but drops about 3° as σ_3' rises from 100 lb/sq. in. to 1000 lb/sq. in. As will be seen later, this drop is closely associated with the rate of volume change at failure.

---

[12] In this context ϕ' is defined by the tangent to the origin from the stress circles at the value of σ_3' under consideration.

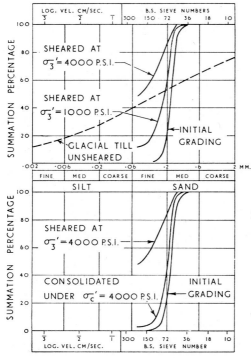

Fig. 20a. Changes in grading resulting (1) from shear at different pressures and (2) from consolidation as compared with complete shear test
Saturated Ham River sand. (Tests by Skinner, 1964–66)

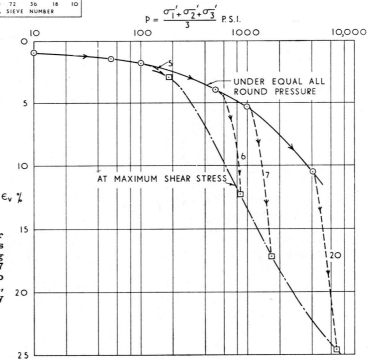

Fig. 20b. Influence of shear stress on volume changes associated with crushing of sand grains. (Test 7 terminated just prior to peak.) Ham River sand, initially loose. (Tests by Skinner, 1964–66)

In Fig. 20(a) the change in grading due to particle breakdown during compression and shear is illustrated. Several points of interest may be noted. Firstly, the combined effect of consolidation and shear leads to very marked particle breakdown even in a medium to fine sand. This effect can also be detected at much lower stresses than illustrated here. Secondly, breakdown results in a grading tending to approximate to that found in naturally occurring glacial tills, for which ϕ' has proved to be relatively insensitive to stress (Fig. 17; see also Insley *et al*, 1965).[13] This suggests the type of grading likely to be suitable for fills to withstand high stresses. Thirdly, at high stresses the particle breakdown occurs to a much greater extent during the shear stage than during the consolidation stage.

This latter point is further illustrated by plotting the associated volume changes against

the average stress $\dfrac{\sigma_1' + \sigma_2' + \sigma_3'}{3}$ in Fig. 20(b). Where the increase in average stress is associated

---

[13] Further data on the breakdown of sand particles with normal and shear stress is given by Vesic and Barksdale (1963) and Borg, Friedman, Handin and Higgs (1960). The breakdown of rockfill is discussed by Marsal (1965). These points are further discussed by Bishop (1965).

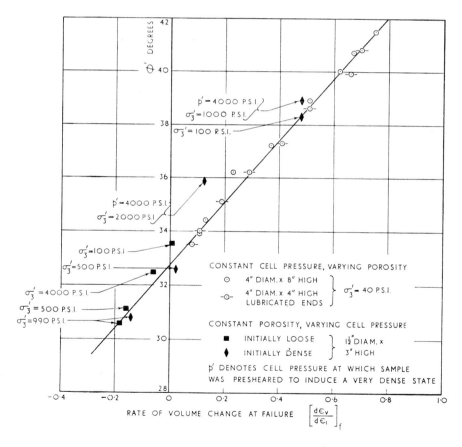

Fig. 21. The relationship between ϕ' and rate of volume change $\dfrac{d\epsilon_v}{d\epsilon_1}$ at failure. (Tests by Green and Skinner, 1964–66)

with a stress difference (or shear stress) the rate of volume decrease is many times greater than under all round pressure, except at low consolidation pressures.

In Fig. 21 the relationship between the value of ϕ' and the rate of volume change $\dfrac{d\epsilon_v}{d\epsilon_1}$ at failure (or dilatancy rate) is given.   At a given pressure the dilatancy rate will vary with the initial density at which the material is placed, and a very close correlation with ϕ' will be noted.   At a given initial density an increase in pressure will reduce the rate of dilatancy, and it is of interest to note how near to the previous line values obtained in this way actually lie.   This is all the more remarkable when the extremely wide stress range is considered, from $\sigma_3' = 40$ lb/sq. in. to $\sigma_3' = 4000$ lb/sq. in.   For this particular sand (Ham River), the maximum departure from the mean line is only $1\frac{1}{2}°$.   The curvature of the failure envelope is thus largely accounted for by the decrease in the rate of dilatancy with increasing stress.

The variation in the rate of volume change at failure with increase in effective stress σ_3' is plotted in Fig. 22.   It appears that for Ham River sand the change from positive to negative rate of dilatancy at failure occurs mainly within the stress range $\sigma_3' = 0-1000$ lb/sq. in.   At higher stresses the trend is reversed and failure at almost constant rate of volume change occurs after the large initial decrease in volume illustrated in Fig. 18.   At failure, however, the material is no longer a fine to medium sand but a well graded silty sand with nearly 50% in the silt sizes or smaller (Fig. 20a).   The greatly increased number of interparticle contacts carrying the stresses must largely counterbalance the effect of the reduction in the basic coefficient of interparticle friction with pressure (see, for example, Hafiz, 1950).

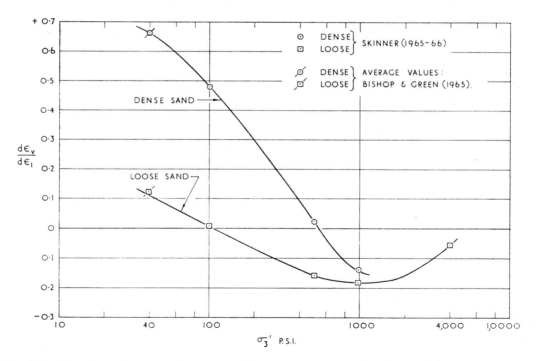

Fig. 22.   Variation of rate of dilatancy at failure with increase in effective stress; saturated Ham River sand

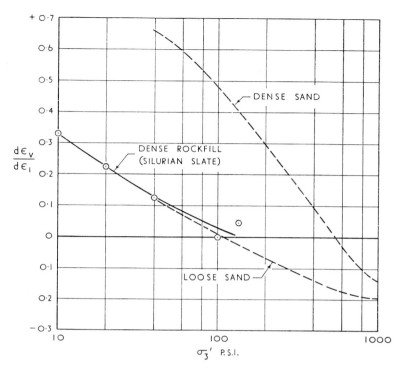

Fig. 23. **Variation of rate of dilatancy at failure with increase in effective stress: dense rockfill (Silurian slate). (Tests by Tombs, 1966)**

A comparison with the results of tests on 1-ft diameter samples of a compacted rockfill is made in Fig. 23. Within the working range of stress the dilatancy characteristics of the compacted rockfill (Silurian slate) approximate more closely to those of a loose sand than those of a dense sand. This is consistent with the very marked particle breakdown observed during the tests.

Provided that the influence of high pressure on ϕ' and on volume change is measured and that designs are not based on the extrapolation of low pressure tests, little difficulty is involved under drained conditions in achieving safe designs. However, fully saturated granular material under these stresses could be very dangerous under undrained or shock loading, as structural breakdown gives it an undrained stress path very similar to that of quick clay. The curves showing the relationships between stress, strain, and the build up of pore pressure are given in Fig. 24. The very small strain at failure in test 8 should be noted. The stress paths are given in Fig. 25.[14]

It will be seen that the shape of the stress path of test 8 is very similar to that observed in the low stress range for very loose sands which are susceptible to flow slides (Waterways Experiment Station, 1950; Bjerrum, 1961), and for sensitive clays (Taylor and Clough, 1951; N.G.I., unpublished data). In particular it will be noted that at the maximum value of the stress difference (represented by $\frac{1}{2}[\sigma_1' - \sigma_3']$) the value of ϕ' mobilized is 21·3° for test 8 (Fig. 25); thereafter the rise in pore pressure more than compensates for the increase in ϕ' as the residual state is approached.

---

[14] Further details of these tests are given by Bishop, Webb and Skinner (1965).

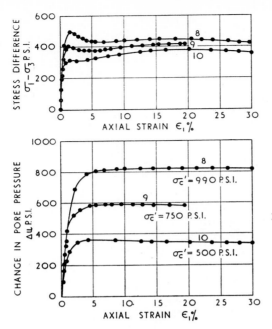

Fig. 24. Results of consolidated–undrained tests on saturated Ham River sand. (σ_c' denotes effective consolidation pressure). (Tests by Skinner, 1964)

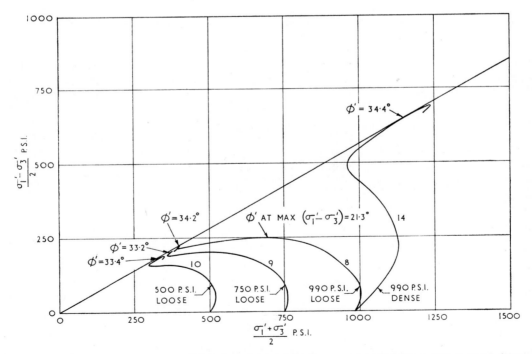

Fig. 25. Stress paths for consolidated-undrained tests on saturated Ham River sand (Tests by Skinner, 1964–66)

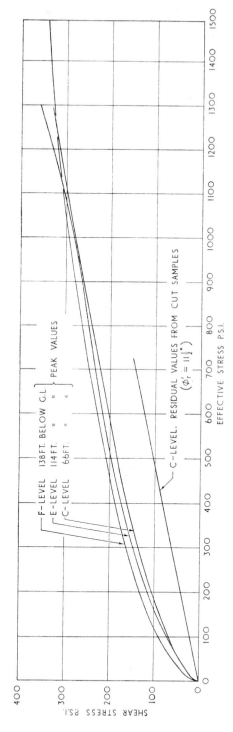

Fig. 26. Mohr envelopes for undisturbed London Clay from Ashford Common shaft (after Bishop, Webb and Lewin, 1965)

It would appear, therefore, that fill to be used fully saturated, and under high stresses, should preferably be well graded and should in any case be placed in a dense state, so that under undrained loading the pore pressure build-up is reduced and the undrained strength increased as illustrated in test 14 (Fig. 25).

There is not space to deal in detail with the behaviour under a wide range of stress of clay as an undisturbed material and as a compacted fill. One illustration must suffice. Fig. 26 shows the Mohr envelopes for undisturbed London Clay from depths of 66, 114, and 138 ft below ground level at the Ashford Common shaft.[15] The change in slope from 30° near the origin to 10° at very high stresses will be seen (the latter corresponds to an origin $\phi'=15°$). For the same material consolidated from a slurry the value of ϕ' obtained from undrained tests with pore pressure measurement (Fig. 17) drops only from 21° near the origin to about 16° (tangent from the origin). The residual angle ϕ' from pre-cut undisturbed samples from a depth of 66 ft dropped only from $11\frac{1}{2}°$ to 11°.

(3) THE IN-SITU UNDRAINED STRENGTH OF A SOIL

In using the undrained strength of a clay in the $\phi_u=0$ analysis for short-term loading the engineer is apt to imagine that, apart from sampling disturbance, a given sample of clay has a unique undrained strength, irrespective of the type of test (triaxial, vane or simple shear test) used to measure it and irrespective of the inclination or direction of the slip surface implied in the problem he is analysing.

In fact, as early as 1949, Professor J. Brinch Hansen and Dr R. E. Gibson showed that on theoretical grounds the laboratory undrained compression test should differ from the field vane test (Table 1) and that the in-situ strength on an inclined failure surface could differ from them both, being greatest in the case of active earth pressure and least in the case of passive earth pressure. This prediction was for a soil consolidated with zero lateral yield, i.e. the initial lateral effective stress was only K_0[16] times the vertical effective stress. The soil was thus subjected to an anisotropic stress history, but no anisotropy of the shear strength

Table 1

Predicted influence of orientation of shear plane on undrained strength (after Hansen and Gibson, 1949)

Value of $\dfrac{c_u}{p}$	Clay 1	Clay 2
Active earth pressure　　.. 　　..	0·331	0·282
Passive earth pressure　　.. 　　..	0·193	0·256
Failure on a horizontal plane　　..	0·213	0·262
Vane test　　.. 　　.. 　　.. 　　..	0·191	0·252
Unconfined compression test:		
condition (a)　　.. 　　.. 　　..	0·170	0·247
condition (b)　　.. 　　.. 　　..	0·250	0·283

Clay 1.　Normally consolidated, sensitive silty clay.
Clay 2.　Normally consolidated, typical British post-glacial clay.
Condition (a) ⎫
Condition (b) ⎭ Probable limits of influence of stress release on sampling.

---

[15] The index properties at the 114 ft level, for example, are $W_L=70$, $W_p=27$, clay friction$=57$, activity $=0·75$, initial water content$=24·2$. For full details see Bishop, Webb and Lewin (1965).

[16] K_0 is termed the coefficient of earth pressure at rest and is generally within the range of 0·4 to 0·7 for normally consolidated clays.

parameters in terms of effective stress was assumed in estimating the undrained strength. Their results thus indicated the influence on the excess pore pressure at failure of stress history and, in particular, of the rotation of principal stress directions in an anisotropically consolidated soil.

Their conclusions have been rather lost sight of in recent years, due to the renewed emphasis on the unique relationship between undrained strength and water content. However, test results both in the field and in the laboratory, though still rather limited, suggest that Hansen and Gibson's conclusions are substantially correct, though complicated by two additional features. These are that

(a) the soil structure may in fact be significantly anisotropic with respect to its shear parameters in terms of effective stress, due to orientation and/or segregation of particles during deposition, and due to orientation arising from its subsequent history;

(b) the degree of mobilization of these parameters (c' and ϕ') at the peak stress difference varies with the orientation of the principal stresses at failure, as does the strain at failure.

Table 2

Some examples in which c_u depends on principal stress directions during shear (tests in situ or on undisturbed samples)

1. c_u from field vane lower than c_u from piston sampler or block samples.   (Vold, 1956; Coates and McRostie, 1963).

2. c_u from field vane for vertical plane lower than for horizontal plane.   (Aas, 1965.)

3. c_u from block samples with axis horizontal lower than with axis vertical in lightly over-consolidated clay.   (Lo, 1965)

4. c_u from block samples with axis horizontal higher than with axis vertical in heavily over-consolidated clay.   (Ward, Marsland and Samuels, 1965)

5. c_u/p for simple shear (max shear stress horizontal) lower than in triaxial compression with axis vertical.   (Bjerrum and Landva, 1966)

6. c_u/p for axial extension much lower than in axial compression for samples consolidated with zero lateral yield.   (Ladd and Bailey, 1964; Ladd and Varallyay, 1965)

Some of the test results which bear on this problem are listed in Table 2.   Of particular interest are the field tests (Fig. 27) carried out by the Norwegian Geotechnical Institute with a series of specially proportioned vanes (Aas, 1965), as they indicate the relative magnitudes of the in-situ undrained strength on the vertical and horizontal planes respectively.   The ratio varies between $\frac{1}{2}$ and $\frac{2}{3}$ for the three normally consolidated clays tested.   Since the conventionally proportioned vane measures mainly the strength on a vertical cylindrical surface it may underestimate the field value relevant to some engineering problems in normally or lightly over-consolidated clays.   The values are for sensitive or quick clays; values for the clays usually encountered in Britain would be of great interest.

The variation in the undrained strength of lightly and heavily over-consolidated clay with the direction of the applied major principal stress is illustrated in Fig. 28.   The samples were all cut from blocks taken from vertical shafts[17] and average values are given based on a large number of tests detailed in the references.   In the lightly over-consolidated Welland clay the

---

[17] With the exception of the tests described by Bishop (1948).

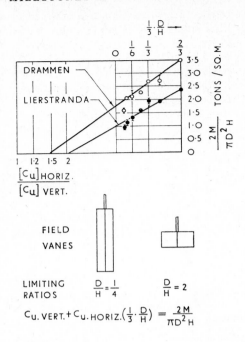

Fig. 27. Determination of **anisotropy** ratio $\dfrac{(c_u)\ \text{horiz.}}{(c_u)\ \text{vert.}}$ from undrained tests with vanes of different

$\dfrac{D}{H}$ ratios. (After Aas, 1965)

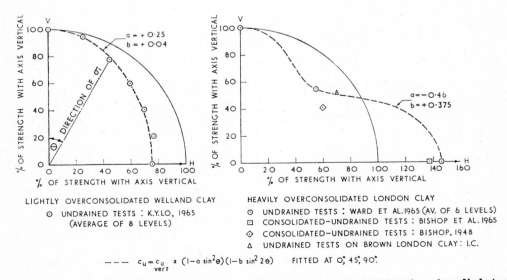

Fig. 28. Polar diagram showing variation of undrained strength with direction of applied stress:
θ denotes inclination of major principal stress with respect to vertical axis

compression strength with σ_1 horizontal was about 0·75 the value with σ_1 vertical.[18]   In the heavily over-consolidated London Clay the ratio of horizontal to vertical strength was 1·46 (range 1·23 to 1·63).   That this difference is primarily a pore pressure phenomenon is indicated by the associated consolidated–undrained tests (Bishop, Webb and Lewin, 1965), which show ratios of the same order (e.g. 1·35), but little difference in the effective stress envelopes, the A values, however, being +0·42 for the vertical sample and +0·19 for the horizontal sample quoted.

However, inclined samples of London Clay show a great reduction in strength, presumably associated with lower shear strength parameters along the bedding planes, the undrained strength with σ_1 at 45° (i.e. the maximum shear stress parallel to the bedding planes) being 0·77 of the vertical value.   A simple expression with two parameters, a and b, can be used to express these results: a reflecting the influence of pore pressures and b the directional character of c' and ϕ' as well as that of pore pressure.[19]   Even in the lightly over-consolidated Welland clay the value of the second term suggests that an orientated structure is becoming manifest.   Undrained tests on block samples from the brown London Clay at Maldon show a similar drop in strength in the direction of the bedding planes, as also do the earlier consolidated-undrained tests on London Clay from Walton (Bishop, 1948).

These strengths are not, of course, identical with the values of the in-situ undrained strengths in plane strain, which are of principal interest in many engineering problems, and the influence, not only of stress release on sampling,[20] but also of sample size, is of particular interest in dealing with over-consolidated clays.

Before examining these factors in more detail it should be pointed out that a drop in strength of 50% in the horizontal direction leads, in the circular arc analysis of a typical slope (Lo, 1965), to a reduction in factor of safety of only 15%–30% since the whole of the slip surface is not inclined at the least favourable angle.   This, together with the reduction in measured strength which always results from sampling, has probably made the $\phi_u=0$ analysis appear more accurate than, theoretically, it should be.

The importance of the two factors, anisotropy and the size of sample, in practical design work may be illustrated by tests carried out on the weathered London Clay foundation of a proposed embankment near Maldon in Essex.   Owing to the great base width of the embankment and to the low coefficient of consolidation of the clay, undrained failure on an almost horizontal slip surface in the weathered zone represented a critical condition.   I therefore asked for the normal site investigation to be augmented by a number of in-situ undrained direct shear tests on samples 2 ft × 2 ft in cross-section with their zone of maximum shear stress in the horizontal plane.

The layout of the testing equipment is shown in Fig. 29.   An intact block of clay was left projecting 6 inches above the floor of the trial pit, and with the minimum of delay the shear box and loading platten were fitted over it.   A load equivalent to the overburden pressure was applied through a hydraulic jack mounted beneath a strut transmitting the load to a joist

---

[18] The interpretation of cylindrical compression tests on samples cut with their axis horizontal is open to some ambiguity in a soil which may have a low undrained strength when the plane of failure is vertical, but the relative motion horizontal, as in the tests by Aas (1965).   Failure may occur on such a plane in the compression specimen cut with its axis horizontal, rather than on an inclined plane forming part of a conventional plane strain failure surface, as assumed by Lo (1965).

[19] The first term agrees with that used by Lo (1965) and Casagrande and Carrillo (1944).   It is simpler than that proposed by Hansen and Gibson (1949), but lack of detailed information hardly justifies a more elaborate expression.   The second term is assumed to represent a satisfactory working hypothesis, though, based on work by Hill (1950) on metals in plane strain, Scott (1963b) assumes a similar term to the power $-\frac{1}{2}$.

[20] Bishop and Henkel (1953), Ladd and Lambe (1963), Skempton and Sowa (1963) and Ladd and Bailey (1964) have dealt with this problem either with no rotation of the principal stresses or (Ladd and Bailey) with the special case of axial extension.

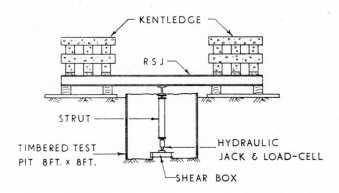

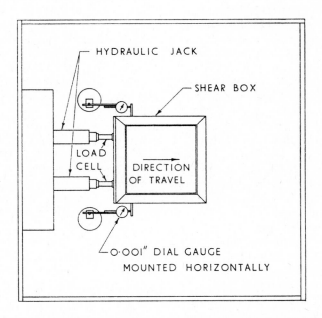

Fig. 29.   Layout of direct shear test on 2 ft × 2 ft samples in the field

passing beneath kentledge on either side of the trial pit.   The horizontal load was applied through two hydraulic jacks fitted with electrical load cells.   Any tendency of the box to run out of the true could thus be controlled.   A pair of dial micrometers recorded the horizontal displacement of the box.

The shear stress–displacement curve for the test at a depth of 11 ft in trial pit 3 is given in Fig. 30.   The very small displacement (0·3 in.) at which the peak stress was reached may be

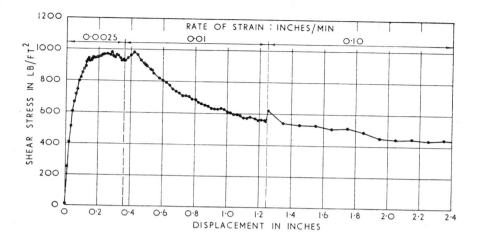

Fig. 30. Shear stress–displacement curve for undrained direct shear test on 2 ft × 2 ft sample of brown London Clay at Maldon, Essex: horizontal shear plane 11·3 ft below surface

noted. The rate of strain was controlled so that the peak stress was reached after about 1 to 2 hours. In this test, which was one of the two deep tests performed, the stress then fell off and appeared to reach an almost constant value when the limit of travel of the shear box was reached. At this stage careful sectioning of the sample revealed one or more pronounced slip surfaces running almost horizontally across the sample near the base of the shear box.

The undrained strength–depth plots are given in Fig. 31. The most notable feature is that the strengths obtained with horizontal shear on large samples are, on the average, only 55% of the strengths obtained by testing compression specimens with their axis vertical either from boreholes samples, or from tube or block samples taken in the trial pits. A reduction of this magnitude makes a conventional factor of safety of 1·5 on a conventional undrained test result on London Clay appear rather inadequate, and it is difficult to see on what grounds we can fault the in-situ tests.

Four factors may be considered in assessing the significance of the difference.

(1) *Time to failure.* The time to failure (about one hour) in the field test is greater than the duration (about 5 minutes) of the laboratory test. Other studies (La Rochelle, 1961) suggest that the effect on strength of this difference amounts to only a few per cent, but in relation to construction work the slower test in any case is the more correct.

(2) *Stress conditions in the direct shear test.* The principal stress directions in the shear box at failure are not known very precisely. An error of $(1 - \cos \phi_e) \times 100\%$ is possibly involved in estimating c_u from a shear box.[21] This is generally less than 5% for a clay of high plasticity.

(3) *Anisotropy.* Tests on block samples in the laboratory orientated so that the slip plane lay in the horizontal direction gave undrained strengths 86% of the strengths

[21] This is still controversial. Reference can be made, for example to Hill (1950), and Hansen and Gibson (1949). The interpretation of the shear box test and simple shear test will clearly be influenced by anisotropy.

with the axis vertical.[22]   Similar tests on samples cut from cores taken in the trial pit with a 4-in. diameter sampler show a reduction of 87% of the strength with the axis vertical.

(4) *Sample size.*   The major part (from 86%–55%) of the reduction in strength must therefore be attributed to the use in the field of a large and more representative sample.

The results of four large plate loading tests are also included on the strength–depth plot for trial pit 4.   These again indicate strengths much below the values given by small laboratory samples, though rather higher than the values given by the large direct shear tests.   This latter difference[23] probably reflects the fact that in the plate loading tests the slip surface is inclined to the direction of the bedding planes over much of its area, and the influence of anisotropy is reduced.

---

[22] Anisotropy in a larger sample may of course be more marked than in a small one due to the inclusion of a more representative structure.

[23] This difference may have been to some extent masked by the limited displacement applied in the plate loading tests.

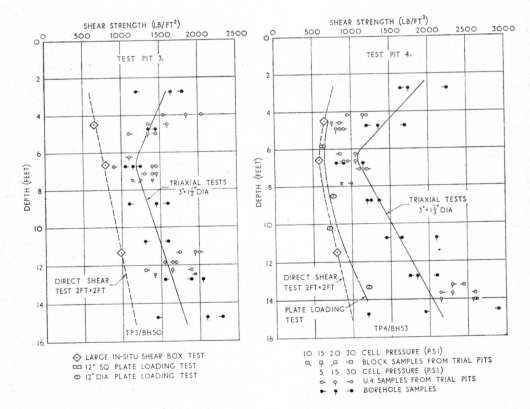

Fig. 31.   Relationship between undrained strength and depth: results of 2 ft × 2 ft direct shear tests and plate loading tests compared with values obtained from 3 in. × 1½ in. dia. triaxial tests: brown London Clay from Maldon, Essex

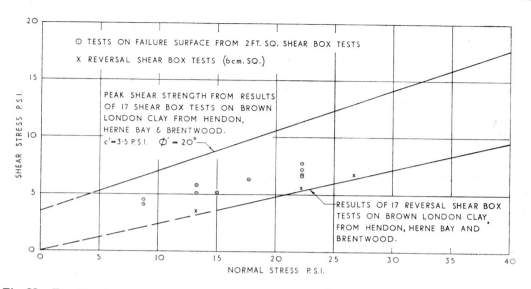

Fig. 32. Results of drained tests on samples from failure surface of 2 ft square in-situ shear box tests. (Tests by Petley, 1966)

Whitaker and Cooke (1966) have reached a similar conclusion for the deeper layers of the London Clay from the ultimate base loads measured on large bored piles. The in-situ undrained strength was, on the average, only 75% of that given by standard borehole samples tested with the axis vertical.

It is of interest to note that, in similar clay at Bradwell, Skempton and La Rochelle (1965) found that the 'undrained' strength mobilized in a slide in the side of an excavation was only about 55% of the undrained strength of 3-in. × 1½-in. diameter samples, either from boreholes or cut from blocks. In this case the slip surface was steep and not in the direction of the bedding planes, but a larger time elapsed before failure, which in itself could have accounted for a reduction to 80% of the value measured in the standard laboratory test. The further reduction of 30% due to size effect in a soil with a fissured structure at Bradwell is thus about the same as the reduction due to size effect at Maldon. This suggests that at this level in the London Clay a 2-ft square sample was adequate.

These differences overshadow refinements in our methods of analysis and suggest that we may need to rethink the means by which we determine undrained strength in engineering practice. Either samples must be large enough to include a fully representative soil structure (this could mean even larger samples in some cases than the size tested at Maldon) and they must be tested with the correct orientation, or we must apply empirical factors to the strength of our conventional laboratory specimens.

To obtain *drained* shear parameters for large samples is much more difficult. The test duration necessary for full pore pressure dissipation in the shear test described above would have been 6 months or more[24] for a clay of the type tested at Maldon. However, large scale drained tests on stiff fissured clays are clearly essential to the rational design of engineering works in or on these strata.

---

[24] At low stresses preferential drainage through the fissures might accelerate the consolidation of weathered samples.

It is perhaps of interest to add that drained tests run on sections cut from the Maldon in-situ tests so as to include part of the actual slip surface showed that the residual value of ϕ' had not been reached at the displacement of 2 to 3 in. applied in the tests. The test results are given in Fig. 32. The values of the residual factor R (Skempton, 1964) for 6 cm. square samples vary between 0·45 and 0·8.

(4) THE INFLUENCE OF TIME ON THE STRENGTH OF SOILS

The strength of a given soil stratum which is available to the engineer depends on time in a number of different ways.

Under a sustained load the available strength of a clay stratum changes from the undrained strength to the drained strength at a rate which depends on the coefficient of consolidation or swelling and on the length of the drainage path. The change is an increase in most foundation problems where the load increases, and a decrease in most excavation or cutting problems, where the load is decreased, and results in the first place from pore-water pressure changes in the field (for a detailed discussion see Bishop and Bjerrum, 1960).

However, as was shown by Professor Skempton in the fourth Rankine Lecture, the shear strength parameters calculated from actual slips based on a knowledge of the field pore pressure differ radically from the peak strength values measured in the laboratory in the case of over-consolidated clays of other than low plasticity.

Several factors may contribute to this discrepancy,

- (a) the size and orientation of the test specimens will influence the values of the shear strength parameters measured in the laboratory;
- (b) in soils showing brittle or work-softening stress–strain characteristics it is likely that failure in the field will be to some extent progressive, i.e. that the peak strength will not be mobilized simultaneously along the complete slip path. As pointed out by Webb, Lewin and myself in 1965, the release of stored energy on stress reduction under drained conditions in clay showing marked swelling characteristics is of special importance in this case. This approach has been developed by Dr Bjerrum in his recent Terzaghi Lecture to the American Society of Civil Engineers;
- (c) the peak values of the drained shear strength parameters may be substantially time dependent in heavily over-consolidated clays and clay shales.

Little precise information exists on all three factors. Almost nothing really appears to be known about the time dependence of the drained peak strength of undisturbed clays. The technical difficulties of maintaining a known constant stress difference on a sample in an apparatus without leaks over periods of months and possibly years are considerable. The apparatus we are currently using at Imperial College is illustrated in Fig. 33. Several important features may be noted. The whole loading and strain measuring system is inside one continuous pressure vessel filled with oil, so that friction due to a seal on the loading ram is entirely avoided. The load is applied by two very long springs in tension, controlled by a screw adjustment at the base of the cell, and is transmitted to the cylindrical sample through a ram guided by a ball bushing. The load can be determined both from the length of the springs and from a proving ring mounted on the ram. Creep in the sample has little effect on the load in the springs due to their large extension, but in the early stages of the test such adjustment as is necessary due to the shortening of the sample and the change in its cross-sectional area can readily be made with the screw at the base of the cell. Deformation is measured by an oil filled dial micrometer reading to 10^{-4} in. and by a linear differential transformer reading to 10^{-5} in.

The sample is enclosed in a rubber membrane and is submerged in mercury to prevent loss of water through the rubber membrane, and to protect the membrane from contact with the mineral oil.   Volume change is measured with a paraffin volume gauge (Bishop and Henkel, 1962, Fig. 141) using a back pressure to ensure full saturation of the system.   Volume change is also measured with a mercury-filled volume gauge, back-pressured from the cell, which is adjusted to maintain the mercury in the inner cell surrounding the sample to a constant level, determined by an electric contact.

The use of a spring-loaded system of low inertia makes the apparatus less susceptible to tremors transmitted by the structure of the building than the use of a dead load system.

The first series of tests (Fig. 34) on block samples of London Clay has been running for about seven months and has already produced some interesting information.   Samples were set up and kept under sustained shear stresses, the stress levels being approximately 90%, 80%, 70%, 60%, 40%, and 16% of the peak drained strength in a test of one week's duration.   These percentages are based on the results of six triaxial tests of this duration.   The percentage shown first in Fig. 34 is calculated from the average of the two highest values observed.   The second percentage is based on the four lower values in the series.

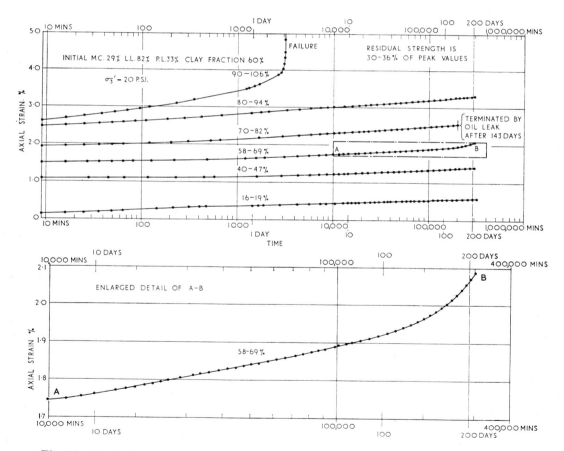

Fig. 34. Drained creep tests on undisturbed brown London Clay from Hendon. The applied principal stress differences as given above are percentages of the peak values measured in drained triaxial tests of 5 days' duration. (Tests by Lovenbury, 1965–66)

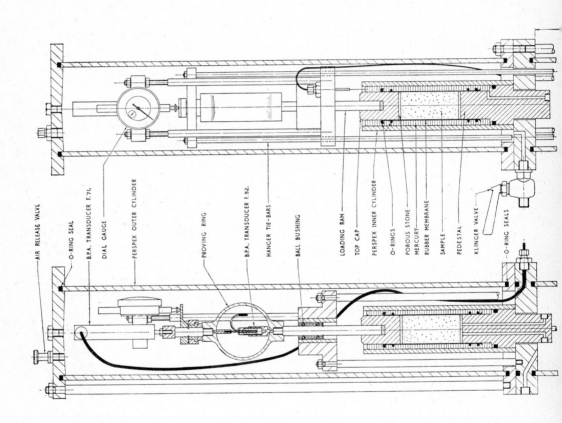

AIR RELEASE VALVE

O-RING SEAL

B.P.A. TRANSDUCER F.7L

DIAL GAUGE

PERSPEX OUTER CYLINDER

PROVING RING

B.P.A. TRANSDUCER F.52.

HANGER TIE-BARS

BALL BUSHING

LOADING RAM

TOP CAP

PERSPEX INNER CYLINDER

O-RINGS

POROUS STONE

MERCURY

RUBBER MEMBRANE

SAMPLE

PEDESTAL

KLINGER VALVE

O-RING SEALS

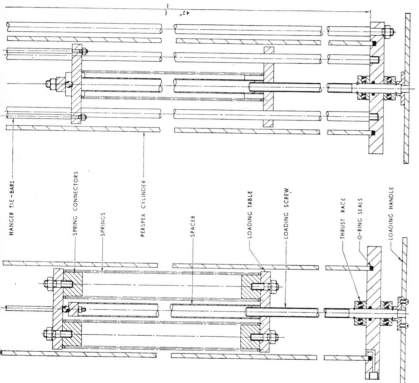

HANGER TIE-BARS
SPRING CONNECTORS
SPRINGS
PERSPEX CYLINDER
SPACER
LOADING TABLE
LOADING SCREW
THRUST RACE
O-RING SEALS
LOADING HANDLE

4.2"

Fig. 33.   Diagrammatic sections of creep cell

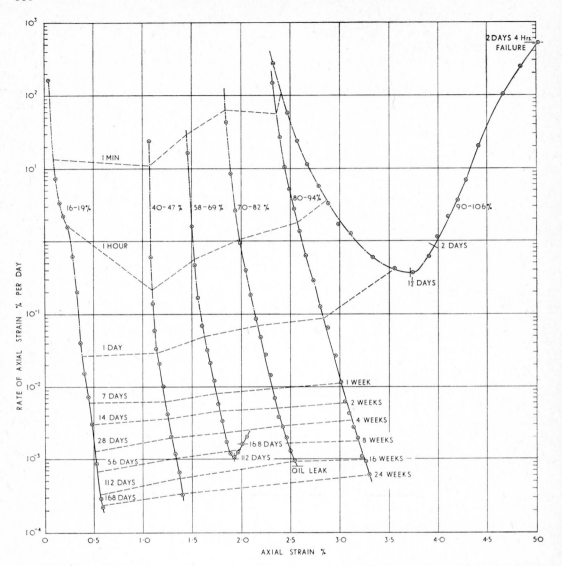

Fig. 35. Strain rate as a function of axial strain for various stress levels. (Stress levels indicated by percentages adjacent to curves). Contours represent times after application of final stress increment; drained tests on brown London Clay from Hendon. (Tests by Lovenbury 1965–66)

It will be seen that the 90% peak strength sample failed after two days, having given (at least in retrospect) sufficient warning of its intention.[25]   The 80% test is still continuing with no sign of impending failure.   The 70% test came to a premature end after 143 days, due, ironically, to creep in a perspex component for which we had not allowed.   The 60% test showed a decreasing rate of strain for the first three and a half months (100 days), but the

---

[25] The period of two days is measured from the time of application of the last increment of the stress difference and full drainage under this increment would not have been achieved in the earlier part of this period.

rate has subsequently increased steadily. Whether, as the enlarged detail might suggest, this presages eventual failure is very difficult to forecast. The creep rates are given in Fig. 35, plotted against strain. Perhaps the most interesting feature of this diagram is that in undisturbed clay the creep rate does not stay constant under constant stress at any stage of the test. It either decreases fairly steadily or increases. The simpler rheological models are therefore not applicable. The 60% test, although it has speeded up, is still only proceeding at two thousandths of 1% per day and at this rate would take another 1200 days to reach the strain at which the 90% sample failed. An extrapolation of the present strain rate path suggests about 65 days more to failure.[26]

Even if the 60% sample did fail, and if we ignore the fact that the 80% sample is not yet showing a speeding-up in its strain rate, we have only accounted for part of the drop to the residual value which is approximately 30% of the higher peak drained strength. But it is a very considerable part, and may make possible a quantitative explanation in terms of the three factors listed above.

The creep tests outlined above are, of course, equally significant in relation to the performance of foundations under sustained load, where current concepts of secondary consolidation are based mainly on the results of oedometer tests with rigid lateral confinement.

CONCLUSION

In conclusion, I hope I have thrown a little light on some of the problems of soil mechanics which are both of intellectual interest and of practical importance. I hope I have also shown, in the last two sections in particular, that there is a great deal still to be found out about the actual strength of soils as engineering materials, and that not all of this can be found out in the laboratory. The investigation of full-scale failures and the carrying out of field tests of a sufficient size to be relevant and in sufficient numbers to be representative are tasks which must be shared by consulting engineers and contractors as well as by universities and research stations, and must be budgeted for.

ACKNOWLEDGEMENTS

In preparing this lecture I have been able to draw on unpublished experimental data obtained at Imperial College by G. E. Green, A. E. Skinner, H. T. Lovenbury, D. J. Petley, S. W. Smotrych, S. K. Sarma, N. N. Som, S. G. Tombs, and Dr B. P. Walker, and at the Building Research Station by P. I. Lewin. In addition I am indebted to Dr L. Bjerrum, Director of the Norwegian Geotechnical Institute for unpublished reports on field and laboratory tests.

The large shear tests at Maldon were carried out by George Wimpey and Co. Ltd under the direction of Binnie and Partners to whom I am indebted for permission to quote the results and also the results of tests on rock-fill. Acknowledgements are also due to the Science Research Council and the Civil Engineering Research Association whose grants made possible some of the tests described in this lecture.

I am particularly indebted to Gordon E. Green for assistance in assembling material for the lecture, to E. W. Harris for assistance with the illustrations, and to Dr R. E. Gibson for reading the manuscript.

---

[26] Since the Rankine Lecture was delivered, the speeding up of the creep rate has not increased and the time to failure cannot be predicted with any greater certainty at the present date (March 1966).

REFERENCES

AAS, G., 1965. A study of the effect of vane shape and rate of strain on the measured values of in-situ shear strength of soils. *Proc. 6th Int. Conf. Soil Mech.*, 1:141–145.

BISHOP, A. W., 1948. Some factors involved in the design of a large earth dam in the Thames Valley. *Proc. 2nd Int. Conf. Soil Mech.*, 2:13–18.

BISHOP, A. W., 1950. *Discussion.* Measurement of the shear strength of soils. *Géotechnique*, 2:1:113–116.

BISHOP, A. W., 1958. Test requirements for measuring the coefficient of earth pressure at rest. *Proc. Brussels Conf. on Earth Pressure Problems*, 1: 2–14.

BISHOP, A. W., 1965. Contribution to panel discussion, Division 2, *Proc. 6th Int. Conf. Soil Mech.*, 3.

BISHOP, A. W. and L. BJERRUM, 1960. The relevance of the triaxial test to the solution of stability problems. *Proc. Res. Conf. Shear Strength of Cohesive Soils*, Boulder (ASCE) 437–501.

BISHOP, A. W. and A. K. G. ELDIN, 1953. The effect of stress history on the relation between ϕ and porosity in sand. *Proc. 3rd Int. Conf. Soil Mech.*, 1:126–130.

BISHOP, A. W. and G. E. GREEN, 1965. The influence of end restraint on the compression strength of a cohesionless soil. *Géotechnique*, 15:3:243–266.

BISHOP, A. W. and D. J. HENKEL, 1953. The pore pressure changes during shear in two undisturbed clays. *Proc. 3rd Int. Conf. Soil Mech.*, 1:94–99.

BISHOP, A. W. and D. J. HENKEL, 1962. The measurement of soil properties in the triaxial test. *Edward Arnold, London*, 2nd ed.

BISHOP, A. W., D. L. WEBB and P. I. LEWIN, 1965. Undisturbed samples of London Clay from the Ashford Common shaft: strength–effective stress relationships. *Géotechnique*, 15:1:1–31.

BISHOP, A. W., D. L. WEBB and A. E. SKINNER, 1965. Triaxial tests on soil at elevated cell pressures. *Proc. 6th Int. Conf. Soil Mech.*, 1:170–174.

BJERRUM, L., 1961. The effective shear strength parameters of sensitive clays. *Proc. 5th Int. Conf. Soil Mech.*, 1:23–28.

BJERRUM, L., 1966. Mechanism of progressive failure in slopes of over-consolidated plastic clays and clay shales. 3rd Terzaghi Lecture, ASCE Conf., Miami.

BJERRUM, L. and A. LANDVA, 1966. Direct simple shear-tests on a Norwegian quick clay. *Géotechnique*. 16:1:1–20.

BORG, I., M. FRIEDMAN, J. HANDIN and D. V. HIGGS, 1960. Experimental deformation of St Peter sand: a study of cataclastic flow. *Rock Deformation*, Geological Society of America, Memoir 79, 133–192.

CASAGRANDE, A. and N. CARRILLO, 1944. Shear failure of anisotropic materials. *J. Boston Soc. civ. Engrs*, 31:74–87.

COATES, D. F. and G. C. MCROSTIE, 1963. Some deficiencies in testing Leda clay. *Symposium Laboratory shear testing of soils*. Ottawa, 1963, ASTM STP 361, 459–470.

CORNFORTH, D. H., 1961. Plane strain failure characteristics of a saturated sand. Ph.D. Thesis, London.

HABIB, P., 1953. Influence de la variation de la contrainte principale moyenne sur la résistance au cisaillement des sols. *Proc. 3rd Int. Conf. Soil Mech.*, 1:131–136.

HAFIZ, M. A., 1950. Strength characteristics of sands and gravels in direct shear. Ph.D. Thesis, London.

HALL, E. B. and B. B. GORDON, 1963. Triaxial testing with large-scale high pressure equipment. *Symposium Laboratory shear testing of soils*. Ottawa. 1963. ASTM STP 361, 315–328.

HANSEN, J. BRINCH and R. E. GIBSON, 1949. Undrained shear strengths of anisotropically consolidated clays. *Géotechnique* 1:3:189–204.

HAYTHORNTHWAITE, R. M., 1960. Mechanics of the triaxial test for soils. *Proc. ASCE*, 86 SM5: 35–62

HILL, R., 1950. The mathematical theory of plasticity. Clarendon Press, Oxford.

HIRSCHFELD, R. C. and S. J. POULOS, 1963. High-pressure triaxial tests on a compacted sand and an undisturbed silt. *Symposium Laboratory shear testing of soils*. Ottawa, ASTM STP 361, pp. 329–339.

HVORSLEV, M. J., 1960. Physical components of the shear strength of saturated clays. *Proc. Res. Conf. Shear Strength of Cohesive Soils*, Boulder (ASCE), 437–501.

INSLEY, A. E. and S. F. HILLIS, 1965. Triaxial shear characteristics of a compacted glacial till under unusually high confining pressures. *Proc. 6th Int. Conf. Soil Mech.*, 1:244–248.

JAKY, J., 1944. A Nyugalmi Nyomas Tenyezoje. *Magyar Mernok-es Epitesz-Egylet Kozlonye*, Oct., 355–358.

JAKY, J., 1948. Pressure in silos, *Proc. 2nd Int. Conf. Soil Mech*, 1:103–107.

JOHANSEN, K. W., 1958. Brudbetingelser for sten og beton. (Failure conditions for rocks and concrete.) *Byningsstatiske Meddelelser*, 19:25–44 Teknisk Forlag, Copenhagen.

KIRKPATRICK, W. M., 1957. Condition of failure for sands. *Proc. 4th Int. Conf. Soil Mech.*, 1:172–178.

KUMMENEJE, O., 1957. 'To-dimensjonale' vakuum-triaxialforsök på törr sand. Norwegian Geotechnical Institute Internal Report F. 80 (unpublished).

LADD, C. C. and W. A. BAILEY, 1964. *Correspondence.* The behaviour of saturated clays during sampling and testing. *Géotechnique*, 14:1:353–358.

LADD, C. C. and T. W. LAMBE, 1963. Shear strength of saturated clays. *Symposium Laboratory shear testing of soils*. Ottawa, 1963, ASTM STP 361, 342–371.

LADD, C. C. and J. VARALLYAY, 1965. The influence of stress system on the behaviour of saturated clays during undrained shear. M.I.T. Report, July.

LA ROCHELLE, P., 1960. The short-term stability of slopes in London Clay. Ph.D. Thesis, London.

LEUSSINK, H., 1965. Contribution to panel discussion, Division 2. *Proc. 6th Int. Conf. Soil Mech.* Vol. 3.

LO, K. Y., 1965. Stability of slopes in anisotropic soils. *Proc. ASCE*, 91: SM4: 85–106.

MARSAL, R. J., 1965. Contribution to panel discussion, Division 2. *Proc. 6th Int. Conf. Soil Mech.* Vol. 3.

MARSAL, R. J., E. M. GOMEZ, A. NUNEZ G., P. CUELLAR B. and R. M. RAMOS. 1965. Research on the behaviour of granular materials and rockfill samples. Comision Federal De Electricidad, Mexico.

NITCHIPOROVITCH, A. A., 1964. Deformations and stability of rockfill dams. *Proc. 8th Cong. Large Dams*, 3:879–894.

NORWEGIAN GEOTECHNICAL INSTITUTE, 1958. Triaxial compression and extension tests on a saturated fine and uniform graded sand. Internal Report, F94.

PELTIER, M. R., 1957. Experimental investigations on the intrinsic rupture curve of cohesionless soils. *Proc. 4th Int. Conf. Soil Mech.*, 1:179–182.

ROSCOE, K. H., A. N. SCHOFIELD and C. P. WROTH, 1958. On the yielding of soils. *Géotechnique*, 8:1: 22–53.

ROSCOE, K. H., A. N. SCHOFIELD and A. THURAIRAJAH, 1963. An evaluation of test data for selecting a yield criterion for soils. *Symposium* Laboratory shear testing of soils, Ottawa, ASTM STP 361, 111–128.

SCHLEICHER, F., 1925. Die Energiegrenze der Elastizitat (Plastizitatsbedingung). *Zeits für ang. Math. Mech.*, 5:478–479.

SCHLEICHER, F., 1926. Der Spannungfzustand an der Fliessgrenze (Plastizitatsbedingung). *Zeits für ang. Math. Mech.*, 6:199–216.

SCOTT, R. F., 1963a. Discussion on the Mohr–Coulomb concept in shear failure. *Symposium* Laboratory shear testing of soils. Ottawa, ASTM STP 361, 75–76.

SCOTT, R. F., 1963b. Principles of soil mechanics. *Addison Wesley*, 440.

SIMONS, N., 1958. *Discussion* Test requirements for measuring the coefficient of earth pressure at rest. *Brussels Conf. on Earth Pressure problems*, 3:50–53.

SKEMPTON, A. W., 1964. Long term stability of clay slopes. 4th Rankine Lecture, *Géotechnique*, 14:2: 77–101.

SKEMPTON, A. W. and P. LA ROCHELLE, 1965. The Bradwell slip: a short-term failure in London Clay. *Géotechnique*, 15:3:221–242.

SKEMPTON, A. W. and V. A. SOWA, 1963. The behaviour of saturated clays during sampling and testing. *Géotechnique*, 13:4:269–290.

SOWA, V. A., 1963. A comparison of the effects of isotropic and anisotropic consolidation on the shear behaviour of a clay. Ph.D. Thesis, London.

TAYLOR, D. W., 1948. Fundamentals of soil mechanics. Wiley, New York.

TAYLOR, D. W. and R. H. CLOUGH, 1951. Report on research on shearing characteristics of clay. M.I.T.

USCOLD, 1963. Oroville Dam. Newsletter No. 10, January, 4.

VESIC, A. and R. D. BARKSDALE, 1963. *Discusion* Test methods and new equipment. *Symposium* Laboratory shear testing of soils. Ottawa, 1963, ASTM STP 361, 301–305.

VOLD, R. C., 1956. Undisturbed sampling of soils. *Norwegian Geotechnical Institute*, Publ. No. 17.

WADE, N. H., 1963. Plane strain failure characteristics of a saturated clay. Ph.D. Thesis, London.

WARD, W. H., A. MARSLAND and S. G. SAMUELS, 1965. Properties of the London Clay at the Ashford Common shaft; in-situ and undrained strength tests. *Géotechnique*, 15:4:321–344.

WATERWAYS EXPERIMENT STATION, VICKSBURG, 1950. Triaxial tests on sands—Reid Bedford Bend, Mississippi River. Report No. 5–3.

WHITAKER, T. and R. W. COOKE, 1966. An investigation of the shaft and base resistances of large bored piles in London Clay. *Proc. Symp. Large Bored Piles*. Instn. civ. Engrs. London.

WOOD, C. C., 1958. Shear strength and volume change characteristics of compacted soil under conditions of plane strain. Ph.D. Thesis, London.

ENGINEERING GEOLOGY OF NORWEGIAN NORMALLY-CONSOLIDATED MARINE CLAYS AS RELATED TO SETTLEMENTS OF BUILDINGS

L. BJERRUM

INTRODUCTION

I would like to express my sincere gratitude to the British Geotechnical Society for the great honour of asking me to present the Seventh Rankine Lecture, and I wish to thank Dr Ward for his extremely kind remarks.

Since rock and mountains constitute 70% of Norway's land area, the great majority of the 3·7 million population lives on a narrow strip of loose sediments fringing the mountains along the shoreline of the country. These sediments are often so soft and unstable that successful and economical development of this part of the country is strongly dependent on the fact that full benefit be made of the assistance offered by the science of soil mechanics. Realization of this fact caused the Norwegian Geotechnical Institute to be established in 1953 with the dual purpose of carrying out research and giving practical advice to civil engineers concerning their design and construction problems.

Shortly after the Institute was established, it was decided to concentrate the research on foundations of buildings in Drammen, a town of 47 000 inhabitants located about 40 km south-west of Oslo where the Drammen River flows into the Drammensfjord (see Fig. 1). Drammen is known for its soft clay, and the settlements of the existing buildings are so large that the effect of the poor foundation conditions can be observed at a glance. In addition, the soil conditions are so uniform over large areas of the town that the behaviour of different types of foundations can be directly compared. Since 1953 the Institute has worked in close co-operation with the consulting engineers and the Municipality of Drammen as geotechnical consultant for the construction of a number of buildings. The behaviour of the buildings was observed during construction and the subsequent settlements were measured. In this way a considerable amount of data was accumulated.

In this lecture we will first review the geotechnical properties of the soft clays in Drammen as they supposedly were shortly after deposition, but most of the time will be devoted to a study of all changes in properties which have occurred since then, and the effect of these changes on the foundation conditions will be illustrated by examples from practice.

GEOLOGICAL HISTORY AND GEOTECHNICAL PROPERTIES OF THE DRAMMEN SEDIMENTS

About 20 000 years ago the climate became milder and Norway started to emerge from the huge ice-sheets which covered the Scandinavian peninsula during the last Pleistocene glaciation. At that time the country was still depressed under the tremendous weight of the glaciers. Simultaneous with the withdrawal of the glaciers, the underlying rock became unloaded and, consequently, an isostatic crustal rebound of the previously glaciated areas took place. In the Drammen area, the land elevation which has occurred since the glaciers retreated from the valley about 10 000 years ago, amounts to 205 m relative to present seawater level, and is still proceeding at a rate of about 30 cm per century (see Fig. 3). When the glaciers withdrew from the valleys they occupied, they left nothing behind them except the bare ice-polished rock, here and there covered with a blanket of morainic material; all

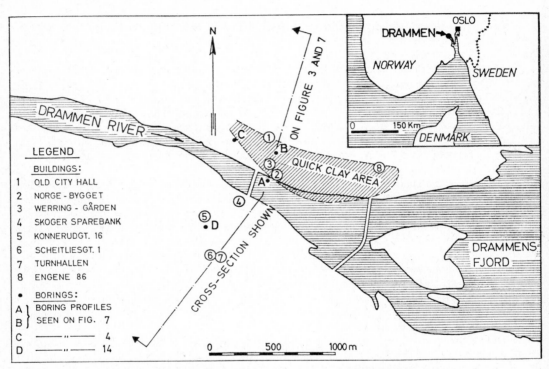

Fig. 1.   Map of Drammen showing location of buildings and borings

Fig. 2.   Aerial view of the town of Drammen (*Widerøes Flyveselskap A/S*)

residual soil and loose rock, pre-dating the Pleistocene, had been removed by the slowly creeping ice masses.   As the glaciers retreated, rivers of melt-water discharged large quantities of sand, silt and clay into the fjord at the front of the ice-sheet.   Due to the depression of the area there was free communication between the Atlantic Ocean and the inner reaches of the Oslofjord and, consequently, the water into which the sediments were discharged was salt. When minute flake-shaped clay particles precipitate in salt water they are electrically charged and have a tendency to flocculate, i.e. to stick together, edge to face, with the result that clay, silt and fine sand settle at an equal rate without any separation and the sediment formed consists of clusters of particles with a very loose cardhouse-like structure.   The late-glacial clay which filled the bottom of the valley (see Fig. 3) is therefore fairly homogeneous and of relatively low plasticity.

As the country gradually rose above the sea level, the valley took on, to an increasing degree, the character of a narrow fjord with only limited communication with the ocean.   The climate again became milder and this is the beginning of the post-glacial period which extends to the present day.   The glaciers had by now retreated so far that only the finer material, silt and clay, was transported down to the lower part of the valley.   The post-glacial clay layers which were now deposited therefore show a somewhat higher plasticity than the underlying clay, and in addition they contain a certain content of organic matter as a result of the increasing biological life of the period.

The isostatic upheaval continued in the post-glacial period and gradually the character of the landscape changed from that of a fjord to that of a valley with a river flowing in the sediments.   The uppermost silt and sand blanket overlaying the clay deposits in Drammen dates back to this period.   The sand originates from a terminal moraine, the remains of which can still be seen some distance upstream.   Knowledge of the rate of isostatic upheaval of the country (Hafsten, 1959; Kenney, 1964) enables us to determine the time at which the terminal moraine was raised above the water level and at which the river started to erode it and deposit the sand in the lower valley.   This was about 3000 years ago.   This was the final stage of

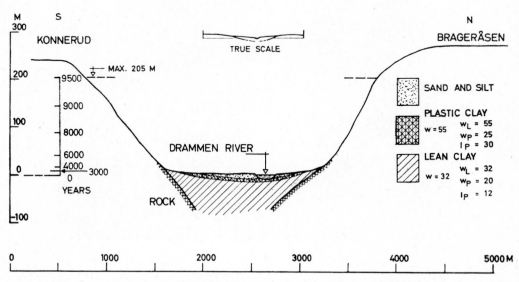

Fig. 3.   Cross–section through the valley of Drammen showing the marine sediments and illustrating the land elevation

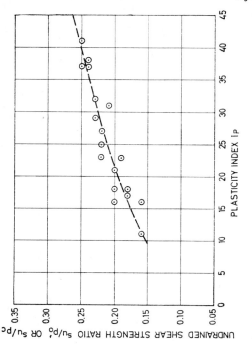

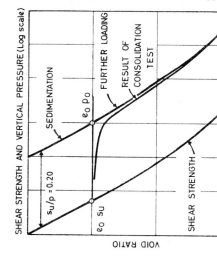

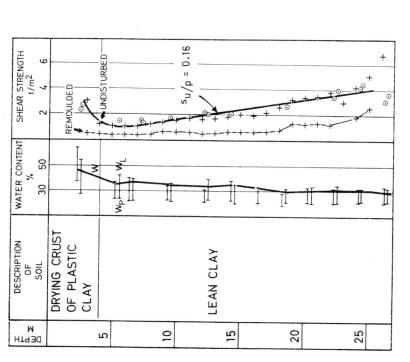

Fig. 4 (above).   Geotechnical profile through a normally consolidated clay in Drammen

Fig. 5 (top right).   Correlation of plasticity index and undrained shear strength ratio for Norwegian marine clays which have not been subjected to leaching.   The undrained shear strength used for plotting the points are all determined by vane tests, and only clays were considered from which results of consolidation tests were available to control that $p_0 = p_c$ (see below).   If p_0 was found to be greater than p_c and the ratio s_u/p_0 was constant throughout the clay layer, this value was used in the diagram.   The curve shown differs only slightly from the previously published correlation for Norwegian clays (Bjerrum, 1954)

Fig. 6 (right).   Typical result of consolidation test on normally-consolidated marine clay

deposition.   The deposits now rose above the sea level to become dry land.   The lower area of Drammen which is considered in this Paper actually emerged from the sea as late as 1000 years ago.

The clays deposited in the manner described have never been subjected to loads greater than the present overburden, and are thus normally consolidated.   In the remaining part of this lecture we will trace the various types of changes which have occurred in the interval between the period of deposition and the present day.   For the sake of comparison we are interested, therefore, in knowing the geotechnical properties of a normally-consolidated clay which has undergone no, or only minor, changes, and for this purpose a geotechnical profile showing the properties of the lower clay of low plasticity has been selected.   It is believed that the changes which this clay has experienced since deposition are so slight that their effect on the geotechnical properties is insignificant.   Fig. 4 shows the geotechnical profile through this clay.

At the site of the boring shown in Fig. 4, the upper sand layer is missing and the plastic clay is located just beneath the surface, where it has been subjected to desiccation and has been converted into what is commonly known as 'drying crust'.   Below the plastic clay we find the 25 m thick deposit of lean marine clay.   The geotechnical data of this clay, presented in Fig. 4, provide us with an example of the characteristic properties of a normally-consolidated marine clay.

In the first place, its relatively loose structure can be observed from the fact that the water content is relatively high, and throughout the profile is approximately equal to the liquid limit.

In the second place, the undrained shear strength of the clay is very low.   Immediately below the drying crust, the shear strength measured by vane tests is as low as 1 ton/sq. m. In addition, it is directly observed that the undrained shear strength increases linearly with depth or, in other words, the undrained shear strength increases proportionally with the effective overburden pressure.   This is one of the most characteristic properties of normally-consolidated clays.   The ratio between the undrained shear strength and the effective over-burden pressure, the s_u/p ratio, is a characteristic property of a clay and, as shown by Skempton (1948), is dependent on the plasticity of the clay.   If the s_u/p ratio for different clays is plotted against the plasticity index, the points will fall on a single curve as shown on Fig. 5 and, from this correlation, we can conclude that the greater the plasticity, the higher the undrained shear strength of a clay.

The third characteristic property of the normally-consolidated clays is their high compressibility.   If an undisturbed sample is placed in a consolidometer and gradually subjected to increasing loads, we can determine experimentally the compressibility of the clay for the conditions of no lateral strain.   Fig. 6 shows the result of such a test, in which the equilibrium void ratio is plotted against the logarithm of the vertical pressure.   The consolidation curve consists of a recompression curve which at a pressure, p_o, equal to the overburden pressure of the sample in the field, bends into the virgin compression curve.   The virgin consolidation curve represents the compression of the clay for additional loading and is approximately a straight line when plotted against the logarithm of the pressure.

If a normally-consolidated clay is consolidated under an increasing load, the shear strength will increase proportionally with the consolidation pressure, as mentioned above.   If, there-fore, in a conventional e–log p diagram the logarithm of the shear strength is plotted against the void ratio, the points will fall on a straight line running parallel with the virgin consolida-tion line, as shown on Fig. 6.[1]   The correlation between void ratio, shear strength and con-solidation pressure established in such a diagram summarizes the essential properties of a

---

[1] The correlation between water content and shear strength of normally-consolidated clays is further discussed in the following papers: WES (1947), Bjerrum (1951) and Henkel (1960).

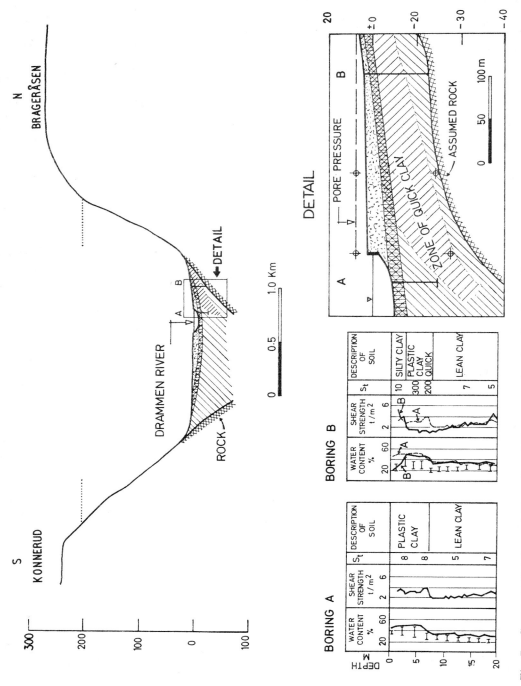

Fig. 7. Cross-section through the valley of Drammen showing the effect of leaching on the geotechnical properties of the clay

normally-consolidated clay, that is, that the modulus of compressibility, $1/m_v$, and the shear strength of the clay both increase proportionally with the consolidation pressure.

EFFECT OF LEACHING

The picture presented above of the properties of a normally-consolidated clay is, strictly speaking, only valid for sediments which are relatively young from a geological point of view. As soon as a clay sediment has consolidated under its own weight, the clay can be classified as a normally-consolidated clay. But now it enters the second stage of its life in which a number of factors come into play which can lead to significant changes in properties from an engineering point of view. In this lecture several such geological factors will be discussed.

The first factor which will be considered is the effect of leaching caused by a slow flow of fresh water through the marine sediments. In order to illustrate this process, let us return to the cross-section through the Drammen valley (Fig. 7) which shows the typical geological setting of clay sediments deposited on rock slopes which rise high above the floor of the valley.

The leaching process

The pore pressures in the sediments were originally in equilibrium at values which increased hydrostatically with depth or which corresponded to a very small upward gradient. The gradual elevation of the rock slopes and the sediments above sea level resulted in a change in the ground water conditions leading to an increase of the upward gradient. The pore water pressures at the bottom of the sediments stayed at values higher than those corresponding to the ground water level in the upper sand. This artesian condition may be the result of a pervious layer between rock and the clay sediments, but in many cases it originates in the presence of cracks and fissures in the rock which communicate with 'free ground water' at a higher elevation in the rock slope. The result of the artesian condition is that the clay sediments are subjected to a slow upward flow of water. The rate of flow will be greatest where the depth to rock is small, but it will also be greatly influenced by the presence of sand and silt layers in the sediments.

A slow flow of water through a clay will not in itself cause any changes in its geotechnical properties, but in this case the percolating water is fresh water, whereas the water confined in the voids of the clay is salt water. The flow therefore results in a gradual exchange of the salt water in the voids with fresh water and such leaching of a marine clay has an almost dramatic effect on the properties of the clay. It transforms the ordinary normally-consolidated clay into a 'quick clay'.

North of the river on the cross-section through the Drammen valley in Fig. 7, the shaded zone indicates a region in which leaching has proceeded so far that the clay has been converted to a quick clay. Fortunately, results are available from two borings, A and B, of which A passes through the unleached clay layers and B passes through the same clay layers, but within the zone where leaching is so advanced that the clays have been changed to quick clays. By comparing the two borings in Fig. 7 we can readily appreciate the effect of leaching on the geotechnical properties of the clay.

In the first place, desalination has produced a reduction in the plasticity of the clay. As an example, the liquid limit of the upper plastic clay has been lowered from 48% to 37%. The water content of the clay has, however, remained practically unaltered during the leaching process and the water content is now considerably higher than the liquid limit. A clay with a water content much higher than the liquid limit will obviously have the consistency of a liquid in the remoulded state, and it is this significant property which has given the leached clays the name of quick clays. The sensitivity of the clay, defined as the ratio of undisturbed to remoulded shear strength, has increased from a value of 8–10 in boring A to a value of 200–300 in the leached zone in boring B.

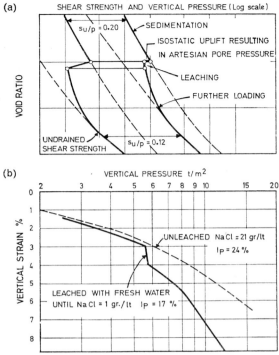

(a)   SHEAR STRENGTH AND VERTICAL PRESSURE (Log scale)

(b)   VERTICAL PRESSURE t/m²

Fig. 8.   Change in compressibility and shear strength of marine clay caused by leaching: (a) general principle; (b) result of leaching tests in the laboratory with a lean clay from Drammen

Secondly, leaching has caused a reduction in the undrained shear strength. The undrained shear strength determined by vane tests in the leached zone in boring B is only 50% of the shear strength of the unleached clay in boring A.

Thirdly, leaching has produced an increase in the compressibility of the clay. It goes almost without saying that the structure of a quick clay is so unstable that even small additional loads will cause a large reduction in water content. The increase in compressibility resulting from leaching is illustrated in principle in Fig. 8a. In the diagram of void ratio against the logarithm of the effective overburden pressure we are able to follow the different stages: sedimentation, when the overburden increased gradually; isostatic uplift leading to a slight decrease of the effective vertical stress due to the increased pore pressures; and finally, leaching during which a very small, if any, reduction in water content may have occurred. If, after leaching, the clay is subjected to additional loading, the reduction in water content will be large for small load increments and it is only after a considerable reduction in water content that the compressibility decreases to 'normal' values consistent with the low plasticity of the quick clay. The e–log p curve for a quick clay is not a straight line, but a curve which starts with a steep section for loads exceeding p_0.

The changes in undrained shear strength are also shown in Fig. 8a. The ratio of undrained shear strength to effective overburden pressure is typically of the order of 0·16–0·25 in the unleached clay, but in the leached clay it has been reduced to a value of 0·09–0·12.

Figure 8b shows the result of a consolidation test in which the geological history of a leached clay is simulated in the laboratory. An undisturbed salt clay was gradually loaded in a consolidometer until the vertical pressure was 5·6 ton/sq. m. The sample was then subjected to a slow flow of fresh water until the salt concentration of the pore water had been reduced from 21 g/l to 1 g/l. The clay was then subjected to an additional loading. In the figure, the consolidation curve for the leached clay is compared with a curve obtained from a test on an identical sample which was not leached, clearly illustrating the increase in compressibility resulting from the leaching.

Foundations on quick clay

From the point of view of foundation engineering, quick clays constitute some of the most troublesome soil conditions. Not only are they extremely soft and very compressible, but their high sensitivity makes them difficult to handle in excavations. Unfortunately, the central part of Drammen is located north of the river near the rock ridge where the clays have been changed to quick clays, see Fig. 1. The result on the buildings is evident. The relatively low but rather heavy masonry buildings that were constructed between 50 and 100 years ago show settlements which in many cases exceed 0·5 m (Engh, 1962).

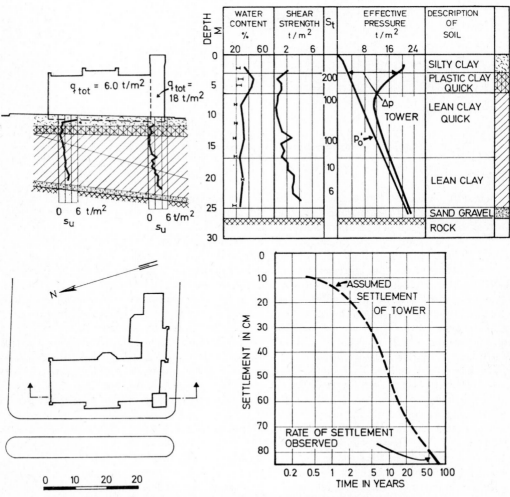

Fig. 9.   Soil data and settlement of Old City Hall, Drammen

Such an example is the old town hall of Drammen shown in Fig. 9.   It was built in 1870 of red bricks with heavy walls and two low towers (see Fig. 12).   The net foundation load varies between 6 ton/sq. m under the main building and 18 ton/sq. m under the towers.   The foundation is placed on a raft of crossed timbers which rests directly on top of the clay. Recent borings have shown that below a 3 m thick drying crust we find the postglacial plastic clay, and below a depth of about 7 m the lean clay extends to a depth of about 25 m.   As seen from the profile in Fig. 9, the clay layers are quick to a depth of about 17 m, the water content being far in excess of the liquid limit, the sensitivity so high that it could not be measured, and the undrained shear strength in places as low as 0·3–0·5 ton/sq. m.   Settlements have only been recorded during the last few years, but on the basis of a study of the building and the soil conditions, the settlement of the tower has been estimated at about 90 cm.

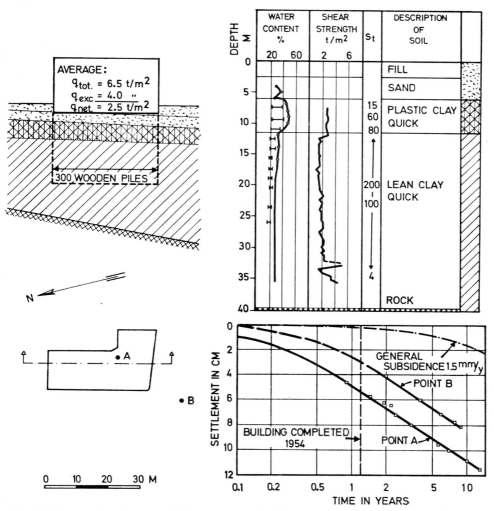

Fig. 10. Soil data and settlement of Norge–bygget in Drammen. Foundation on spliced wooden friction piles

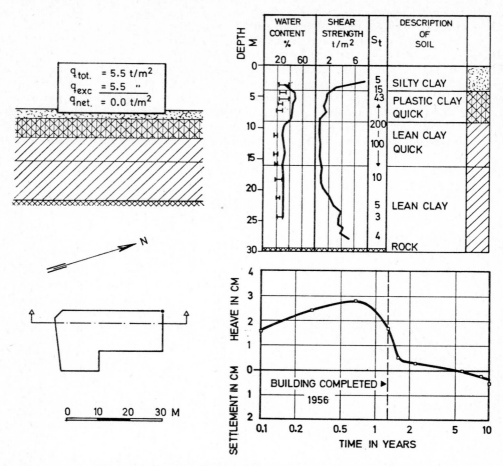

Fig. 11. Soil data and settlement of Werring-gaarden, Drammen: compensated foundation

The differential settlements are of the order of 40 cm and the building has obviously suffered considerable damage.

The use of driven piles is an obvious means of reducing settlements, but in the central part of the town the settlements of the surroundings, caused by the displacement of the piles, are normally so large that the applicability of this method is very limited.

To illustrate this effect, the case of Norge-bygget[2] in Drammen will be described, see Fig. 10.   Since the proposed site for the building was so close to the steep bank of the river and, in addition, the upper sand here had a high content of organic material, it was decided to carry the building on 23 m long spliced wooden piles acting as friction piles in the clay. Today, twelve years after completion of the building, the settlement is 12 cm but, as seen in the settlement diagram, driving of the piles has caused the surroundings to settle by about 8 cm.

[2] Consulting engineer was Mr O. A. Engh, Drammen, and Norsk Teknisk Byggekontroll, Oslo, were geotechnical advisers.   Mr J. Friis, Norsk Teknisk Byggekontroll, has kindly permitted use of the data in this Paper.

Soil mechanics can only provide a solution to the problems involved in foundations on quick clays by taking into full account the instability of the structure of the clay. Acknowledgement of this fact led to the application of 'floating' or 'compensated' foundations, designed such that the weight of the excavation is equal to the weight of the building.

In 1954, in co-operation with the consulting engineers, the Institute introduced the principle of compensated foundations for buildings in the central part of Drammen, and since then the principle has found widespread application. The problem involved in its use in Drammen is that the quick clay is at many sites so soft that an excavation will fail by a bottom heave at a depth of about 3 m. In order to successfully compensate a 4–5 storey building and at the same time maintain a reasonable safety factor against a shear failure in the clay below the bottom of the excavation, it has in general proved necessary to carry out the excavation and pour the foundation raft in small sections.

Figs 11 and 13 show an example of a compensated foundation in the centre of Drammen. Werring-gaarden[3] was constructed in 1956 at a site where the clay is quick and the shear strength is lower than 1 ton/sq. m to a depth of 20 m. The settlement of the building is 4 cm, equal to the elastic rebound observed during excavation.

Werring-gaarden is only one of several examples of successful application of the principle of compensated foundations on quick clays in Drammen, all of them showing settlements smaller than 5 cm (Bjerrum, 1964). When one takes into consideration the extremely poor soil conditions in the central part of Drammen and the small settlements experienced, it is easy to understand that the method of compensated foundations has now been generally adopted.

EFFECT OF DELAYED CONSOLIDATION

The next factor to be considered will here be called delayed consolidation. Obviously the individual clay layers suffered tremendous settlements as the deposit was gradually built up and they became loaded with the increasing weight of the overburden sediments. Settlement continued, however, after the excess pore pressures set up during deposition had dissipated and the clay structure effectively supported the overburden pressure. This settlement which occurs under constant effective stress, and in some clays continues for thousands of years, is due to what might be called delayed or secondary consolidation.

Effect of time on compressibility

The compressibility characteristics of a clay showing delayed consolidation cannot be described by a single curve in an e–log p diagram but require a system of lines or curves as illustrated in Fig. 14.[4] Each of these lines represents the equilibrium void ratio for different values of effective overburden pressure at a specific time of sustained loading. Consolidation tests have shown that the system of lines is approximately parallel (Taylor, 1942; Crawford, 1965), indicating that the rate of delayed consolidation is about the same throughout a homogeneous deposit or, as the lines are actually slightly curved, it decreases slightly with increasing overburden pressure.

The diagram in Fig. 14 is believed to represent a unique relationship between void ratio, overburden pressure and time. This means that to any given value of the overburden pressure and void ratio there corresponds an equivalent time of sustained loading and a certain rate of delayed consolidation, independent of the way in which the clay has reached these values.

The volume change which has occurred in a clay sediment can thus be divided into two components:

---

[3] Consulting engineer was Mr J. Harbitz, Drammen. Geotechnical adviser: The Norwegian Geotechnical Institute.

[4] The curves in Fig. 14 represent an estimate of the behaviour of the plastic clay in Drammen.

Fig. 12 (above).   The Old City Hall (Sønstrød, Drammen)

Fig. 13 (right).   Werring-gaarden (Sønstrød, Drammen)

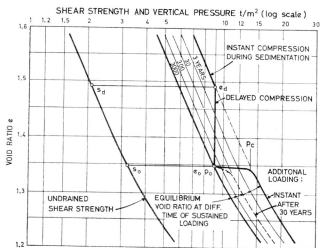

Fig. 14. Compressibility and shear strength of a clay exhibiting delayed consolidation

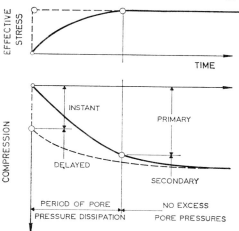

Fig. 15. Definition of 'instant' and 'delayed' compression compared with 'primary' and 'secondary' compression

(a) an 'instant compression' which occurred simultaneously with the increase in effective pressure and caused a reduction in void ratio until an equilibrium value was reached at which the structure effectively supported the overburden pressure;

(b) a 'delayed compression' representing the reduction in volume at unchanged effective stresses.

The two new terms 'instant' and 'delayed' compression clearly describe the reaction of the clay with respect to an increase in the *effective* stresses. They are contrary to the well-known expressions, 'primary' and 'secondary' compression, which separate the compression into two components occurring before and after the excess pore pressures have dissipated. In order to clarify the definitions, Fig. 15 shows how the compression of a clay layer develops with time if loaded with a suddenly-applied uniformly-distributed pressure. The dotted curve shows the reaction of the soil structure that would occur if the pore water in the voids of the clay were incapable of retarding the compression, and the applied pressure were transferred instantaneously to the clay structure as an effective pressure. This curve defines the 'instant' and the 'delayed' compression. Due to the viscosity of the water, the effective stresses will increase gradually as the excess pore pressures dissipate and compression will occur along the fully-drawn curve. As the time required for dissipation of the excess pore pressures is dependent on such factors as the thickness of the clay layer, its permeability and the drainage conditions, separation of the compression into a primary and a secondary contribution is rather arbitrary, and this division is unsuited to describe the behaviour of the soil structure with respect to effective stresses.

In Fig. 14 an additional curve is shown representing the undrained shear strength that can be mobilized at a given void ratio. Combining this line with any of the compression curves gives directly the shear strength which we would measure, for instance by vane tests, at the various depths of the sediment at any given time after sedimentation. Similarly, it represents the gain in shear strength at any given depth occuring as a result of the reduction in void ratio during delayed consolidation. There is ample evidence to verify that the shear strength of a plastic clay increases as the void ratio decreases during delayed consolidation.[5] The unique relationship between undrained shear strength and void ratio postulated in Fig. 14 is, however, only a working hypothesis that has been found valid for the plastic clay in Drammen.

Effect of additional loading

The reduction in water content during delayed consolidation will clearly lead to a more stable configuration of the structure. The number of contact points between clay particles will increase and in plastic clays the cohesive component of the shear strength will increase. This means that during delayed consolidation a cohesive clay will develop increased strength and a reserve resistance against further compression. Such a clay can support an additional load in excess of the effective overburden pressure without any significant volume change produced by slippage of the contact points. This means that for additional loads smaller than a certain critical value the clay will behave similarly to an overconsolidated clay and the instant settlements will be limited to an elastic compression. In Fig. 14 this behaviour is illustrated by considering a clay layer located at a depth where the effective overburden pressure is p_o. Imagine the clay layer to be 3000 years old and to have reached equilibrium at a void ratio e_o, $e_o p_o$ being located on the 3000-year curve. During the 3000 years of delayed consolidation, the shear strength, measured by vane tests for instance, increased from s_d to s_o. If the clay is subjected to an additional load, such as the weight of a building, the instant compression will be small provided the vertical stress does not exceed the critical pressure, p_c. If the additional load is so large that the effective stress exceeds p_c, it is only that part of the load exceeding p_c that will lead to large instant settlements.

The reserve resistance against compression developed during delayed consolidation obviously increases with the reduction in void ratio, that is with time of sustained loading. As the e–log p curves for different times are nearly parallel, the ratio p_c/p_o is approximately equal throughout a clay deposit, or in other words, the critical pressure developed during delayed compression increases linearly with the effective overburden pressure.

When it was stated above that the compression of the clay is small for additional loads up to p_c, this referred only to the instant compression, i.e. the compression which occurs immediately the effective stresses are increased.

The instant compression, however, is followed by a delayed compression, the rate of which can be estimated directly from the vertical distance between the curves in the diagram. It increases very rapidly as the effective stresses approach p_c, and in Fig. 14 a dotted line shows the magnitude of the total compression after thirty years. If we take account of delayed compression we can talk about a 'field value' of the critical pressure which depends on the

---

[5] The increase in shear strength resulting from delayed consolidation has previously been discussed by Taylor (1955), Osterman (1960), Ladd (1964), and Schmertmann (1965).

time of loading, in accordance with the corresponding value of the shear strength (Crawford, 1964). If, for instance, the load acts for 3000 years, the additional compression will occur along the 3000-year curve, and the effect of the reserve resistance of the deposit will have vanished. The engineering significance of the p_c-values developed in clays exhibiting delayed consolidation is thus limited to deposits whose 'age' is great compared with the lifetime of a building.

The development of a reserve resistance against compression during delayed consolidation can be very easily demonstrated in the laboratory. The first tests in which this effect was observed were carried out by Moretto (1946). The most comprehensive study of this effect has been performed by Leonards and the results are published in various papers listed in the references. In Fig. 16, a plastic clay sample from Drammen was consolidated to 13 ton/sq. m and the load was applied for thirty days. Subsequently the sample was loaded in steps, each step lasting one day. The curve thus obtained shows that the sample had developed a critical pressure, p_c, which for the selected rate of loading amounted to 16 ton/sq. m, 1·25 times the pressure at which the delayed consolidation took place.

In the above discussion, for the sake of clarity it was ignored that the voids of a clay are saturated with water and that the very slow rate at which this water can be squeezed out of the clay will govern the rate of change in volume upon application of a load. The hydro-dynamic retardation is insignificant for the relatively low rate of volume change prevailing during delayed compression, but completely governs the rate of compression in the so-called 'instant compression.' It is of practical importance to note that if the additional pressure is smaller than $p_c - p_o$, the pore pressure will dissipate relatively rapidly. In this range the instant compressibility is low and the total amount of pore water to be squeezed out during the period of consolidation is therefore relatively small. As the effective stresses exceed p_c, the importance of the hydrodynamic time lag increases. In Fig. 17 a system of curves is shown which illustrate in principle the type of settlement curves which can be expected for loads of various magnitudes relative to p_c. These types of curve are well-known from consolidation tests when different values of $\Delta p/p$ are used (Leonards and Girault, 1961).

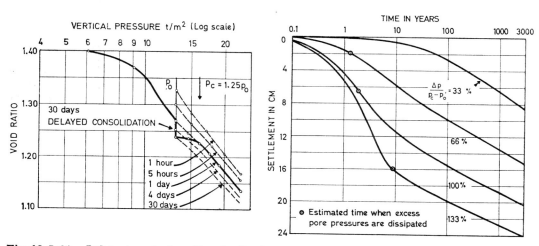

Fig. 16 (left). Laboratory test on the plastic clay in Drammen demonstrating the development of reserve resistance against further compression during 28 days of delayed consolidation

Fig. 17 (right). Shape of time–compression curves for different degrees of mobilization of reserve resistance against compression. The curves are computed for a 5 m thick layer of the plastic clay in Drammen assuming $p_c/p_o = 1·6$

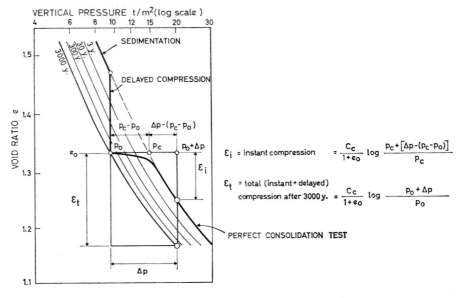

Fig. 18. Principle of settlement computation

Before leaving these rather general considerations one important conclusion should be drawn concerning settlement calculations.   For this purpose we will consider the compression of a clay layer exhibiting delayed consolidation as represented by the system of curves in Fig. 18.   A perfect consolidation test will in the first place provide us with the value of the critical pressure, p_o, and in the second place the inclination of the curves, i.e. the value C_c. If the additional stress is Δp, based on the results of the consolidation test we can compute two values of the compression, ϵ_t and ϵ_i, as shown in Fig. 18.   The computation of ϵ_t starts at the point (e_o, p_o) and the total value of Δp is used.   The starting point for computing ϵ_i is (e_o, p_c) and only that part of Δp which exceeds $p_c - p_o$ is used.   The significance of the two components is as follows:

ϵ_i predicts the instant component of the settlement which occurs on increase of the effective stresses.   The value of ϵ_i and the time required for the excess pore pressure to dissipate will therefore provide us with an initial theoretical point on the time-settlement curve, which does not include, however, the delayed compression occurring during the period of pore pressure dissipation.

ϵ_t predicts the total additional[6] compression of the clay layers, including the instant as well as the delayed compression, and it represents the compression which can be expected at a time after the load has been applied equal to the time elapsed since the clay was loaded with its present overburden pressure.   If the additional load Δp is smaller than $p_c - p_o$, ϵ_t is valid at a time equal to the difference between the 'age' of the sediment and the equivalent time of sustained loading which corresponds to the point $(e_o, p_o + \Delta p)$ on the diagram, but in practice this reduction in time is insignificant.

---

[6] This means relative to the surroundings not subjected to additional loads.

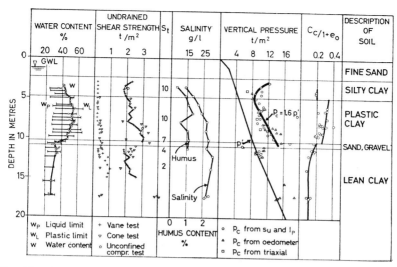

Fig. 19. Geotechnical profile typical of the considered area in Drammen

The conclusion concerning calculation of settlements on normally-consolidated clays exhibiting delayed consolidation is believed to be of some practical importance. Previously there has been no available means of estimating the delayed settlements following the period when dissipation of the excess pore pressures governed the rate of compression. The above finding permits us now to obtain some idea of the magnitude of the delayed consolidation provided we have an approximate estimate of the 'loading age' of the deposit.

Soil conditions south of the river in Drammen

The concepts presented above on the effect of delayed settlements on the compressibility of a normally-consolidated clay emerged from a detailed study of the soil conditions in an area south of the river in Drammen. The soil conditions within this area are fairly uniform and, fortunately, in this area there are six buildings for which complete settlement records have been collected. Because the settlement behaviour of these buildings deviated from any predictions based on conventional procedures, the soil conditions at each site have been studied in great detail. The results of these studies will be published in separate papers but in order to illustrate the importance of the above concepts on the settlement of buildings, a brief review of the findings will be presented here.

The soil conditions in the area are shown in Fig. 19 and consist of four different layers of soil. The upper layer is a 2·5 m thick deposit of fine sand, which is underlain by a silty clay having a thickness of about 2·5 m. Below the silt we find a 5·5 m thick deposit of the post-glacial plastic clay with a high water content, and it is this clay layer that is of main interest in the present discussion as the greatest contribution to the settlements, about 60%, originates in this layer. The plastic clay has a content of organic matter of about 1% and its liquid limit ranges from 50 to 65%. It belongs to the type of clay exhibiting a relatively large delayed consolidation. The vane shear strength of the clay is about 2 ton/sq. m at the top of the deposit and increases with depth to a value of 3 ton/sq. m in the lower stratum.

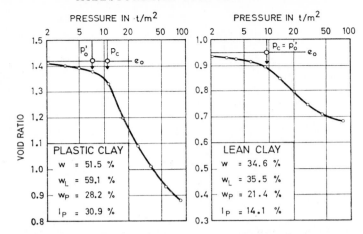

Fig. 20. Typical results of consolidation tests on plastic clay and lean clay from Drammen for determination of p_c

Below the plastic clay, we find a thin layer of sand separating it from an approximately 20–25 m thick deposit of a lean clay of low plasticity. The liquid limit of this clay ranges from 30 to 35%. At the boundary between the plastic clay and the lower clay the shear strength drops abruptly from 3 to 2 ton/sq. m. Throughout the lower clay the shear strength increases linearly with depth. At a depth of about 35 m below ground surface the late-glacial clay rests on soil layers which are probably of glacial origin, and what lies below this depth is of no interest in the present discussion.

Figure 19 also shows the effective vertical overburden stress at each depth, the value of which is calculated from the total vertical stress and the pore pressures observed in piezometers. In the upper layers, the pore pressures increase hydrostatically, corresponding to a ground water level 1·30 m below the ground surface. At greater depths there is a small artesian pressure. It should be mentioned, however, that the resulting slow upward-flow of water has caused no significant reduction in the salt concentration of the pore water.

In our studies of the soil conditions in Drammen attention was focused on the determination of the critical pressure, the p_c value, observed in consolidation tests on undisturbed samples. In spite of the fact that the sampling and testing techniques used by the Institute were especially developed to handle soft and sensitive clays, the values that we obtained for the critical pressure scattered so much that they never provided a consistent picture of the properties of the clay in this respect (Kenney, 1966). Consequently we decided to improve the technique. A new 9·5 cm thin-walled fixed-piston sample was used and special care was exercised in the sealing, handling, transport and storage of the samples. New equipment and procedures were developed for transferring the samples in as undisturbed a condition as possible from the sampling tube directly into the consolidometers (Clausen, 1966). Application of these techniques to the clays in Drammen yielded much more consistent values of the critical pressure. For illustration purposes, typical results of consolidation tests carried out on samples of the plastic and the lean clays are presented in Fig. 20. As seen from the figure, the value of p_c is easily determined, being the pressure at which the consolidation curve shows a sharp bend.[7] In Fig. 19 the critical pressures obtained from about 40 consolidation tests are plotted so that they can be compared directly with the effective overburden pressure.

[7] See Casagrande (1936) and Casagrande and Fadum (1944).

From a geological point of view, the clay deposit in Drammen is obviously normally-consolidated. This fact is strongly confirmed by the general agreement between the critical pressures and the effective overburden pressure observed in the lower clay layer. In contrast, the critical pressure in the plastic clay is unquestionably greater than the present overburden. The test results are so consistent that it has been concluded (Clausen, 1966) that the critical pressure increases with the effective overburden pressure at a ratio of 1·6. The same value has been obtained at other locations, the ratio showing a tendency to decrease slightly with the depth at which the plastic clay is located. In the light of the concepts presented above, it seems logical to conclude from this finding that the reserve resistance against compression represented by the critical pressure is a result of the delayed consolidation which the plastic clay has undergone during the 3000 years it has supported the present overburden. In contrast, the lean clay, which is less cohesive and shows small delayed consolidation, possesses no measurable reserve resistance.

The studies of the critical pressure resulted in one more finding of some practical interest, namely that the critical pressure can also be determined quite reliably from the results of vane tests. As mentioned above, the ratio between the undrained shear strength and the effective overburden pressure is a characteristic constant for a given normally-consolidated clay, being primarily dependent on the plasticity index. The correlation between this characteristic ratio and the plasticity index as observed in Norwegian marine clays is shown in Fig. 5. If we know the plasticity index of a clay and its undrained shear strength, from the correlation in Fig. 5 we can compute an 'equivalent critical pressure' for the clay (Bjerrum, 1964). This has been done for the plastic clay in Drammen with the result shown on the effective-stress diagram in Fig. 19. The values of p_c computed from the vane tests show a reasonably good agreement with the results obtained from consolidation tests and the same agreement has been found at other locations and in other types of clay. An exception is leached clays of low plasticity where errors involved in the determination of the plasticity index produce large

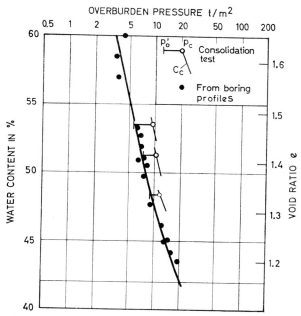

Fig. 21.   Field consolidation curve for the plastic clay in Drammen

scattering of the p_c values determined from the vane tests. Taking into consideration the fact that a reliable determination of p_c from consolidation tests on undisturbed samples is a demanding and time-consuming operation, it goes without saying that the use of the vane test for the same purpose has considerable practical and economical advantages.

In Fig. 19 the compressibility of the clays expressed by the value of $C_c/1 + e_0$ obtained from consolidation tests is also shown. It can be seen directly from the diagram that the plastic clay is the most compressible clay layer in the profile, the value of $C_c/1 + e_0$ being about 0·30. Fortunately, the plastic clay is so uniform over a large area in Drammen that it has proved possible from the results of borings to derive the field relationship between the water content and the effective overburden pressure, from which the field value of $C_c/1 + e_0$ can be computed. Due to an increasing depth to rock, the plastic clay dips regularly towards the river and in the various borings available the plastic clay is found at depths varying from 4–21 metres, and as a result the field consolidation curve has been determined for a relatively wide range of over-burden pressures. The field consolidation curve determined in this way is shown in Fig. 21. The points from the individual borings determine a slightly curved line from which we can compute that the value of $C_c/1 + e_0$ in the field varies from 0·18 to 0·30, the lowest value being determined where the clay had the greatest overburden pressure. These values are similar to the values observed in consolidation tests on the most undisturbed samples, and for comparison the results of some consolidation tests are also shown schematically on Fig. 21. We can thus conclude that for the plastic clay in Drammen at least the field e–log p curve, which includes about 3000 years of delayed consolidation, shows compressibilities similar to those observed in consolidation tests.

Settlement of six buildings

The soil conditions shown in Fig. 19 are representative of an area in Drammen within which six buildings have been constructed, for each of which comprehensive soil data and complete settlement records are available. The data for four of these buildings are given in Figs 23, 25, 26 and 27, and their locations are shown on the map in Fig. 1 and on the photograph in Fig. 22.

Skoger Sparebank,[8] located near the river, is a 10-storey building whose central block measures 13·5 m × 28 m, see Figs 23 and 24. The building rests on a continuous concrete raft and the design of the foundation is such that the excavation for the basement compensates about 70% of the weight of the building, the average net load on the ground thereby being reduced to 3·0 ton/sq. m. The soil conditions are shown in Fig. 23. Since the site is close to the river, the plastic clay is located deeper than in the profile described above, and the thickness of the sand blanket is correspondingly greater. From vane tests and consolidation tests it has been found that the plastic clay shows a critical pressure of about 1·5 times the effective over-burden pressure. Fig. 23 also shows the additional vertical pressure at various depths result-ing from the weight of the building. The stress distribution was computed on the assumption that the upper sand layer had a modulus of elasticity five times as large as that of the under-lying clay layers. As seen from the pressure diagram, the resulting effective vertical pressure in the plastic clay is well below the critical pressure and on the average only 37% of the re-serve resistance has been utilized. Today, five years after the completion of the building, the settlement amounts to 4 cm and the rate has already diminished to a fraction of one centi-metre per year.

For the sake of comparison it can be mentioned that if the 35 metres of clay supporting this building had behaved as a recent normally-consolidated clay, the primary settlements would have been about 19 cm, of which 10 cm would have originated in the plastic clay.

---

[8] Consulting engineer was Mr O. A. Engh, and the Norwegian Geotechnical Institute was geotechnical adviser.

Fig. 22.   View of Drammen showing location of buildings (*Widerøes Flyveselskap A/S*)

Fig. 24. Skoger Sparebank (Sønstrød, Drammen)

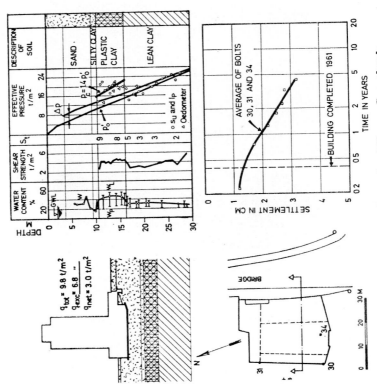

Fig. 23. Soil data and settlements of Skoger Sparebank

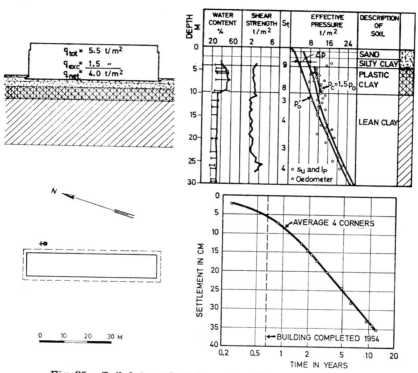

Fig. 25.   Soil data and settlements of Konnerud gate 16

Konnerud gate 16,[9] Fig. 25, is representative of four identical four-storey apartment blocks built between 1950 and 1956, and is located about 300 m from Skoger Sparebank. The soil conditions are the same as those shown in Fig. 19 and described in detail above. The building is founded on a continuous raft extending 1·5 m beyond the area of the building. Its total weight including 25% of the live load corresponds to an average pressure on the raft of 5·5 ton/sq. m. Excavation for the basement reduced the net pressure on the soil beneath the foundation to 4·0 ton/sq. m. Fig. 25 shows the additional vertical stress at various depths. In the plastic clay the resulting effective stress approaches the critical pressure and the average mobilization of reserve resistance against further compression is about 80%.

The settlement of Konnerud gate 16 is shown in Fig. 26. The shape of the settlement curve plotted on a logarithmic time-diagram is such that one would expect the building to be in the middle of a period of pore pressure dissipation and that in a few years time it would 'turn the corner' and embark on a period of delayed consolidation. Actually we have been expecting this to happen for several years and it was only recently, after developing the concepts presented above, that we realized that the interpretation was incorrect. The settlement curve for Konnerud gate is characterized by the fact that the 'instant settlement' is small and by far the greatest proportion of the settlement is the result of delayed consolidation occurring mainly in the plastic clay. The excess pore pressures dissipated very rapidly, probably within a couple of years of completion of the building. Piezometers installed in 1964 confirmed that the excess pore pressures had dissipated ten years after the load was applied. The settlements in the past years have thus occurred at constant effective stresses and can therefore only be explained by delayed consolidation of the plastic clay. The reason why they are so large is obviously that the effective stresses in the plastic clay approach the critical load. Today the total settlement of the building amounts to 35 cm. This settlement is larger than that generally accepted for buildings of this type but the differential settlement is as small as 10 cm and no damage has been caused to the building.

It is of interest to examine the large difference in settlement between Konnerud gate 16 and Skoger Sparebank, the ratio being as large as 10 to 1. A comparison of the stress conditions indicates that the net load on the soil and the stresses in the clay beneath the two buildings are not very different, those at Konnerud gate being four thirds of those at Skoger Sparebank. The properties of the clay layers on which they rest are almost identical and the only difference in soil conditions is that below Skoger Sparebank the plastic clay is found at a depth from 11–17 m compared with 4–10 m below Konnerud gate. The difference in settlements can only be comprehended when it is appreciated that the plastic clay has developed a reserve resistance against further settlements which increases proportionally with the effective overburden, being about 50% of p_o. Under Skoger Sparebank the effective overburden in the plastic clay is large and consequently the reserve resistance is also large; only 37% is mobilized by the additional stresses resulting from the weight of the building. On the other hand below Konnerud gate the effective overburden in the plastic clay is low. This is reflected in the reserve resistance, which in this case is almost completely mobilized by the additional stresses. From the above concepts we know that the rate of delayed consolidation increases very rapidly as the effective stresses increase from p_o to p_c. It is this difference in degree of mobilization of the reserve resistance that explains why the settlements of Konnerud gate are about ten times greater than those of Skoger Sparebank.

About 300 metres from the apartment blocks in Konnerud gate, two buildings are located within 40 metres of each other, Turnhallen and Scheitlies gate 1. In this area the soil conditions are essentially similar to those at Konnerud gate, but the plastic clay is somewhat thicker and has a more gradual transition towards the upper and lower deposits.

---

[9] Consulting engineer: Mr J. Harbitz, Drammen.

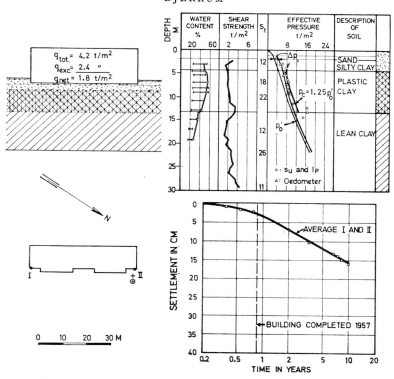

Fig. 26. Soil data and settlements of Scheitlies gate 1

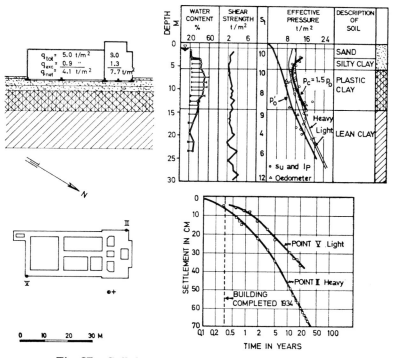

Fig. 27. Soil data and settlements of Turnhallen

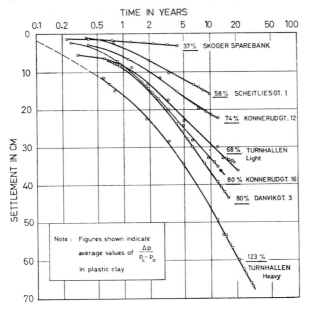

Fig. 28. Comparison of settlements of six buildings in Drammen

At the apartment block Scheitlies gate 1 (see Fig. 26), the plastic clay is considerably softer and the critical pressure considerably smaller than at the other sites, which include the nearby Turnhallen.   The ratio p_c/p_o at Scheitlies gate is only 1·25 compared with 1·4–1·5 at the other sites within this area.   This irregularity is due to the location of the site at a point where a local depression containing a brook previously existed, and the upper layers of sand and fill were placed quite recently in connexion with the urban development of the area. The low value of p_c/p_o is therefore the result of a recent increase in p_o.   To the value of p_c/p, equal to 1·25, there corresponds an equivalent 'loading age' of the plastic clay which is estimated to about 150 years (see Fig. 14).

The building at Scheitlies gate[10] is a conventional three-storey block resting on a raft foundation with a net pressure of 1·8 ton/sq. m.   From the stress distribution diagram it is seen that the additional stresses in the plastic clay are so low that they are well below the critical load and on the average only 58% of the reserve resistance is mobilized.   The settlement curve of the building again has the characteristic shape of small instant and large delayed settlement.   Today the total settlement amounts to 16 cm.

The settlement of Turnhallen[11] has been described in detail by Simons (1957).   The building was completed in 1934 and consists of a heavy western section and a lighter eastern section housing the gymnastic hall, see Fig. 27.   The light section is carried by strip footings, while the heavy section is supported by a raft.   The plastic clay here has a critical pressure of 1·5 p_o.   The additional stresses below the heavy section are so high that the effective stress exceeds the critical pressure, but below the light section only 68% of the reserve resistance is mobilized.

Today, 32 years after construction, the settlement of the heavy section is about 70 cm. Due to the fact that the critical pressure was exceeded, the 'instant contribution' to the settlements is appreciable and it required quite a few years for the excess pore pressures to dissipate.

---

[10] Consulting engineer was Mr Stener Sörensen, Drammen, and the Norwegian Geotechnical Institute was geotechnical adviser.
[11] Consulting engineer was Mr H. Lorentz Aass, Drammen.

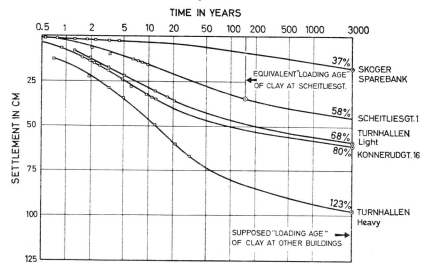

Fig. 29.   Future settlements of five buildings in Drammen

During the past 25 years, the settlement has plotted on a straight line on a logarithmic time scale, and since piezometers recently installed below the building indicate that all excess pore pressures have dissipated, this suggests that the settlements which have occurred over the past 25 years are due to delayed consolidation in the plastic clay.   The settlement of the light section is considerably smaller, amounting at present to about 40 cm.

In Fig. 28 a comparison is made of all recorded settlements of buildings in the area.   The buildings fall into two groups.   The first group consists of Turnhallen and Scheitlies gate below which the plastic clay has a thickness of about 9 metres, and the second group includes all the other buildings studied, where the thickness is about 6·5 metres.   The percentage of reserve resistance mobilized in the plastic clay is shown for each building.   Before drawing any conclusion from this diagram, attention is drawn to the fact that the critical pressure used for this purpose is a laboratory value determined from consolidation tests during which the load was only sustained for a period of about a day.   However, considering the degree of mobilization assigned to each building in Fig. 28 as an empirical value, it is obvious that this figure to a large extent governs the magnitude of the settlements and, in particular, the rate of the delayed consolidation.   It may be too early to conclude how far it is advisable to go in the design of a new building, but for the plastic clay in Drammen it seems reasonable that, if more than 50% of the reserve resistance measured in consolidation tests is mobilized, the delayed consolidation will be larger than that normally desirable for conventional buildings.

It is clearly of some interest to compare the calculated settlements with the observed values. As demonstrated in Fig. 15, a computation can be made of the total settlement ϵ_t, including the instant and the delayed contribution, which can be expected at a time after completion of the building equal to the time during which the clay has carried its present overburden. The calculated values of ϵ_t for the buildings in Drammen will therefore tell us how large the additional settlements referred to the surroundings will be when the buildings are about 3000 years old.   Fig. 29 shows the observed settlements of five buildings and their extrapolation to the computed values at an age of 3000 years (150 years for Scheitlies gate).   These curves are believed to be relatively realistic.   The first part of the curves is directly observed and, at least for the plastic clay, which accounts for most of the settlement, the computation is based on the 'field consolidation curve.'

The curves in Fig. 29 are of considerable interest as they represent our first piece of information concerning the variation of the rate of delayed consolidation with time. Hitherto it has been assumed that the delayed settlements would continue along the straight line normally observed in the first 10–50 years after the dissipation of the excess pore pressure. The curves in Fig. 29 show that the settlements do not plot on a straight line, but follow a slightly bent curve that gradually approaches a horizontal line.

It is interesting to observe that the curves for all buildings in Fig. 29 gradually become more and more parallel with the passage of time. This means that with time, the rates of delayed consolidation are becoming equal. This finding is in agreement with the concepts presented above, according to which the rate of delayed consolidation is independent of the effective stress provided sufficient time has elapsed for the effect of the original loading conditions to disappear. It should furthermore be noticed from Fig. 29 that the effect of the reserve resistance of the plastic clay on the settlements is most pronounced during the initial period after completion of the buildings, that is, a short period compared to the 3000 years 'loading age' of the sediment. As the age of the building increases and approaches 3000 years the effect gradually disappears. The values of void ratio and effective stress in the clay below the buildings will eventually plot on a single e–log p curve valid for a time of sustained loading equal to the age of the buildings.

DEVELOPMENT OF ADDITIONAL STRUCTURAL STRENGTH BY CHEMICAL BONDING

The development of reserve strength during delayed consolidation is important in areas like Drammen where the compressibility of the upper, rather plastic, postglacial clay governs the settlement of buildings. The majority of the Norwegian marine clays, however, do not belong to the type exhibiting pronounced delayed consolidation. A review of settlements observed on buildings and embankments (Bjerrum, 1964) indicates that normally-consolidated clays of medium or low plasticity under certain conditions have also experienced changes since their deposition which have resulted in a reduced compressibility. These changes will be discussed in this section under the heading 'development of additional structural strength by chemical bonding,' independent of their fundamental nature.

It is a well-documented fact that if a clay is allowed to stand for a certain time in a laboratory apparatus under unchanged stresses it will develop additional structural strength. The clay becomes more brittle and the resistance against deformations for small load increments increases with the age of the clay. There is good reason to believe that such a change in behaviour is the result of the development of cohesive bonds between the particles. Experimental evidence of the effect of aging of a clay can be found in papers by Moretto (1946), Leonards and Ramiah (1960) and Bjerrum and Lo (1963). Experience is also available to indicate that the same type of phenomena can occur in the field (Terzaghi, 1941; Bjerrum and Wu, 1960; Keinonen, 1963).

In our quest for an explanation of the nature of these cohesive bonds, we soon become aware of the fact that there are a variety of processes, covered by the term diagenesis, which with time produce inter-particle bonds in clays. Most of these processes, however, are associated with much more fundamental modifications or alteration of the clay minerals than can have occurred in the relatively young Norwegian clays. The only processes which are believed to have any influence on the Norwegian clays are:

(*a*) cold-welding of mineral contact points between particles;
(*b*) exchange of cations;
(*c*) precipitation of cementing agents.

The cold-welding, leading to inter-particle van der Waal forces, probably exists in all clays and these forces may explain why the water content of a quick clay remains practically unchanged during leaching.   Cold-welding in Norwegian clays is believed to be so weak, however, that its effect on the compressibility for additional loading is insignificant.

Exchange of cations

The second process, the exchange of cations, is believed to be by far the most important for Norwegian clays and it will therefore be discussed in some detail.

As mentioned above, the clay particles are in general of a flake-type shape of lattice minerals of various types.   The most common clay minerals present in Norwegian clays are hydrous mica and chlorite.   Mineral crystals of most common clay minerals possess a net negative electric charge.   These charges are balanced by cations on the surface of the minerals and since the cations can be readily exchanged with other cations, they are termed exchangeable ions.[12]   In marine clays, the clay particles were initially saturated with sodium cations. If, however, the type and relative concentration of cations in the pore water changes, the ions on the surface of the clay particles will exchange with the ions of the solution.

It can be easily demonstrated that the geotechnical properties of a clay can be radically modified by exchange of the cations attached to the surface of the particles, an exchange bringing about changes in plasticity, shear strength and compressibility.

Table 1 contains a list of the types of cations which exist in Norwegian marine clays, or which may be produced as a result of disintegration of the minerals and other constituents. The table also shows the effect of exchange of the different ions on the properties of a typical Norwegian clay.   A remoulded clay was saturated with the different ions in turn and the corresponding plasticity indices were determined for each ion.   In addition, the undrained shear strength was determined at a water content about equal to the natural water content of the clay.   The values obtained in these tests show clearly that, when the type of cation change follows the order shown in the table, the plasticity and the shear strength will increase and the compressibility will decrease.   Any ion-exchange leading to a development of structural strength of a marine clay requires that the relative concentration of one or more of the cations of higher order than the Na^+ ion be increased compared to that of seawater.   Such a change can only take place as a result of some type of disintegration of either the minerals or of the remaining constituents of the clay.   The development of structural strength in clay is

Table 1.   Common types of cation participating in ion-exchange phenomena in Norwegian clays

Type of cation	Origin or possible source	Effect on hydrous-mica/chlorite type clays	
		Plasticity index I_p	Remoulded shear strength s_u* $ton/sq.\ m$
H^+ pore water	Water, dissolved CO_2 decomposing organic matter	7·5	<0·01
Na^+	Seawater	16·4	0·11
Ca^{++}	Seawater, microfossils	16·7	0·15
Mg^{++}	Seawater, disintegrating chlorite	17·9	0·13
Al^{+++}	Disintegrated chlorite and felspar	21·6	0·42
$(Fe^{++}), Fe^{+++}$	Disintegrating chlorite	22·4	0·21
K^+	Seawater, disintegrating felspar and mica	22·7	0·29

* Tested at natural water content of clay, about 48%.

[12] For a more detailed discussion, see for instance Lambe (1960) and Van Olphen (1963).

therefore dependent on a change in environmental conditions capable of producing the types of disintegration listed in Table 1.

The basic factor governing the chemical stability of minerals in clay is the pH value of the porewater; any change reducing the pH value of the porewater will increase the rate of disintegration of the minerals, and vice-versa.

The geological and topographic conditions in Norway are such that as soon as a clay deposit rises above seawater level it will in almost all cases be subjected to a slow exchange of the original porewater by percolating rainwater. As described above, this will lead to a gradual removal of the Na^+ ions. This in itself has no great effect on the pH value, but rainwater contains dissolved O_2 and CO_2. CO_2 lowers the pH of the porewater and the O_2 coming into contact with organic matter forms humic acids which also reduce the pH-value. If this slow but persistent process advances to such an extent that the pH is reduced to a sufficiently low value, then a disintegration of felspar, mica and chlorite will commence. The disintegration results in liberation of cations of higher order than Na^+ which collect on the surface of the clay particles. The effect of this base-exchange is to raise the plasticity of the clay and additional strength is developed. The disintegration also causes the liberation of other chemical compounds which tend to increase the pH and thereby prevent the process. The development of structural strength by exchange of Na^+ ions by ions of higher order thus requires a continuous supply of pH-reducing agents to the clay.

It is well beyond the scope of this lecture to discuss in detail the various types of ions involved in this process.[13] To keep the discussion simple, attention will be focused on the K^+ ions liberated from the mineral lattice of felspar and mica, two minerals which exist in all Norwegian clays. The K^+ ions are believed to be the dominant ones in the early phase of this process and therefore they, more than the other types of ions in Table 1, govern the development of additional structural strength in the relatively young Norwegian clays.

The effect of base-exchange, resulting from the type of weathering described, is illustrated in Fig. 30, which shows soil conditions typical of Norway (Moum and Rosenqvist, 1955). Since the normally-consolidated clay deposit in Fig. 30 rose above seawater level, the upper two to three metres of clay have been subjected to drying and the result is a reduction in water content and an increase in shear strength. Below the drying crust there is a zone of clay extending to a depth of 6 to 7 metres and, though showing no reduction in water content, it has developed additional strength due to weathering. In this case, base-exchange is promoted by the seepage of rainwater through the clay from the surface and consequently the weathering effect diminishes with depth. That the increase in shear strength is the result of base-exchange is verified by measurements of the type of adsorbed ions on the clay. The results of these measurements are shown in the plot of the ratio K^+/Na^+ in Fig. 30. This ratio expresses the proportion of the Na^+ ions that have been exchanged by K^+ ions (the original value in the freshly-deposited clay being about 0·20), and is thus a measure of how far the base-exchange process has proceeded. As observed from Fig. 30, the K^+/Na^+ ratio is low in the drying crust where the K^+ ions have been absorbed by vegetation. Just below the drying crust the ratio is about 1, and it decreases gradually with depth to the value of 0·20, typical for the unaltered clay at 6 to 7 metres. The undrained shear strength is used to measure the effect of base-exchange on the geotechnical properties of the clay in Fig. 30. In the diagram the observed shear strengths of the clay are compared with the values that the clay is assumed to have had before the weathering process started. As can be seen, there is a correlation between increase in shear strength and increase in the K^+/Na^+ ratio.

Figure 31(a) shows in principle how the compressibility of a normally-consolidated clay is altered as the result of a base-exchange in which Na^+ ions are replaced by ions of a higher order. As the plasticity and the shear strength increase, the clay develops an increased

---

[13] For a detailed discussion, see Rosenqvist (1955 and 1959), Moum and Rosenqvist (1957 and 1961).

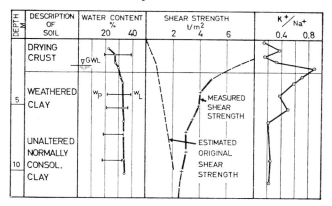

Fig. 30. Geotechnical profile of typical Norwegian marine clay showing effect of weathering on properties of clay (Moum and Rosenqvist, 1955)

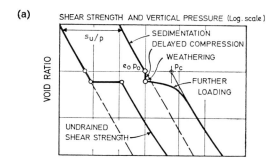

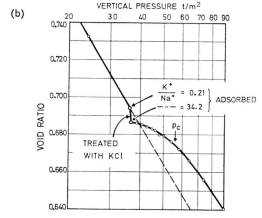

Fig. 31. Effect of base-exchange on compressibility and shear strength of a normally-consolidated clay: (a) general principle; (b) result of laboratory tests on lean clay from Drammen

resistance against deformation from additional loading. The clay has developed a critical pressure, p_c, and provided the additional load does not exceed this value the compression will be small. If the additional load is exceeded, the clay will consolidate along a new e–log p curve corresponding to the increased plasticity of the clay.

Figure 31(b) shows an experimental example of the effect of a base-exchange on the compressibility. A sample of the lower lean clay in Drammen was consolidated at a pressure exceeding the previous overburden, and was then permeated with a water rich in K^+ ions. When the K^+/Na^+ ratio had increased from 0·21 to 34·2 the sample was loaded in small steps. As observed from Fig. 31(b), the clay had developed a critical load of 56 ton/sq. m compared with the 36 ton/sq. m at which the sample was consolidated. The base-exchange has not only resulted in the development of a critical pressure, but the e–log p curve representing the compressibility of the clay for loads exceeding p_c has shifted as a result of the increased activity of the clay.

North of the river in Drammen there are, as mentioned above, large areas where the clays have been leached as a result of an artesian ground-water condition. Within this area there are zones of quick clay where the conditions for some reason are such that disintegration of the clay has occurred and the clay has developed additional structural strength.

An example of this phenomenon and its effect on the settlement of a building is shown in Fig. 32. The apartment block Engene 86,[14] was built in 1957 (Bjerrum, 1964). The soil conditions are characterized by the presence of a 4·5 m thick very stiff crust of dried and weathered clay below which is found a 10 m thick layer of quick clay overlaying rock. Consolidation tests on the quick clay indicate a critical pressure greater than the present overburden, the difference being appreciable just below the upper crust, but decreasing to an insignificant value just above rock. Correspondingly, the undrained shear strength has increased in comparison with the values observed in unaltered quick clays of the same type. Since the lowest part of the quick clay is very nearly normally consolidated, the additional strength of the quick clay must be the result of chemical changes producing base-exchange. This theory is confirmed by the values of the K^+/Na^+ ratio measured on samples from various depths and listed in Fig. 32.

The effect of base-exchange on the compressibility is directly observed from the settlement of the building. The building has a foundation of strip footings and the average net pressure on the ground is 2·7 ton/sq. m. The settlement is only 3 cm. The small settlement is clearly due to the fact that the additional stresses in the quick clay are smaller than the critical pressure. For comparison it can be mentioned that if the quick clay had not been altered by weathering, the settlements would have been of the order of 20 cm.

It was mentioned above that the general geological setting in Norway is such that the marine clays are subjected to a slow flow of freshwater which gradually leaches out the salt in the porewater and transforms the clay to a quick clay. If this geological factor were the only one acting, an increasing number of landslides and a general aggravation of the foundation conditions in Norway could be expected in the future. It is very comforting to know that, at least in some places, the leaching process is accompanied by a base-exchange process which tends to change the clay in the opposite direction, and which after a clay has become quick will gradually lead to the development of additional strength.

Precipitation of cementing agents

The third process leading to the development of additional strength of a clay is precipitation of cementing agents. The effect of such a precipitation is principally limited to a strengthening of the links of the clay structure, the clay itself not otherwise being affected.

---

[14] Consulting engineer was Mr J. Harbitz, Drammen. Geotechnical adviser was the Norwegian Geotechnical Institute.

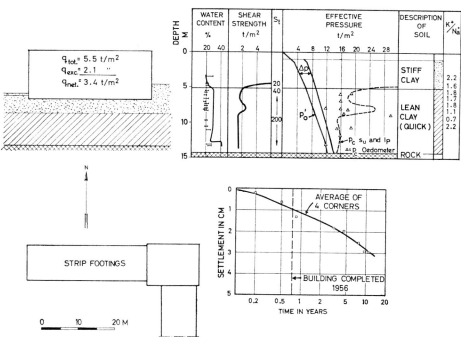

Fig. 32.   Soil data and settlement of Engene 86

We know that in many clays there exist considerable quantities of soluble chemical agents such as organic matter, carbonates, gypsum, aluminium and iron compounds which under certain conditions could precipitate and form chemically stable cements, crystalline or gels, possessing considerable strength.

It should be admitted straight away, however, that it has never been possible to prove the existence of cementation bonds in Norwegian clays, which means that they are either only very weakly cemented or not cemented at all.   Studies of a Swedish clay from the Göta valley led to the conclusion that its strength and compressibility were influenced by some type of cementation of the clay (Bjerrum and Wu, 1960).

In the eastern part of Canada late-glacial and post-glacial clays can be found which have many similarities with Norwegian clays.   Their mineralogy, plasticity and water contents are about the same, and their sensitivity is as high as that observed in Norwegian clays.   The shear strength of the Canadian clays is, however, considerably greater than that of the comparable Norwegian clays.   A detailed study of a quick clay from Labrador carried out by Kenney (1967) clearly showed that the difference in strength of the Norwegian and this particular Canadian quick clay could be explained by the cemented structure of the Labrador clay.   The details of the tests carried out with Labrador clay will be described in a paper by Kenney, but in order to include this geological factor in the present lecture some of his findings will be briefly described.

Two samples of the Labrador clay were placed in consolidometers and loaded to a pressure well below the critical load.   Both samples were then subjected to a slow flow of liquid.   One sample, the neutral sample, was permeated with liquid of the same salt concentration as that of the porewater.   The second sample was permeated with a chemical named EDTA (a disodium salt of ethylene-diamine-tetra-acetic acid).   EDTA dissolves carbonates, gypsum and iron compounds, the type of materials which can act as cementing agents, but for short

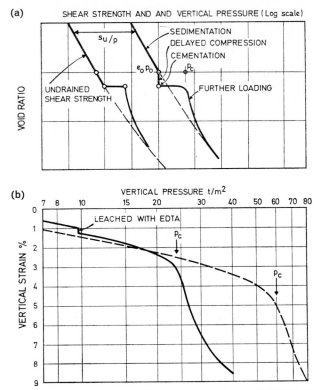

(a)

SHEAR STRENGTH AND AND VERTICAL PRESSURE (Log scale)

VOID RATIO

s_u/p

SEDIMENTATION
DELAYED COMPRESSION
CEMENTATION

$e_o P_o$ P_c

UNDRAINED
SHEAR STRENGTH

FURTHER LOADING

(b)

VERTICAL PRESSURE t/m²

7 8   10   15   20   30   40   50 60 70 80

VERTICAL STRAIN %

LEACHED WITH EDTA

P_c

P_c

Fig. 33. Effect of cementation on compressibility and shear strength: (a) general principle; (b) result of laboratory tests showing the effect of removal of cementing agents on the compressibility of a quick clay from Labrador (Kenney, 1967)

periods of treatment it is incapable of altering the minerals. The treatment lasted for 38 days and the EDTA was then removed by 34 days of saltwater treatment using the same concentration as the original porewater. The two samples were finally loaded in small steps. The results of the tests were plotted in a conventional e–log p diagram on Fig. 33(b). The untreated sample showed a critical pressure of 60 ton/sq. m. While the sample from which the cementing agents had been removed showed a critical pressure of only 24 ton/sq. m. From these tests we can therefore draw the conclusion that, since its deposition, the Labrador clay has developed a very considerable additional resistance against deformation, a major part of which is the result of cementation. Chemical analysis of the water permeating the sample showed that the cementing agent in this clay consisted mainly of iron compounds.

CONCLUSION

A review of the past fifteen years work on the soft Norwegian clays shows that we have progressed from an initial period of uncertainty and incompetence to a stage at which we are gradually reaching a better understanding of the properties of our clay deposits, and thus are developing an improved ability to take into account the factors responsible for the previous discrepancies between theory and practice. This progress is almost exclusively due to three factors.

First, careful measurements of the behaviour of buildings have provided an invaluable collection of data to guide us both in research and in our work as consultants on new foundations. It is against these observations that we have tested our methods, and the ultimate aim of all new developments has been to bridge the gap between prediction and observation.

Second, improvement of the technique of taking, handling and testing soil samples has increased our possibility of discovering the true properties of our clays. In areas of soft clay such as Norway the use of conventional techniques in soil exploration provides too pessimistic an assessment of the soil conditions, and it is therefore a worthwhile investment to use the most up-to-date methods even on everyday consulting jobs. It was only by the development of these new techniques that we were able to obtain so consistent a picture of the reserve resistance of the clays in Drammen that we dared to take this factor into account in the design of foundations.

The third factor that has greatly contributed to a better understanding of the behaviour of soils is the incorporation of engineering geology into our way of thinking. If by engineering geology we mean the study of all geological factors and processes of importance for the engineering properties of soils and rock, then it is this field which in recent years has most contributed to irradicate the discrepancy between theoretical predictions and actual behaviour of soils in nature.

ACKNOWLEDGEMENTS

The study of settlements of buildings in Drammen is the result of twelve years work at the Norwegian Geotechnical Institute. A great number of the Author's colleagues have contributed to this study and their assistance is gratefully acknowledged. Mr O. Eide, chief engineer of the foundation section of the Institute, has borne the responsibility for all consultant assignments and field studies and during these many years of daily co-operation the Author has profited very much from Mr Eide's wide experience with Norwegian clays.

In 1964, Dr G. A. Leonards, Professor of Soil Mechanics at Purdue University, spent the summer at the Institute and the study of the settlement of Engene 86 is the result of his stay in Norway. In addition, he participated in the study of the other buildings and the Author expresses his thanks to Dr Leonards for his contribution.

Between 1964 and 1966 new investigations carried out in the field and in the laboratory contributed substantially to an understanding of the problems. The Author wishes to express his gratitude to Mr I. J. Foss, Mr T. Berre and Mr C. F. Clausen for their enthusiastic co-operation during this phase of the studies. Mr F. Jörstad and Mr J. Moum assisted the Author by reviewing those parts of the manuscript dealing with the geological and geochemical aspects respectively.

The material presented in this Paper could never have been collected and made available without the generous and never-failing interest and co-operation of the civil engineers in Drammen. Their help is greatly appreciated.

REFERENCES

BJERRUM, L., 1951. Fundamental considerations on the shear strength of soil. *Géotechnique*, 2 : 209–218.
BJERRUM, L., 1954. Geotechnical properties of Norwegian marine clays. *Géotechnique*, 4 : 49–69.
BJERRUM, L. and K. Y. Lo, 1963. Effect of aging on the shear-strength properties of a normally consolidated clay. *Géotechnique*, 13 : 147–157.
BJERRUM, L., N. Simons and I. Torblaa, 1958. The effect of time on the shear strength of a soft marine clay. *Proc. Conf. Earth Pressure Problems, Brussels*, 1 : 148–158. See also Norwegian Geotechnical Institute, Publication, 33.
BJERRUM, L. and T. H. Wu, 1960. Fundamental shear-strength properties of the Lilla Edet clay. *Géotechnique*, 10 : 101–109.
BJERRUM, L., 1964. Relasjon mellom målte og beregnede setninger av byggverk på leire og sand. *NGF-foredraget, Oslo*. 92 pp.
BJERRUM, L., 1966. Secondary settlements of structures subjected to large variations in live load. *Proc. Symp. Rheol. and Soil Mech., Grenoble, 1964. International Union of Theoretical and Applied Mechanics*, pp. 460–471.
CASAGRANDE, A., 1932. The structure of clay and its importance in foundation engineering. *J. Boston Soc. Civ. Engrs*, 19 : 168–209.

CASAGRANDE, A., 1936.   The determination of the pre-consolidation load and its practical significance. *1st Int. Conf. Soil Mech., Cambridge, Mass.*, 1:60–64.

CASAGRANDE, A. *and* R. E. Fadum, 1944.   Application of soil mechanics in designing building foundations. *Trans Am. Soc. civ. Engrs*, 109:383–416.

CASAGRANDE, L., 1964.   Effect of preconsolidation on settlements.   *Proc. Am. Soc. civ. Engrs*, 90:SM5:349–362.

CLAUSEN, C.-J. F., 1966.   Bestemmelse av leirers for-konsolideringstrykk.   Det store eksamensarbeidet i Geoteknikk og fundamenteringslaere, høsten 1966.   *Norwegian Geotechnical Institute.*   Internal report, F. 315, 5 vols.

CRAWFORD, C. B., 1964.   Interpretation of the consolidation test.   *Proc. Am. Soc. civ. Engrs*, 90:SM5:87–102.   See also National Research Council, Canada.   Division of Building Research.   Research paper 239.

CRAWFORD, C. B., 1965.   Resistance of soil structure to consolidation.   *Can. Geotech. J.*, 2:2:90–115.   See also National Research Council, Canada.   Division of Building Research.   Research paper 247.

ENGH, O. A.,1962.   Geoteknikkens anvendelse i praksis sett fra en bygningsteknisk konsulents synspunkt. *Norwegian Geotechnical Institute.*   Publication 47, pp. 37–43.

FEYLING-HANSSEN, R. W., 1964.   Foraminifera in late quaternary deposits from the Oslo-fjord area. Thesis, Oslo, Universitetsforlaget, p. 383.   See also *Norges geologiske undersøkelse.*   Publikasjon, 225.

FOSS, I., 1965.   Settlement of Skoger Sparebank, Drammen.   *Norwegian Geotechnical Institute.*   Internal report, F. 272–2, 9pp. +pl.

FOSS, I. *and* O. EIDE, 1965.   Settlement of Konnerudgaten 16 and two neighbour buildings in Drammen. *Norwegian Geotechnical Institute.*   Internal report, F. 272, 18 pp. +pl.

FOSS, I, *and* O. EIDE, 1966.   Settlement of Turnhallen, Drammen; a supplementary study.   *Norwegian Geotechnical Institute.*   Internal report, F. 272–3, 5 pp. +pl.

HAFSTEN, U., 1959.   De senkvartaere strandlinjeforskyvningene i Oslotrakten belyst ved pollenanalytiske undersøkelser.   *Norsk geografisk tidsskrift*, 1957–58, 16:1/8:74–99.

HAMILTON, J. J. *and* C. B. CRAWFORD, 1959.   Improved determination of preconsolidation pressure of sensitive clay.   *Am. Soc. Test. Mat.*   Special technical publication, 254, pp. 254–271.

HENKEL, D. J., 1960.   The strength of saturated remolded clay.   *Proc. Res. Conf. Shear Strength Cohesive Soils*, pp. 533–554.   *American Society of Civil Engineers.*

KEINONEN, L., 1963.   On the sensitivity of water-laid sediments in Finland and factors inducing sensitivity. *Statens tekniska forskningsanstalt*, Helsinki.   Publikasjon, 77, 131 pp.

KENNEY, T. C., 1964.   Sea-level movements and the geologic histories of the postglacial marine soils at Boston, Nicolet, Ottawa and Oslo.   *Géotechnique*, 14:203–230.

KENNEY, T. C., 1966.   Disturbance and damage of quick-clay samples from Manglerud, determined from laboratory measurements other than shear strength.   *Norwegian Geotechnical Institute.*   Internal report, F. 264–5, 7 pp. +pl.

KENNEY, T. C., 1967.   Shearing resistance of natural quick clays.   Thesis submitted to University of London.   *Norwegian Geotechnical Institute, Oslo.*   138 pp.   (In preparation.)

LADD, C. C., 1964.   Stress-strain modulus of clay in undrained shear.   *Proc. Am. Soc. civ. Engrs*, 90:SM5:103–132.

LAMBE, T. W., 1960.   A mechanistic picture of shear strength in clay.   *Proc. Res. Conf. Shear Strength Cohesive Soils*, pp. 555–580.   *American Society of Civil Engineers.*

LANDVA, A., 1961.   Belastnings- og setningsforløp for 8 bygninger i Drammen.   *Norwegian Geotechnical Institute.*   Internal report, F. 31, 6 pp. +pl.

LEONARDS, G. A. *and* B. K. RAMIAH, 1960.   Time effects in the consolidation of clays.   *Am. Soc. Test. Mat.* Special technical publication, 254, pp. 116–130.

LEONARDS, G. A. *and* P. GIRAULT, 1961.   A study of the one-dimensional consolidation test.   *Proc. 5th Int. Conf. Soil Mech.*, 1:213–218

LEONARDS, G. A., 1964.   Compressiblity of clay.   *Proc. Am. Soc. civ. Engrs*, 90:SM5:133–155.

LO, K. Y., 1961.   Secondary compression of clays.   *Proc. Am. Soc. civ. Engrs*, 87:SM4:61–87.

MORETTO, O., 1946.   An investigation of the effect of certain factors on the strength and compressibility of clays.   Ph.D. Thesis, University of Illinois.

MOUM, J. *and* I. Th. ROSENQVIST, 1955.   Kjemisk bergartsforvitring belyst ved en del leirprofiler.   *Norsk geologisk tidsskrift*, 34:2/4:167–174.   See also *Norwegian Geotechnical Institute*, Publication, 8.

MOUM, J. *and* I. Th. ROSENQVIST, 1957.   On the weathering of young marine clay.   *Proc. 4th Int. Conf. Soil Mech.*, 1:77–79.   See also *Norwegian Geotechnical Institute*, Publication, 26.

MOUM, J. *and* I. Th. ROSENQVIST, 1961.   The mechanical properties of montmorillonitic and illitic clays related to the electrolytes of the pore water.   *Proc. 5th Int. Conf. Soil Mech.*, 1:263–267.   See also *Norwegian Geotechnical Institute*, Publication, 45.

OSTERMAN, J., 1960.   Notes on the shearing resistance of soft clays.   *Acta Polytech. Scand.*   Civil engineering and Building Construction Series, Ci 2 (263/1959), 22 pp.

ROSENQVIST, I. Th., 1955.   Investigations in the clay-electrolyte-water system.   *Norwegian Geotechnical Institute*, Publication, 9, 125 pp.

ROSENQVIST, I. Th., 1959.   Physico-chemical properties of soils; soil water systems.   *Proc. Am. Soc. civ. Engs*, 85:SM2:31–53.

SCHMERTMANN, J. H., 1955.   The undisturbed consolidation behavior of clay.   *Trans Am. Soc. civ. Engrs*, 120:1201–1233.

SCHMERTMANN, J. H., 1965.   Discussion Crawford, C. B., 1964.   *Proc. Am. Soc. civ. Engrs*, 91:SM2:131–135.

SIMONS, N., 1957. Settlement studies of two structures in Norway. *Proc. 4th Int. Conf. Soil Mech.*, 1:431–436.

SKEMPTON, A. W., 1948. Vane tests in the alluvial plain of the River Forth near Grangemouth. *Géotechnique*, 1:111–124.

TAYLOR, D. W., 1942. Research on consolidation of clays. *Massachusetts Institute of Technology.* Department of Civil and Sanitary Engineering. Serial, 82, 147 pp.

TAYLOR, D. W., 1955. Review of research on shearing strength of clay 1948–1953. *Massachusetts Institute of Technology.* Soil Mechanics Laboratory. 41+26 pp.

TERZAGHI, K., 1941. Undisturbed clay samples and undisturbed clays. *J. Boston Soc. civ. Engrs*, 28:3: 211–231.

TERZAGHI, K., 1955. Influence of geological factors on the engineering properties of sediments. *Econ. Geol.*, 50 (aniversary volume):557–618. See also Havard soil mechanics series, 50.

Van OLPHEN, H., 1963. An introduction to clay colloid chemistry; for clay technologists, geologists and soil scientists. *Interscience Publishers, New York and London*, 301 pp.

WAHLS, H. E., 1962. Analysis of primary and secondary consolidation. *Proc. Am. Soc. civ. Engrs*, 88:SM 6:207–231.

WATERWAYS EXPERIMENT STATION, 1947. Triaxial shear research and pressure distribution studies on soils. Vicksburg, Mississippi. 332 pp.

THE RISE OF GEOTECHNOLOGY AND ITS INFLUENCE ON ENGINEERING PRACTICE

R. GLOSSOP, B.Sc., M.I.C.E.

INTRODUCTION

Three periods can be distinguished in the development of soil mechanics: an early period, which extended from the end of the 17th century to the beginning of the 20th century; Classical Soil Mechanics, founded on the work of Terzaghi, which dates from the publication of his first book in 1925 and is now an important branch of engineering science; and a new phase of the subject, now developing, which includes rock mechanics and is strongly influenced by geological thinking; by a renewed appreciation of the importance of minor geological structures in engineering problems; and by the use of essentially geological techniques, such as those of optical mineralogy. It might be argued that this whole subject is in fact Engineering Geology, but it is better described as Geotechnology. In any case, Classical Soil Mechanics remains its basic discipline.

The central problem of the early period was earth pressure theory, an important element in the design of fortifications and of canal locks. About 1690 Vauban gave empirical rules for the design of retaining walls (Kerisel, 1956), and inspired work on this subject which continued in France during the 18th century, and culminated in Coulomb's famous essay (Coulomb, 1773).

The next important advance was made by Collin, a true natural philosopher, who studied the stability of clay slopes (Collin, 1846). These were based on field observation and laboratory tests, and incidentally it was he who first gave a name to the subject—'méchanique terrestre'.

It has been said that by this time '... essentially the earth pressure problem had been solved ... and the way lay open for the evolution of a reasonable, practical solution' (Golder, 1953), but nothing of the sort occurred. Indeed, except for Rankine's conjugate stress theory (Rankine, 1857), little was done on the borderland of civil engineering and the earth sciences for eighty years, although mention should be made of Darcy who published an account of his studies on the flow of water through sand (Darcy, 1856); of Boussinesq, who worked on a branch of elasticity theory applicable to foundation problems (Boussinesq, 1885) and of Atterberg, who between 1908 and 1914 published a series of papers on the plasticity of soil. His Plastic and Liquid Limit tests were adapted for engineering purposes by Terzaghi, and are in constant use to this day (Blackall, 1952).

It has been suggested that the great advances made in mechanical and structural engineering during this period made them more attractive as subjects for study than were the apparently intractable problems of retaining walls and foundations.

During this same period a number of 'geotechnical processes' were invented. Coulomb published a pamphlet which probably establishes him as the inventor of the compressed air caisson (Coulomb, 1779) (Fig. 1), but the air-lock as we know it was invented in 1830 by Lord Cochrane (Cochrane, 1830), a brilliant naval commander with a genius for mechanical science, and modern practice shows little advance over the system illustrated in his Patent Specification of 1839. Triger was the first man actually to sink a shaft in compressed air, which he did in 1841 (Triger, 1841). Before undertaking this remarkable work he carried out experiments on the physiological effect of working in compressed air, using himself as a subject; it is a wonder that he survived. Bérigny invented alluvial grouting with clay and hydraulic lime in 1802

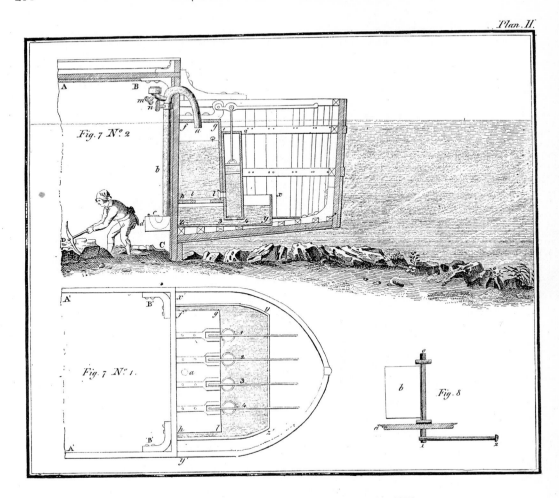

Plan. II.

Fig. 1.   Coulomb's compressed air caisson, 1779

(Bérigny, 1832), and in 1867 Hawkesley introduced cement grouting for the foundations of dams on rock (Glossop, 1961).   Telford in 1811 grasped the principle of the consolidation of clay, and applied the method of pre-loading to reduce settlement under a lock in Scotland (Telford, 1838).   In 1836 Robert Stephenson applied groundwater lowering by means of wells on the Kilsby Tunnel (Boyd-Dawkins, 1898).

The freezing process was suggested by Michoux in 1852 and first used successfully in shaft sinking through water bearing sand at a colliery in South Wales in 1862, but, strange to say, no detailed account of this remarkable achievement has survived (Schmidt, 1895).

By the early years of the 20th century, such had been the advances in structural theory and the increase in the number and magnitude of engineering works, that failures when they occurred were often associated with the soil beneath, or adjacent to, a structure rather than

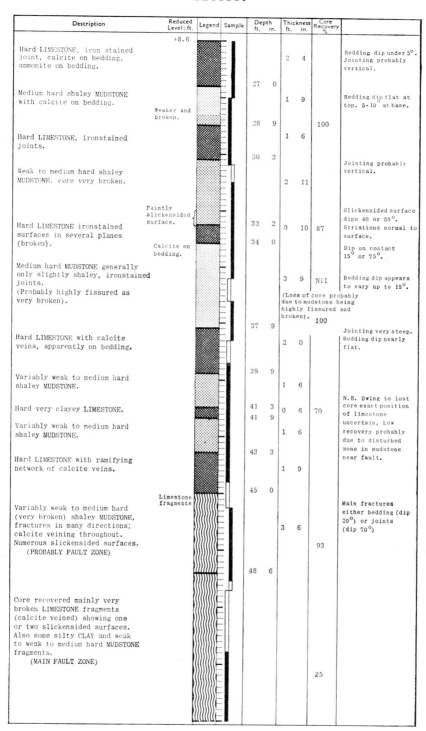

Fig. 2.   Log of borehole from Hinkley Point

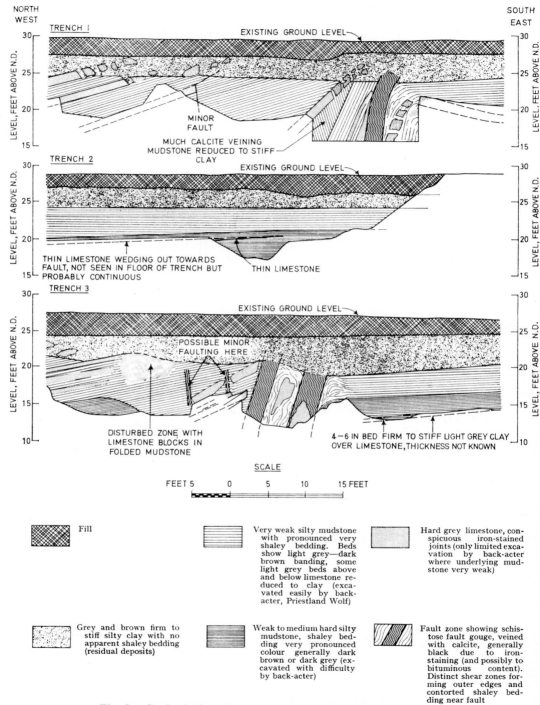

Fig. 3.   Geological section of trenches at Hinkley Point

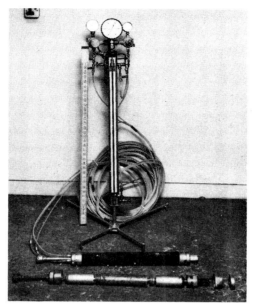

Fig. 4.   Menard pressure meter

with the structure itself.   This led to a revival of interest in the properties of soils and to further research, notably in Sweden and in the Netherlands, for these are countries where many towns and lines of communication are underlain by soft and compressible Post-Glacial deposits.

Undoubtedly the outstanding centre of research at that time was Sweden, for its coast is fringed by highly sensitive Post-Glacial clays, which as a result of isostatic movements may be found at elevations as much as 600 ft above sea level.   These clays are subject to landslides and present many problems to the engineer (Bjerrum & Flodin, 1960).

In 1908 the Swedish State Railway set up a committee to examine this matter, and in 1913 the Geotechnical Commission of the Swedish State Railways was formed; incidentally, this is the first example of the use of the word 'geotechnical.'   The committee was very active, and the names of Fellenius, Hultin and Olssen will always be associated with it.   In 1914 a soil mechanics laboratory was established, and it is claimed that this was the first of its kind in the world.

Within ten years so much had been achieved that it was in Sweden that soil mechanics first became a useful and accepted branch of engineering science.   Methods of undisturbed sampling had been devised, the cone test for the rough measurement of shear strength of clay had been invented, the consolidation of clay was partially understood, and the $\phi = 0$ method for the analysis of circular/cylindrical slope surfaces had been developed and applied (Fellenius, 1927).   As regards foundations, the bearing capacity of friction piles and of groups of friction piles had also been investigated.

In 1920, following the failure of an embankment at Weesp in the Netherlands, which led to a serious railway accident, the Dutch Government formed a committee of enquiry into foundation soils, to which Professor A. S. Buisman was appointed.   Encouraged by the publication of Terzaghi's book in 1925, he set up a private laboratory which, in 1930, was incorporated with the newly formed soil mechanics laboratory at the Technical University of Delft, of which he became Director. Here he developed the Dutch Cell Test (Buisman, 1934), and his attempts to apply the formulae of Prandtl to the measurement of the shear strength of soil by means of a penetration cone test led to the development of the Dutch Deep Sounding apparatus, still a most useful tool in site investigation. His untimely death in 1944, in a prison camp, was a great loss to engineering science, but the laboratory of which he was the first director remains among the more important in Europe.

In Germany Krey, in 1910, became Director of the Preussische Versuchsanstalt für Wasserbau und Schiffbau at Berlin, where he did experimental work on the shear strength of soils, and investigated the stability of slopes and the lateral pressure of soils (Schultze, 1954). This work was stimulated by problems associated with the Kiel Canal. At about the same time slope failures on the Panama Canal led the American Society of Civil Engineers to set up a committee for the study of earthworks.

In Austria Forchheimer developed the use of flow nets in tracing the flow of water through sand, a valuable contribution to the design of earth dams, replacing the empirical approach of Bligh. His results were published in 1917 and certainly influenced the thinking of Terzaghi.

About this time Résal and Frontard in France once more attacked the earth pressure problem, basing their work on Coulomb's ideas, as did Bell in England, whose paper on the lateral pressure exerted by clay and the supporting power of clay foundations was published in 1915. His researches were made while he was working in the Admiralty service, on the construction of the new dockyard at Rosyth. He made box shear tests on a variety of clays under conditions which approximated to the undrained state, and showed their shearing resistance to be in accordance with Coulomb's law, rather than that of Rankine. He checked these results by installing diaphragm pressure cells on the faces of the monoliths which were sunk to form the walls of the dock, and thus obtained readings at various depths. 'These tests . . . opened a new era in soil mechanics; for previous knowledge concerning the shear strength of clays was chaotic. A real understanding of the subject had to await the discovery of the principle of effective stress by Terzaghi; but Frontard "who was working on the problem at this time in France" and Bell showed that the shear properties of clay could be measured and expressed in terms of a reasonable physical law' (Skempton, 1958).

In spite of all this activity the fact remains that during this period the study of soils had very little influence on civil engineering practice, except perhaps in Sweden.

Looking back, it is now clear that by about 1920 the time was ripe for a synthesis of all this knowledge to form a coherent branch of engineering science. This was achieved by Karl von Terzaghi.

Terzaghi was born in 1883, and in 1904 he graduated from the Technische Hochschule at Graz as a mechanical engineer. He was a mathematician with a natural gift for experiment, and his favourite subject was geology. He started work with a firm of civil engineering contractors, where he had first hand experience of difficult foundation problems, including the case of a dam failure by piping. In 1908 he took charge of a geological survey for a hydro-electric scheme in Croatia, and later he published a paper on the hydrology of the Karst region (Terzaghi, 1913). He soon realized that geology would be of far more use to engineers if physical constants of rocks and soils were available for design.

In 1916 he was transferred to the staff of the Imperial School of Engineers at Istanbul, and later he worked at the American Roberts College in that city. There he carried out his early work on the consolidation of clay, and between 1921 and 1924 he published his mathematical theory of consolidation, which led him to the concept of effective stress.

During this same period he made experiments on the nature of the friction term in Coulomb's equation, and performed consolidated-undrained tests on samples of clay. These researches, together with his work on lateral earth pressures and other subjects, formed the basis of his book *Erdbaumeckanik* which was published in 1925—a date which marks the emergence of

Classical Soil Mechanics Theory, of which the cornerstone is the concept of Effective Stress (Terzaghi, 1925).

From 1925 to 1929 he was working at the Massachusetts Institute of Technology, and in his laboratory Arthur Casagrande made observations on volume changes during shear tests on clay, and on the effect of the rate of shear on the resistance of normally consolidated clays. Here, too, Jürgensen developed a form of triaxial compression device which, when adopted by the United States Bureau of Reclamation laboratory at Denver, led to improvements in the design of earth dams. On Terzaghi's return to Vienna in 1930 the triaxial device was further developed by Rendulic, a research assistant, who made both drained and undrained tests with measurement of pore-water pressures within the specimen.

If the year 1925 marks the birth of Classical Soil Mechanics, the year 1936 is scarcely less important, for in that year the Proceedings of the First International Conference on Soil Mechanics and Foundation Engineering were published. This conference was held at Harvard. It brought together many workers in the subject, and made Terzaghi's theories better known. A study of these volumes must have convinced every unprejudiced reader that a new and powerful branch of engineering science had emerged. Indeed, a year or two later it was said that 'Engineering Science is based on three disciplines: theory of structures, hydraulics, and soil mechanics.' At the time this seemed an absurd exaggeration, but few people would dispute it now.

By 1937 the foundations of Classical Soil Mechanics had been well established.

Looking back on this fruitful period it can be seen that the extraordinary impact of Terzaghi's work—for there were many able men working in this field at the time—was due to his particular interests and talents, and to the enthusiasm and strength of character which enabled him to inspire a new and fertile school of thought, founded on the following principles: that every problem in this field is basically geological, and that the first step should always be an exploration of the geological structure and of the hydrology of the site, and he emphasized the fact that minor geological details may have a critical influence on engineering problems (Terzaghi, 1929); and secondly, that the methods of physics should be used to measure the mechanical properties of soils and rocks, so as to provide data for rational designs. These principles are clearly stated in the first paragraphs of *Erdbaumechanik*.

So much of the theoretical background of soil mechanics still rests on Terzaghi's early physical researches that this aspect of his work has overshadowed the fact that an important part of his achievement was to revive engineering geology, and to establish it as a quantitative science.

It will be my endeavour to show here how far these principles have influenced civil engineering practice.

SITE INVESTIGATION

Their immediate effect was to stimulate a geological approach to engineering problems, and this led to a new attitude to site exploration.

William Smith, the founder of modern geology, was himself a civil engineer, and as a rule the early constructors of canals and railways had a good practical knowledge of the subject. After their time the influence of geology on civil engineering declined. Of course, engineers concerned with major projects sometimes consulted a geologist, but the fact is that engineering geology remained non-quantitative, and was not regarded as an important branch of engineering science.

In 1898 the title of the James Forrest Lecture, by Professor Boyd-Dawkins, was 'On the relation of geology to engineering' (Boyd-Dawkins, 1898). He felt strongly that geology and engineering are 'so intimately interwoven that sometimes it is impossible to separate them.

Geology stands to engineering in the same relation as faith to works.' This lecture, with its theological undertones, is interesting to read; but it only deals with hydrology in a non-quantitative way, and with exploration for mineral deposits and in particular for coal. No mention is made of problems associated with the foundations for dams or other structures.

The nature of this revival can be judged by the fact that in England as late as 1946 it seems that not a single firm of civil engineers, whether consultants or contractors, employed a full-time professional geologist; whereas a recent enquiry showed that nearly all the leading consultants employ one or more full-time geologists, and that six of the larger national contractors employ 27 full-time geologists between them. Also the Geological Society of London, founded in 1807 and the oldest body of its kind in the world, has set up an Engineering Group which holds regular meetings of geologists and engineers who have learnt to speak the same language. This Group edits *The Quarterly Journal of Engineering Geology*.

Coming back to site exploration and setting aside feasibility surveys (which although within the province of the engineer may be concerned with questions of finance and economics, and are thus outside the scope of this Paper), then a site investigation to provide data for designs should be basically an exercise in engineering geology, for if at the very start the geological structure of the site is misinterpreted, then any subsequent sampling, testing and calculation may be so much labour in vain.

The first stage is normally a topographical survey on which the surface geology can be mapped, and here modern methods for the interpretation of aerial photographs are valuable, and include such techniques as automatic electronic dodging which will reveal such soil structures as solifluction and cryoturbation (Dowling & Williams, 1964).

The second stage of site investigation is that of exploration in depth. To a younger generation the methods used until about 1945 must seem unbelievably crude. Boreholes were generally put down by well-boring firms with no knowledge of the engineering problem involved, and in soft ground 4 in. diameter boreholes were usual. With holes of so small a diameter, and hence light chisels, it was not possible to penetrate even a moderate sized boulder, and hence boulders were quite often mistaken for bedrock, as was done with disastrous results in the case of the Silent Valley Dam near Belfast (McIldowie, 1936). It was not until 1946 that in England clumsy shot drills were replaced in civil engineering practice by modern diamond drills for this purpose.

In soft ground borings undisturbed samples were never taken, nor were they needed, since there was no means of testing them.

Disturbed samples were generally stored in wooden egg boxes with compartments 2 or 3 in. square, and since they were not protected in any way, specimens of clay and silt soon bore no resemblance to their natural state, particularly if they had been stored behind the stove in the clerk of works' office. The practice of taking undisturbed samples and of preserving disturbed samples in air-tight jars was introduced to the U.K. by the Building Research Station.

Until that time there had been no attempt to classify soils from an engineering standpoint, and consequently there was no accepted nomenclature. Borehole logs were prepared by drill runners, and all kinds of dialect terms were used to which no definite meaning could be assigned. In Britain this state of affairs was at last set right when the first edition of the *Code of Practice for Site Investigation* was published in 1950 (Glossop & Skempton, 1945 (*see* Appendix); Casagrande, 1947).

Modern site investigation can be considered from the points of view of its philosophy, if that is not too grand a term, and of its techniques.

For reasons given later, there is now a renewed interest in undisturbed sampling which has led to the development of large diameter samplers, and of continuous samplers such as the Delft sampler.

As regards the philosophy, the late Professor Collingwood, who was a philosopher, said of archaeological excavation, his second interest:

'Experience soon taught me that one found out nothing at all except in answer to a question; and not a vague question either, but a definite one. That when one dug saying merely "Let us see what there is here," one learnt nothing, except casually, in so far as casual questions arose in one's mind while digging: "Is that black stuff peat or an occupation soil?" ... "Are those loose stones a ruined wall?" That what one learnt depended not merely on what one turned up in one's trenches but also on what questions one was asking; so that a man who was asking questions of one kind learnt one kind of thing from a piece of digging which to another man revealed something different, to a third something illusory, and to a fourth nothing at all' (Collingwood, 1939).

This is equally true of our subject.

To put it in different terms: if you do not know what you should be looking for in a site investigation, you are not likely to find much of value. What you look for should be suggested by the natural environment, and by the nature of the constructional problem to be solved. Thus, a detailed programme of investigation cannot be decided on day one and adhered to, and the engineer who in the long run is responsible for the solution of the constructional problem should not expect to order a site investigation and then dismiss the matter from his mind until a report is placed upon his desk. The number and location of boreholes, trenches and pits, and the number and nature of the tests to be made, whether in situ or in the laboratory (in other words, the questions to be answered), should be decided as work proceeds at meetings between the engineer and those responsible for the investigation. In the case of a large structure, such as a dam, modifications may be necessary during the progress of the main work as yet more knowledge of the site is gained from excavations. In 1948 engineers of the United States Bureau of Reclamation referred to the '"Design-as-you-go" principle ... an essential part of earth dam design,' and in a recent and most important paper to the Institution of Civil Engineers on the Mangla Dam, the authors write: '. . . if an engineer is not diligent in continuing to investigate foundations after they have been opened up and if he is reluctant to review his designs in the light of information obtained after the award of a contract or to admit the need for changes in design, such an attitude can be very dangerous' (Binnie et al, 1967).

An example of modern methods in site investigation is the case of a nuclear power station. The maps and memoirs of the geological survey were first consulted, and indeed contact was maintained with the survey staff as work proceeded. Their records showed the area to be underlain by the Lower Lias series of the Jurassic Period, although the full depth of these beds to the underlying Rhaetic shale was unknown. Vertical and oblique aerial photographs revealed a well marked fault zone on the foreshore.

Guided by this information the positions of the first boreholes, pits and trenches were agreed with the client. In this first stage nine vertical holes were drilled to explore the strata in depth, and two inclined holes to explore the extension of the fault zone. The boreholes were logged in detail by a geologist, and showed the Lower Lias formation to extend to a depth of about 200 ft, and to consist of beds of limestone and mudstone, the limestone rarely being more than two feet thick, and the proportion of mudstone increasing with depth.

Four trenches were excavated to a depth of about 20 ft, at right angles to the inland extension of the fault. These proved the depth of recent alluvium, the depth and degree of weathering of the rock, and the extent of faulting.

It is interesting to compare the kind of information yielded by these two methods.

Figure 2 shows the log of one of the inclined boreholes which records fractured rock with slickensides, but the trenches when mapped gave a clear and detailed picture of the disturbed zone (Fig. 3).

This work showed that the fault had a horizontal displacement of 180 ft, and a vertical movement of 25 ft, and that near the suggested position for the reactors there was a zone of brecciated rock and clay gouge 25 ft wide, weathered to a depth of 50 ft.

An 8 ft by 6 ft trial pit was sunk to a depth of 36 ft, which revealed the comparative degree of jointing in the limestone and the mudstone.

It will be seen that to this point the investigation was neither more nor less than a very detailed mapping of the geological structure; indeed, the reaction of a geologist might be that such detail was unnecessary. The influence of geology on engineering has already been mentioned, but this is the other side of the picture—the way in which the requirements of the design engineer have drawn the attention of the geologist to the importance of recording small details.

As regards hydrology, piezometers were installed in five wells, and a pumping test was made from the trial pit. It was found that the inflow was confined to the vertical joints in the limestone beds. From this test an approximate estimate was made of the amount of water to be expected in the main excavation. Although the groundwater was confined to vertical joints in the limestones, it was thought that stress relief in open excavation might lead to bedding separation, and thus to a lateral distribution of water pressure. For this reason a system of relief wells was proposed.

At this stage important decisions were made. The entire station was re-located so that no major structure was placed within 100 ft of the fault, and the sites of the pump house and tunnel were moved 225 ft westwards to be clear of the fault zone.

In the second stage the mechanical properties of the rocks and soils were measured, both by in situ methods and by laboratory tests. In the overburden and the zone of weathered rock the Menard pressure meter was employed (Fig. 4).

In the harder rock the Centex cell was used. This consists of two semi-cylindrical sleeves which can be expanded hydraulically against the walls of the borehole. The pressure is recorded by gauge at the pump, and the displacement by means of a miniature transducer. As expansion is unidirectional, it is possible to obtain measurements of the modulus of the rock in different directions by rotating the cell. This cell was described by Mayer (1963) in the Third Rankine Lecture.

Laboratory measurements were made on rock cores to determine the elastic constants and the crushing strengths of both the limestone and the mudstone. From these measurements calculations of the safe bearing capacity and probable settlement of the reactors were made.

This short case history illustrates the modern approach to site investigation, including the collaboration between engineer and those undertaking the work, the geological approach, the increased use of pits and trenches made convenient by the introduction of easily portable, hydraulically operated excavating machinery, the increasing use of in situ tests, and the extension of the methods of soil mechanics to weak rocks.

EARTH DAMS

No structure has been more profoundly modified, both in design and construction, by the influence of soil mechanics, than the earth dam. Earth dams have certain distinct advantages over those of masonry and of concrete, but until about thirty years ago they were less in favour than they are now, since design methods were empirical, and the height to which they were built was limited by natural prudence.

About 1940 the United States Bureau of Reclamation first applied the principles of Classical Soil Mechanics to the design of earth dams, and from that time on engineers have gained confidence and have built them to greater and greater heights (Fig. 5). This increased confidence has also led to an increase in the ratio of the number of earth dams built to those of masonry and concrete.

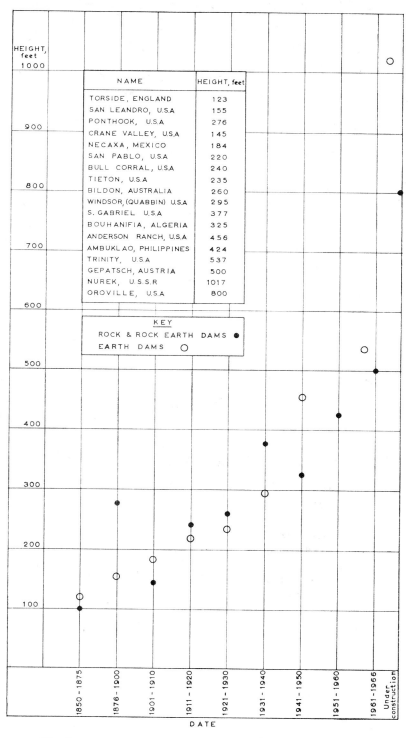

Fig. 5. Maximum heights of earth dams from 1850 to date

As regards the historical background, the first improvement over a simple homogeneous earth embankment was made in 1827, when Telford introduced the idea of a core wall of puddle clay. This was the first step towards the increased complexity of cross section which is a feature of modern dams.

Jacob (1866), when discussing the design of earth dams, said that in the absence of data on soil properties it was 'idle to pursue the investigation by a mathematical mode of reasoning,' and recommended a three to one slope on the upstream side, and a two to one slope on the downstream side, since 'These slopes have been determined by long practice and by success and failure in pre-existing instances.' In fact, these slopes were accepted without question until about 1940.

In 1898 a paper on 'Reservoirs with high earthen dams in Western India' was presented to the Institution of Civil Engineers by Strange (1898), a member of the Indian Engineering Service, and the first graduate of Coopers Hill to read a paper to the Institution. Since during the 19th century the British Government in India probably carried out more irrigation works than were built in the rest of the world put together, this paper, together with a discussion in which all the leading British engineers of the day took part, gives a clear picture of the 'state of the art' at the end of the 19th century.

A typical profile of an earth dam at the time was that recommended by Jacob: a three to one slope on the upstream side and a two to one slope on the downstream side, but there were differences of opinion as to the internal structure of the embankment. In India a puddle clay trench, with battered sides, was carried down into sound rock, and was carried up one foot above ground to key in with the body of the dam. The core of the dam was of impermeable clay, and both slopes were covered with a layer of weathered decomposed rock. It was usual to place a dry-stone drain at the bottom and downstream of the puddle trench, surrounded by gravel so as 'to prevent the flow of the superincumbent earth into the interstices' (Fig. 6).

British practice differed in that, following Telford, a core wall of puddle clay was carried up to the full height of the dam to form an impermeable membrane, which was considered 'economical by limiting the amount of careful construction.'

There was much argument about this point, the British engineers maintaining that since the quantity of puddle was relatively small it could be 'heeled in' under very careful control, and was completely impermeable; so much so that some believed that drains in the downstream side of the embankment were unnecessary, and might be positively dangerous, one speaker saying that 'he did not follow the author's meaning as to leakages having to be dealt with, because the endeavour in England was to stop all leakage.' However, the author very wisely maintained the importance of thorough draining of the embankment on the downstream side of the puddle core.

Although the choice of slopes was empirical, several speakers said that it should be based on the observation of natural slopes in similar material. It was recognized that fatter clays, although less permeable, were 'treacherous' and limited the height of the dam. Majority opinion was that 60 ft was the maximum height to which an earth dam could be built with safety, and this had the support of informed opinion in France, but in the discussion some engineers, including Sir Alexander Binnie, pointed out that dams in England had been built up to 100 ft. The fact is that the English design with a central puddle core enabled a dam to be carried safely to a greater height, so long as the rest of the bank was constructed of sandy clay or other frictional material. The Indian practice of a much larger impermeable fill of fat clay was obviously less stable.

In the higher dams it was suggested that an 'empirical' section might be used, the slope being flattened progressively from top to bottom (Fig. 6). Two speakers justified this section on the grounds that it approximated to the shape of Mount Fujiyama, but a third pointed out that the shape of this mountain was an accident of its mode of accumulation and of erosion,

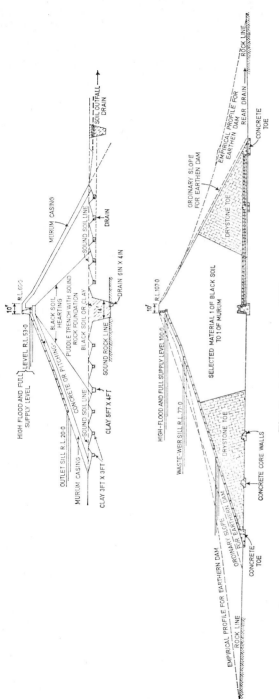

Fig. 6.   (after Strange, 1898)

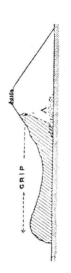

Fig. 7.   Slip at the Crystal Palace (Molesworth, 1898)

Fig. 8.   Puddle core at Chingford Reservoir during construction.   The
puddle clay is covered with hessian sheets to prevent drying, and the
tension crack at the head of the slip can be seen on the right-hand
side of the photograph

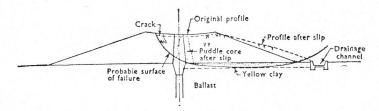

Fig. 9.   Analysis of the failure at Chingford Reservoir (after Cooling
& Golder, 1942)

not necessarily connected with the stability. Berms were sometimes used, and were said to 'weight the surface of the dam,' and thus to prevent its bulging.

In this paper Strange proposed the use of a composite section for dams. This may well have been an important and original invention for it approximates to much modern practice (Fig. 6).

Slips during construction were accepted as inevitable, and one speaker described ten dams, of which five had slipped before completion.

Perhaps the most interesting feature of this paper and of the discussion is the way in which it reveals a lack of understanding of the mechanism of slips, and shows that Collin's work had been completely forgotten. Thus one speaker describes a slope of $1\frac{1}{2}$ to 1 and says, 'the stone pitching really supported the dam,' and another, quoting George Stephenson, said that London Clay 'would sooner run up-hill than stand still,' and illustrated this by his experience when building a railway embankment 30 ft high at the Crystal Palace (Fig. 7).

Hawkesley's invention of foundation grouting in 1874 had not been appreciated.

The traditional design gave good service, and continued in use for many years, one of the later examples of the type to be built in England being the William Girling Reservoir at Chingford, which was started in 1936. Although the finished height of the bank was only to be 36 ft, an extensive slip occurred in 1937 when a portion of the bank reached the height of 26 ft (Figure 8, page 226). This failure was investigated by the newly formed soil mechanics department of the Building Research Station, and it was shown that the failure was due to a stratum of soft, recent clay immediately below the surface of the ground on which the bank had been built. The complex surface of failure was analysed by an original extension of the Fellenius method (Fig. 9), and the necessary instability of the original bank was demonstrated (Cooling & Golder, 1942). Terzaghi, who was consulted, confirmed the work of the Building Research Station, and put forward a revised design for the embankment which entailed a minimum of rebuilding (Fig. 10).

This was the first application of soil mechanics to a major engineering work in the British Isles, and many civil engineers were first made aware of the value of this new science on reading the description of the incident which was later published in the *Journal of the Institution of Civil Engineers*; and here I acknowledge the help and support which this Institution gave to a small band of enthusiasts in those early days.

The first really important advances in earth dam construction did not follow directly from Classical Soil Mechanics, but were due to a scientific study of the compaction of soil made by Proctor (1933) for the Bureau of Waterworks and Supply of the City of Los Angeles. About the same time, and quite independently, similar studies were made by Kelso (1936), in Australia. Proctor's work was most thorough. It established the fundamental relation between dry density, moisture content, and the compactive effort. It defined the optimum moisture content, and developed techniques for measuring the degree of compaction achieved in the field. It is a surprising fact that so little attention had been paid to the control of moisture content in embankments before this time. Indeed, during the early work on the autobahn system of Germany, although much attention was paid to the development of new forms of compaction machinery, there was no proper control of the moisture content of the soil.

The control of compaction thus made possible by Proctor's work has led plant manufacturers to introduce new and more effective machines for the compaction of soil, such as vibrating rollers. Indeed, soil mechanics has had an important influence in plant design.

The first systematic application of Classical Soil Mechanics to the design of earth dams, making use of effective stress, was at the laboratories of the United States Bureau of Reclamation at Denver, and started soon after the Harvard Conference of 1936. The primitive Triaxial cell, invented by Jürgensen and adapted for pore pressure measurement, was much

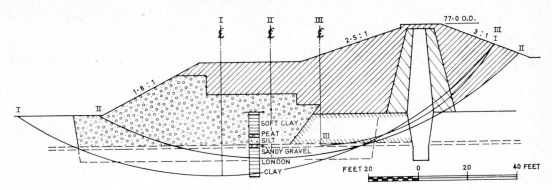

Fig. 10.   Re-design of the Chingford embankment by Terzaghi, 1938

improved by Donald Taylor.   It could supply the data needed for a design method based on the parameters of effective stress and on measurements of pore pressure.   Regular observations on pore pressures within dams under construction were made by the United States Bureau of Reclamation, and these results were published at the Rotterdam Conference in 1948 (Walker, 1948; Hilf, 1948; Walker & Daehn, 1948; Daehn & Hilf, 1951).   These methods were further refined by the introduction of the pore pressure coefficients A and B (Skempton, 1954), and by the application of these coefficients to the calculation of slope stability by Professor Bishop (1952), who also put forward a method for including the forces between slices in stability analyses.   Work at the Road Research Laboratory and at Imperial College led to methods of distinguishing between air and water pressure in compacted fills.

These design concepts led to corresponding changes in construction procedure.   For example, by keeping a constant check upon pore pressures within a dam during construction, the placing of fill could be temporarily stopped if dangerously high pressures were recorded by the piezometers, and time could be allowed for excess pressures to dissipate before the resumption of work.   Also the design itself might be modified by the introduction of filter drains within the dam, which by shortening the drainage paths allowed the excess pressures to dissipate more rapidly (Middlebrook, 1948).   It is undoubtedly procedures of this sort which gave confidence to engineers and led to the great increase in the height to which earth dams are now built.

The introduction of flow net studies by Casagrande, based on the work of Forchheimer, also removed uncertainties in the design of embankments, and led to the use of a variety of patterns of gravel filter drains within the embankment to accelerate consolidation or to prevent erosion and piping.   A formula for the granulometry of such filter drains was first proposed by Terzaghi in about 1922.

An example of a dam built quite recently on a difficult site where full use was made of such modern devices, is the Derwent Dam on the borders of Northumberland and County Durham, which was completed in 1967 (Ruffle, 1965).

The dam, 119 ft high, occupies a glacial valley in which rock lies at a maximum depth of 180 ft below ground level.   A preliminary investigation showed this buried channel to contain a variety of glacial deposits varying from boulder size to silt and clay, and as it was proposed to construct a conventional cut-off to bedrock, this presented a formidable problem.   A number of expedients were suggested, including ground freezing, but it was finally decided to make use of groundwater lowering by means of deep wells, aided by some alluvial grouting above bedrock.   To obtain data for the design of this installation a number of trial wells were put down under the immediate supervision of a geologist, and piezometers were placed in the principal aquifers. This work revealed a most interesting geological section (Fig. 11). Bedrock across the entire width of the valley was overlain by a blanket of boulder clay which, although it contained small lenses of sand, was impermeable and formed a complete barrier between the artesian groundwater in the rock beneath it and the artesian groundwater in the several permeable glacial deposits overlying it. Above this ground-moraine, Lake deposits were identified with a total thickness of about 60 ft. These were named the Lower Lake Deposits, and consist of four sub-divisions:

(i) the lower silty sandy phase;

(ii) the lower clay phase;

(iii) the middle silt phase;

(iv) the upper silty sand phase.

These must have been deposited after the retreat of the ice, and in a temporary lake, perhaps caused because the valley had been dammed by a terminal moraine. There followed a short period when the valley was occupied by a river. Part of the Lower Lake Deposits were eroded, and fluvio-glacial sandy gravel was deposited over half the width.

A middle Lake Deposit was then laid down, perhaps because an advance of ice in a tributary valley downstream of the site had once more dammed the main valley.

The ice then advanced for a second time down the main valley, depositing the Middle Boulder Clay, which is overlain in turn by the Upper Lake Deposits; and finally a third advance of the ice was responsible for the Upper Boulder Clay, above which recent alluvium occurs.

Neglecting its engineering significance for a moment, this is a most beautiful section, and holds the key to the glacial history of the region; but unfortunately, in spite of the closest examination, no trace of fossils or of organic matter have been found, so that no absolute system of chronology based on C_{14} dating has been possible. Evidently, at the time, the whole region was an Arctic wilderness, devoid of life.

From the engineering point of view it was apparent that any form of excavation in the Lower Lake Deposits would be difficult indeed, and it also seemed likely that the Upper Lake Deposits and the Upper Boulder Clay would be adequate as a seal for a cut-off.

The Engineer then ordered a further investigation, which proved that these clay beds extended for a considerable distance upstream and downstream, and this led him to re-design the dam, with an impermeable core wall of clay extending down to ground level, a horizontal clay blanket extending from this core upstream to the toe of the dam, which in turn led to a relatively shallow cut-off sealed into the Upper Boulder Clay (Fig. 12).

This elegant solution proved entirely satisfactory and avoided the difficult and dangerous operation of sinking a cut-off trench to a great depth through difficult ground. It is an admirable example of the principle proposed by the United States Bureau of Reclamation in 1948, and by Binnie et al in their paper on the Mangla Dam in 1967, to the effect that, if necessary, decision should be reviewed in the light of information obtained after the work has begun.

There are many other interesting features in the design of this dam, for example:

(i) Since the laminated clay would evidently consolidate under the weight of the structure, a large number of vertical sand drains were put down into it so as to increase its rate of consolidation during the construction of the embankment.

(ii) Horizontal drainage blankets were placed at regular intervals in the embankment to prevent a build-up of pore pressures; and finally, relief wells were installed downstream of the dam to prevent any danger of piping and the build-up of high pressures in the lower aquifers.

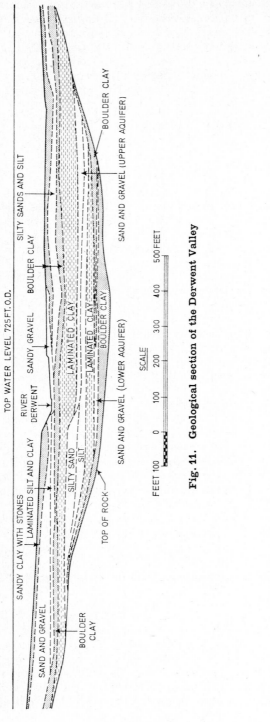

Fig. 11. Geological section of the Derwent Valley

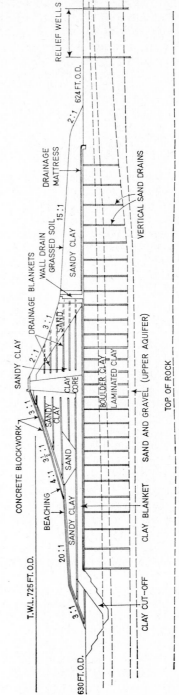

Fig. 12. Section of the Derwent Dam (after Ruffle, 1965)

(iii) Piezometers were placed both in the laminated clay and in the embankment fill to register pore-water pressures, and indeed at one stage construction was halted until excess pressures had dissipated (Figure 13, page 232).

NATURAL SLOPES AND CUTTINGS

Although the $\phi = 0$ method of analysis gave reasonably satisfactory results in the case of short term failures of cuttings and slopes in soft, normally consolidated clay, it failed when applied to the long term case, and in particular to the long term case in fissured clay. The methods mentioned which were developed at Denver for the design of earth dams in terms of effective stress marked an important advance but still did not explain the long term behaviour of stiff fissured clays in natural slopes and cuttings.

This indeed was an old problem, for the early engineers knew that the strength of stiff fissured clays decreased with time; that slips occurred in cuttings long after excavation; and that large retaining walls failed many years after construction.

The first scientific attack on this problem was recorded in a remarkable paper by Terzaghi (1936), read to the Harvard Conference. In it he classified clays as 'soft intact' clays, 'stiff intact' clays, and 'stiff fissured' clays. He also defined 'normally compacted' and 'over-compacted' clays, and introduced the Liquidity Index. He compared values of shear strength calculated from actual landslips with those obtained from compression tests in the laboratory, and showed that in the stiff fissured clays they differed widely—an effect which he attributed to softening along those fissures which had been opened by stress release. His analyses were not in terms of effective stress, and indeed, as late as the Rotterdam Conference in 1948, few slopes had been analysed in this manner, although its use was becoming more general by the time of the Stockholm Conference in 1954.

At last an adequate solution was found in field work on landslides, principally by Skempton, and summarized in his Rankine Lecture in 1964. Ten years earlier the analysis of a landslide at Jackfield (Henkel & Skempton, 1954) in terms of effective stress suggested that c' was zero, and that with the water table at the surface the stable angle of slope was $\frac{1}{2}\phi$. This was confirmed by the investigation of a region underlain by London Clay, where it was found that ϕ' was 20°, and that slopes flatter than 10° were stable, and no slopes steeper than 12° had survived in nature (Skempton, 1957). This was regarded as the terminal state of progressive failure, the earlier stages being exemplified by the failures of cuttings several decades after excavation. A critical step towards a full understanding of the problem followed from observations on a large landslide at Waltons Wood, in Staffordshire, where laboratory shear tests on samples of gouge from old slip surfaces, recovered from pits and boreholes, showed that c' was very nearly equal to zero, and that the value of ϕ' was much lower than anticipated. More-over, shear box tests in the intact clay from this site, taken to large strains, showed that the shearing resistance reached a peak and thereafter diminished to a residual value, which under any effective pressure was the same, whether the clay was normally consolidated or over-consolidated. In fact, the value of c'_r was nearly zero, and the angle ϕ'_r small, and dependent on the proportion of the clay fraction and on the mineralogy of the specimen, and not on its consolidation history. A re-analysis of several other case records then showed a systematic tendency for the strength of stiff fissured clays in cuttings to diminish from the peak to the residual strength; and that in natural clay slopes the strength had reached the residual value (Skempton, 1964).

This concept of residual strength is a unifying principle which has brought order to a branch of soil mechanics previously in a state of confusion. As a particular example it has explained the fact that old landslide debris is most sensitive to disturbance, so that excavation within it, or the placing of fill upon it, often restarts movement, for such debris almost always includes secondary slip surfaces. This is of practical value since new road lines are often sited

Fig. 13.   Derwent Dam.   Part of the piezometer installation

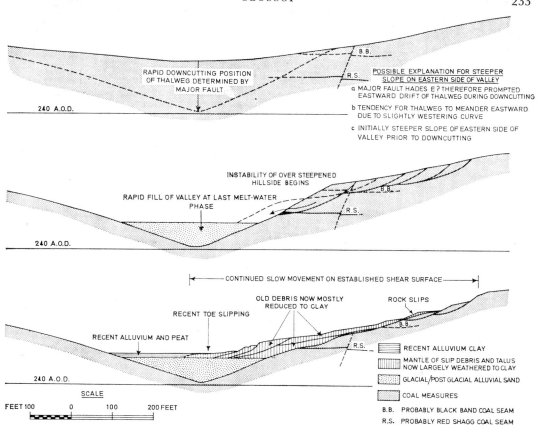

Fig. 14. Landslide at Waltons Wood (after Early)

along the sides of valleys where it is easy to achieve acceptable gradients, and where land may sometimes be purchased more cheaply than elsewhere, but whereas in the pre-motor age roads were narrow and required little cut and fill, modern roads—and in particular motorways, being very much wider—require deep cuts and heavy fills.   Hence, if they cross old landslides, they may well upset the natural stability of the slope.

Two cases of the instability of landslide debris are now described, the first of which illustrates the concept of residual strength and is, indeed, the site on which its significance was first fully established.   They both demonstrate the value of a preliminary geological reconnaissance 'to suggest what to look for before planning a complete investigation' the importance of attention to detail in site investigation, since slip surfaces are easily overlooked in boreholes; and lastly they are excellent examples of the quantitative approach to geological problems.

The first example is from Waltons Wood (Fig. 14) in Staffordshire.   Here the line of a road was planned on a substantial side-hill embankment along one side of a valley.   After filling had started, cracks appeared in the fill, and sheet piles at the toe of the embankment were displaced.   Records soon showed that two separate phenomena were involved: the cracks in the fill were due, and the movement of the piles partly due, to circular slips caused by shear failure in the weak eluvial soil beneath the embankment; but there was also a general downhill movement of the entire valley side over a length of about 900 ft, due to the reactivation of an old landslide.   As soon as this was established the Engineer ordered further investigation, with a view to planning remedial measures.

A preliminary geological survey and a study of the literature (Yates & Mosely, 1958) showed that the valley, which was V-shaped with side slopes of about 12°, had been cut by melt water in Late Glacial times, and that the bedrock, which was mudstone and shale with subordinate sandstone and coal of Upper Coal Measure age, weathered rapidly when freshly exposed; the mudstone being converted to clay, this alteration extended to a considerable depth where movement, due to slipping, had opened up fissures.   In this preliminary survey the old landslide area, with its main scarp and the slipped mass, traversed by the scarps of many subsidiary slips, was mapped in detail.   From the survey which was supplemented by boreholes an interesting picture of the slip and its genesis emerged.   The boreholes revealed that the narrow alluvial plain was underlain by a deep buried channel filled with sand.   On the east side of the valley the toe of the slip rests directly on this sand, although elsewhere the plain has a thin cover of recent clay and peat.   Evidently the valley had been rapidly deepened, and its sides were oversteepened to such a degree that progressive softening of the mudstone, aided by the seepage of groundwater through it, led to the original landslip.   Subsidiary slips continued over a long period as fragmented mudstone in the slipped mass was further softened by exposure.   A detailed investigation of the slipped mass was then made and the geometry of the principal slip surfaces was established by means of trial pits and by continuous undisturbed samples taken from boreholes.   Piezometers were also installed in some of the boreholes to trace the average piezometric line and to search for perched bodies of water.

The final stage of investigation was a programme of laboratory testing to measure shear strength parameters for use in stability calculations, and it was here that an important observation was made by Early, who had previously suspected that old shear plans were a controlling factor in this type of instability.   He noticed that samples which included the 'gouge' of a slip surface, when tested by hand, sheared much more easily along this surface than in the adjacent material, and he decided to investigate this phenomenon in the laboratory. The first specimens were tested in a Casagrande shear-box.   They were hand trimmed so that the slip plane in the sample coincided with the plane of shear of the apparatus, consolidated under the calculated natural overburden pressure, and sheared at a low rate of strain.   The results were most surprising, for the angle of effective shearing resistance on this plane was found to be exceedingly low, of the order of $10\frac{1}{2}°$ to 14°, that of the associated clay being about 25°.   A microscope slide of the gouge showed orientation of the platy minerals parallel to the direction of movement, which suggested an explanation of the phenomenon.

Research was then started at Imperial College, which has led to the important discoveries already referred to, and indeed research on the subject is still active there and elsewhere.

From these shear strength parameters, together with a knowledge of groundwater conditions and of the geometry of the slip surfaces, stability calculations were made and remedial measures suggested, of which the most important were the placing of a massive berm of colliery waste at the toe of the embankment, and thorough drainage of the valley side above the embankment by counterfort drains.   Finally the slope was graded off and re-afforested.

These measures have proved successful, for no further significant movement has been observed during the four years since the completion of the work.

This case history shows the influence of soil mechanics on engineering thought, for until recently it is more than likely that piecemeal measures would have been taken, and the road would have remained in a troublesome state for years.   In this instance the Engineer, being confident that the problem could be solved, tackled it boldly and with complete success.

In the old text books diagrams were often given showing a case where steeply inclined beds parallel to a hillside slipped on their own bedding planes into excavations.   In fact, these cases are quite rare.   A complex example of such a failure is now described which again illustrates

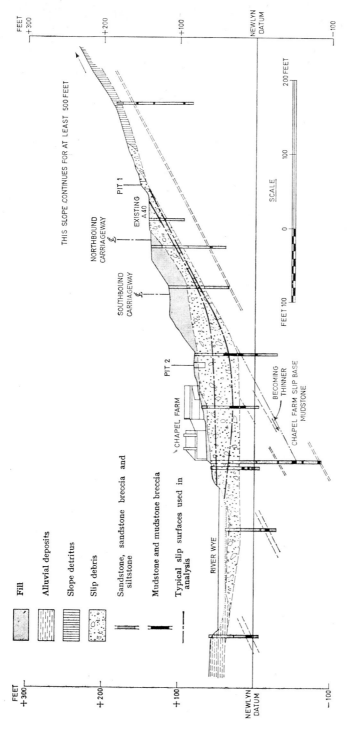

THIS SLOPE CONTINUES FOR AT LEAST 500 FEET

NORTHBOUND CARRIAGEWAY

SOUTHBOUND CARRIAGEWAY

EXISTING A40

PIT 1

PIT 2

CHAPEL FARM

RIVER WYE

BECOMING THINNER

CHAPEL FARM SLIP BASE MUDSTONE

NEWLYN DATUM

FEET +300 / +200 / +100 / NEWLYN DATUM / −100

SCALE

FEET 100 / 0 / 100 / 200 FEET

Fill

Alluvial deposits

Slope detritus

Slip debris

Sandstone, sandstone breccia and siltstone

Mudstone and mudstone breccia

Typical slip surfaces used in analysis

Fig. 15. Landslide near Monmouth (after Early)

the need for the most detailed investigation of hillsides where old slip planes may exist, which will certainly have a low residual shear strength.   This second site lies on the west bank of the River Wye, two miles north of Monmouth, where for a distance of one mile the river flows from north to south at the base of a wooded hillside which rises with a slope of 30° to a height of 500 ft above it.   The hillside is underlain by sandstones and subordinate mudstones of the Brownstone group of the Lower Devonian, and as the area lies on the western edge of the Forest of Dean syncline, the local dip is 30° to the east, and thus the stratification is parallel to the surface of the hillside.   At three points along the river there are bluffs of clay and sandstone blocks which are the debris of old landslides (Fig. 15).

Although these landslides differ in size, and probably in age, the mechanism of failure was in each case the same, and may be illustrated by the largest and most ancient which is found at the southern boundary of the area.   It would seem that it occurred in late Glacial times, when the Wye was cutting a buried channel against the western side of its valley, and the mudstone stratum on which the slide took place was exposed at the foot of the slope.   As the residual ϕ' for the mudstone lies between 12° and 24°, and the dip is about 30°, the mudstone eventually failed in shear, and no doubt this process was repeated more than once, the rocks overlying the plane of weakness being released section by section up the hillside.   Since borings put down at the lower end of the slide showed its debris to occupy the buried channel, this landslide is ancient.

As the debris weathered, fragments of mudstone were reduced to clay and further movement took place within it along at least two surfaces of failure, as a result of which the hillside at this point is only just stable.

The knowledge thus gained was essential to the design of this section of the road.

It should be noted that such dangerous slip surfaces will scarcely be recognized in boreholes unless the boreholes are intended to search for them, a preliminary study of the surface geology having already posed the question—do they exist?

I hope that in due course detailed case histories of these two investigations will be published by my colleagues.

It has been said that certain types of unstable slopes, such as old landslide areas, can always be recognized in a preliminary geological survey, and that roads should not be routed over them.   The first part of this statement is certainly true, but I am not wholly in agreement with the second.   There may be compelling reasons, such as convenience and cost, which determine that a road should be located along a certain valley side.   If this is so then it is the function of the engineer to devise the means for building it there with safety.

Following on these recent advances in our knowledge, we can now stabilize such slopes, so their existence is no longer decisive but merely one of the several factors which determine the choice of a route.

The concept of residual strength has given a new look to this branch of soil mechanics, and it is now generally used in the analysis of slopes in fissured clay.   For example, it was successfully applied on the South Saskatchewan Dam, and also at Weirton, Pennsylvania, where the reactivation of an old landslide threatened the site of a steel works (d'Appolonia and d'Appolonia, 1967), and, of course, at the Mangla Dam in Pakistan.

SHALLOW FOUNDATIONS

It is surprising that throughout the 19th century there was no systematic approach to foundation problems.   Indeed, both as regards foundations and retaining walls, there seems to have been a positive reluctance to accept a scientific approach to their design.   If Brunel put down 175 borings on the site of the centre pier of the Saltash Bridge, there is no record of any at all on the site of Tower Bridge, London, and even if there were, it is significant that they are not mentioned in the literature.

Of course, engineers of talent carried out remarkable foundation works, as, for example, Brunel at Saltash, but the emphasis was on ingenious devices for particular cases, rather than on the establishment of a consistent body of knowledge applicable in every case.

This is confirmed by a study of the early text books, for only in Rankine's *A manual of civil engineering* does one find mention of a theory of the bearing capacity of earth based on his theory of congugate stress.   This attitude of mind is well illustrated in a paper read to the Institution of Civil Engineers by Cruttwell in 1893 on 'The foundations of the river piers of the Tower Bridge' (Cruttwell, 1893).   On the first page he stated that the dimensions of the pier footings had been calculated on the assumption that a load of 4 tons/sq. ft was permissible, but he did not say how this figure was decided upon ; indeed there is no mention of any subsurface exploration in the paper itself.   In the discussion several speakers maintained that a higher load would have been perfectly safe, and would have reduced the obstruction to the waterway. This led the consulting engineer, Mr John Wolfe Barry, to intervene and to say, 'Some question has been raised about the pressure on the London Clay.   He had considerable experience as to what that formation would bear.   One of his earliest works was connected with the Charing Cross Bridge, where the total pressure on the London Clay was about 7 tons/sq. ft.   At Cannon Street Bridge it was considerably reduced, being $4\frac{1}{2}$ to 5 tons/sq. ft, but in both these bridges subsidence had occurred. . . .'   'He was anxious, in the present case, not to have any considerable subsidence, looking to the lofty structure which had to be erected upon the piers ; and he thought it well to err on the safe side and reduce the unit of load rather below what it had been in previous bridges.   He believed that calculations showed the unit of load to be something under 4 tons/sq. ft.'

Calculations based on data from recent boreholes near the bridge show that Sir John Wolfe Barry's judgement was sound, and that it would have been unwise to exceed the chosen value of 4 tons/sq. ft.   These boreholes, however, also show that there were factors of which he presumably had no knowledge, which might—but fortunately did not—affect the situation. For example, the upper surface of the Woolwich and Reading beds is probably only about 10 ft below the under side of the foundations, and had they been penetrated there might have been serious difficulty with fine sand.

The fact is that until about thirty years ago the estimation of bearing capacity was empirical and based upon past experience with what was believed to be a similar soil, and sometimes, but not always, with reference to the soil profile.   With an engineer of experience and judgement dealing with a homogeneous soil well known to him and with uniform loading, this gave a safe, if not necessarily an economical, design ; but as the phenomenon of consolidation was not understood, heavy buildings with load bearing walls and brick or masonry columns, and with uneven loading, were often damaged by long term settlements, as can be seen on the north face of Westminster Cathedral where the massive tower has settled more than the rest of the structure.

Following the work of Bell, the systematic study of the bearing capacity of soils starts with Carruthers (1924), who assumed the soil to be homogeneous and elastic, and applied the theory of elasticity to calculate the distribution of maximum shearing stress and of normal stress on a horizontal plane beneath a footing.   He suggested the pressure exerted by the footing should be such that the shear stress beneath it should nowhere exceed the shear strength of the soil, since should this occur at any point a plastic zone would develop.   This criterion is still useful although it does not give a numerical value for a factor of safety against ultimate failure.

The point at which overstress leads to shearing failure in the soil, with the probability of catastrophic settlement, at the 'ultimate bearing capacity,' was investigated by means of model tests during the 1930's for various shapes of footing and for various soils, by Fellenius, Krey and others, who developed methods of solving particular cases by trial and error on assumed shapes for the surface of failure (Golder, 1942), and by Jürgensen and Hencky, using the theory of plasticity developed for metals by Prandtl (Jürgensen, 1934). During this same period the method of estimating long term settlements on clay by means of Terzaghi's consolidation theory, was developed and tested (Cooling & Skempton, 1941).

Thus, by about 1940, there was a rational explanation of the causes of settlement, and approximate methods of calculating them existed. Types of settlement had been classified as the immediate elastic settlement, excessive settlement due to consolidation and deformation; and catastrophic settlement due to shear failure of the soil. The allowable settlement had been defined as the smaller of two values: (i) the pressure causing a settlement which did not exceed a specified limit; and (ii) the pressure which gave a chosen factor of safety against failure. Also a better understanding of stress distribution in the soil had shown the danger of small scale loading tests on complex soil profiles. This was illustrated in 1942 when the Soil Mechanics Laboratory at the Building Research Station—which was already working on these problems—investigated a foundation failure of exceptional interest at Kippen, on the Firth of Forth, which illustrated the danger of an empirical approach in the case of a complex soil profile (Skempton, 1942) (Fig. 16).

This failure was of a stanchion of a single-storeyed building with a heavy concrete roof. The stanchion was designed to carry a load of 100 tons and was placed upon a mass concrete footing 8 ft by 9 ft in plan, founded at a depth of $5\frac{1}{2}$ ft below ground surface on a fairly firm clay. Unfortunately this clay was the desiccated crust of a bed of soft blue Post Glacial estuarine clay 20 ft thick. This particular column had been the first to take its full load, and within a week it had settled by 10 in. because, as was shown later, the clay beneath it had failed in shear. So many data were available that the incident could scarcely have been more informative had it been planned as a full scale plate bearing test to failure. It showed the ultimate bearing capacity of the soil to have been 2500 lb/sq. ft.

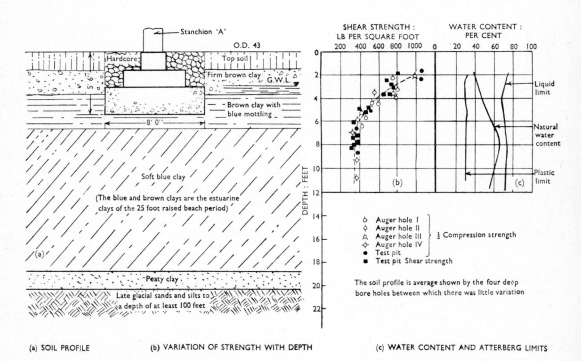

(a) SOIL PROFILE   (b) VARIATION OF STRENGTH WITH DEPTH   (c) WATER CONTENT AND ATTERBERG LIMITS

Fig. 16.   Failure of a foundation at Kippen (after Skempton, 1942)

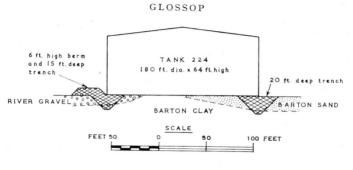

Fig. 17

This gave a wonderful opportunity to test current theories, and after laboratory shear strength measurements had been made on undisturbed samples from the site, the value of the ultimate bearing capacity was calculated by means of various formulae, and the results when compared with the actual value brought conviction to many unbelievers.

Since the properties of soil are so variable, and since soil profiles are often so complex, it cannot be said that, even in the present state of our knowledge, settlements can be predicted accurately; so that in structures likely to be sensitive to settlement it is wise to design them so that they are capable of adjusting themselves to vertical movements of at least 50% more than estimated value. Even greater caution may be needed when dealing with differential settlement.

Nevertheless, foundation theory has influenced engineering practice in two ways. In the first place a general understanding of the mechanics of settlement has given confidence that if it is correctly applied, even where the magnitude of loads and the loaded areas have been extrapolated beyond previous experience, nothing totally unexpected will occur such as did occur at Kippen.

Second, these principles are used to design new forms of foundation for special cases. A simple example is that of a method now much used for large oil storage tanks. These tanks must often be built on weak strata (Penman & Watson, 1967). Since the cost of piled foundations would be high, an alternative has been adopted whereby a test load of water, pumped into the tank, is used to consolidate and thus to increase the shear strength of the clay beneath it. In principle this is neither more nor less than Telford's invention of 1811, but with certain refinements based on our knowledge of stability problems.

An example is the case of a tank 180 ft in diameter and 64 ft high, recently built at the Fawley Oil Refinery (Fig. 17). The soil profile consisted of Barton Clay overlain in places by Barton Sand, and elsewhere by River Gravel. Since the upper surface of the clay had a shear strength of only 750 lb/sq. ft, it would have been incapable of sustaining a load of 2 tons/sq. ft over a circular foundation 180 ft in diameter without edge failure. Accordingly a gravel filled perimeter trench, with the addition of a balancing berm where necessary, was constructed to raise the minimum factor of safety under full water test load to about 1·25. The effect of the trench was to force any potential slip surface into the stronger clay, which occurred in depth. A well-point dewatering system was used during the excavation of the trench, and the gravel was placed and compacted in the dry.

After the tank had been constructed the test load was added over a period of rather more than two months, and settlements and pore pressures were recorded regularly. The full test load was maintained for about three weeks until the pore pressures were seen to be dissipating rapidly and the rate of settlement to be decreasing. The average edge settlement under full test load was eight inches.

Figs 18 and 19.   Prestressed buoyant foundation for sugar store in British Guiana

Fig. 20.   Working site rue Auber

This case may appear elementary, and so it is, but it is essentially based on the principles of Classical Soil Mechanics, and could not have been devised without them.

Another device, suitable for use on very soft soils of great depth, such as may be found in deltas, is the buoyant foundation. In principle it is simple. Instead of being supported by the shear strength of the soil, the structure is supported by buoyancy, although it will, of course, exert a small residual pressure. The depth of a buoyant foundation must be such that the building load is balanced against the weight of excavated materials.

This has been adopted in the town of Drammen, in Norway, which is underlain by very soft Post Glacial Clay, and has enabled the maximum of height of building to be raised from two storeys to five or even six storeys. The foundation is excavated in short lengths with battered sides, and the bottom of the excavation is temporarily loaded with building materials to prevent bottom heave until the superstructure has reached a safe height. Figs 18 and 19 illustrate a buoyant foundation for a building in British Guiana intended for the storage of 20 000 tons of raw sugar. The foundation consisted of six 'egg box' caissons which were built up from precast panels and post-tensioned by the Freyssinet system.

A far more sophisticated example of foundation design based on a knowledge of the pre-consolidation loading and of the geological history of the site was described by Bjerrum (1967) in his Rankine Lecture.

PILED FOUNDATIONS

As regards piled foundations, Classical Soil Mechanics has done little to explain the behaviour of a driven pile, or to correlate the result of a loading test on a single pile to the behaviour of a group of piles, but at least it is now generally appreciated that the problem of the bearing capacity and the settlement of a group of piles exists. Also the effect of the consolidation of a compressible stratum beneath that in which a group of piles have taken their set is fully understood, and this state of affairs is not uncommon, as, for example, in the Lower Thames Estuary, where a soft deposit of solifluction chalk may underlie a compact alluvial gravel.

In the case of bored piles, soil mechanics has had a marked effect on practice, and this is in a large part due to the work of Whitaker and others at the Building Research Station. In the past, bored piles were suspect, and as a rule they were used under exceptional circumstances only, as, for example, in basements or beneath bridges where there was little head-room. Recently their use has greatly increased for, as in the case of shallow foundations, engineers have confidence that although the bearing capacity of such a pile cannot be calculated with precision, yet the physical principles on which it depends are understood, and it is known that given good workmanship the unexpected will not occur if the soil profile has been investigated in depth.

In the case of a homogeneous stratum such as the London Clay calculations of bearing capacity based on soil tests are most valuable for the preliminary assessment of a foundation problem, although it is always wise to supplement them with a loading test on a single pile. In complex soil profiles the N values obtained from penetration tests may be used to supplement the information from boreholes.

In England the effect of all this has been dramatic, and now in London nearly all high buildings are founded on large diameter bored piles. As late as 1950 there was a popular idea—an idée reçue—that 'sky scrapers' could not be built in London since the city was underlain by clay. Now the use of large diameter bored piles for high buildings is so usual that one can almost speak of a revolution in foundation engineering, and this has led to the development of powerful rotary drills of large diameter (*see Symposium on large bored piles.* London: Institution of Civil Engineers, 1966).

ROADS

Structures ancillary to road construction, such as bridges and embankments, have been influenced by soil mechanics in ways already described, but road engineering has one problem peculiar to itself—the determination of pavement thickness.   This has become of increasing importance in recent years, but Classical Soil Mechanics has contributed relatively little to it. As late as 1930 most good roads were of waterbound macadam.   As first built, stone pitching was placed by hand, graded road metal was added and well rolled in, while quarry fines and water were brushed over the surface.   The road was then 'given to traffic' for some weeks, and as pot-holes developed, they were filled in with broken stone.   Thus the road base adjusted itself to the strength of the underlying soil : the weaker the soil the thicker the base.   Finally, the surface was graded to the required profile.   When repairs were needed the road surface was scarified and more stone added ; thus equilibrium was eventually reached, and in many cases an unsuspected thickness of base was formed.   This comfortable state of affairs came to an abrupt end with the introduction of concrete roads.

After an early period of experiment, concrete roads were first built on a large scale in the 1920's.   At first failures were not uncommon, and were often attributed to the quality of the concrete, for the relationship between the thickness of base, the nature and strength, of the underlying soil, and the area of contact of the tyres and their intensity of loading, had not been generally appreciated.

In England the moment of truth came with the start of airfield construction during the last war, for between 1939 and 1945 four hundred and forty-four airfields were built in the United Kingdom, and during 1942 they were completed at an average rate of one every three days (Hudson, 1948).   At the start of this gigantic operation no accepted method existed for pavement thickness design, and hence it was left to the superintendent engineers to decide on the need for any increase over a specified slab thickness of six inches.   In the circumstances no other procedure was possible, but since in case of a bomber the area of contact of the tyres and their intensity of loading was far greater than for any road-using vehicle, there were naturally failures where runways had been built on clay.

In the United States the problem of pavement thickness had been attacked immediately before the war, and the Californian bearing ratio test was developed ; this test is still in use today.   In England an attempt was made in 1942 to apply the principles of Classical Soil Mechanics to the problem in the so-called shear strength method, which could only be used with sub-grades of saturated clay (D.S.I.R., 1952).   Both gave useful results in particular cases, but both over-simplified the problem, which is indeed a very complex one, for a rational approach must take into account many other factors besides the strength of the soil, such as the equilibrium soil moisture conditions and the effect of climate (Croney & Lister, 1965), the elastic properties of the pavement which itself may consist of more than one layer, the intensity of traffic, the maximum wheel load, and so on.

However, there is another aspect of road engineering which would make even a perfect solution to this problem, were such a thing possible, of only limited value, and that is the relatively enormous surface area of foundation for a road as compared with that of any other engineering structure, so that the soil strength factor in design can vary greatly along the road line ; all the more so since, as the contact area of vehicle tyres is not great, the maximum stress which they impose is concentrated—except in deep cuttings—in the top few inches of the sub-grade ; that is to say, in a zone where weathering effects are dominant, where soil moisture conditions are variable, and where pedological processes may be active.

This has led to a new approach to the problem of road base design, based on traffic intensity and on a system of terrain evaluation related to a minimum of testing of the C.B.R. type, leading to the build-up of a store of information on road behaviour under differing conditions of climate, geology, and other natural factors.   It is believed that this will be most valuable in solving design problems on large road projects, particularly in undeveloped countries.

In other fields soil studies have contributed to road construction, as for example, in the development of soil stabilization techniques (Millard, 1962) which are now very widely used in tropical countries.   Also a number of devices and processes have been invented for road construction which have proved useful in other branches of engineering, such as the accelerated consolidation of soft clay and peat by means of sand drains (Porter, 1938).

EXCAVATIONS

As regards excavations, in the case of open excavation with battered sides, increased knowledge of slope stability, particularly in the case of the short-term stability of slopes in fissured clay, is of value in practice (Skempton & La Rochelle, 1965), and in such excavation in sand and gravel below ground water level, the use of ground water lowering and of alluvial grouting has proved most valuable.   The design of sheet pile cofferdams has been influenced by recent work in lateral earth pressure theory, and in shafts and similar excavations where the lining is placed as sinking proceeds, an understanding of base failure has proved useful. This problem is, of course, the converse of that of the ultimate bearing capacity of a foundation (Bjerrum & Eide, 1956).

GEOTECHNICAL PROCESSES

In the first part of this Paper the geotechnical processes which were invented during the 19th century were mentioned.   Of these some, including ground freezing and the use of compressed air, have been little influenced by the science of soil mechanics since they are in any case effective over a wide range of particle size.   Others, such as grouting, compaction and groundwater lowering, have been much improved, and there have been some new inventions, such as that of the application of electro-osmosis to drain fine grained soils, which was first developed and applied by Dr Leo Casagrande.   For some years this process was more remarkable for the number of papers published upon it than for the number of its successful applications, but its use is now becoming more frequent.

Perhaps the most important influence of soil mechanics in this field has been to dispel the aura of oddity and distrust which was once attached to it, for we now understand the physical principles upon which these processes depend.   That which has most benefited by a scientific

Table 1.   Injectability of main types of grouts

Ground nature	Coarse sand and gravel	Medium to fine sands	Clayey sand, silts
Characteristics of ground	$d_{10} > 0.5$ mm	0.02 mm $< d_{10} < 0.5$ mm	$d_{10} < 0.02$ mm
	$S < 100$ cm^{-1}	100 cm$^{-1} < S < 1000$ cm^{-1}	$S > 1000$ cm^{-1}
	$K > 10^{-3}$ m/s	10^{-5} m/s $< K < 10^{-3}$ m/s	$K < 10^{-5}$ cm/s
Nature of grout	Bingham type suspension	Colloidal solution	True solution
Strengthening	*Neat cement* ($K > 10^{-2}$ m/s) Grout with air entraining agent	*Joosten* ($K > 10^{-4}$ m/s) High strength gel with organic reagent	Resins
Reduce permeability	*Clay cement* Grout with air entraining agent Clay based gel	*Gel* Lignochrome	Resin A M 9

(a)

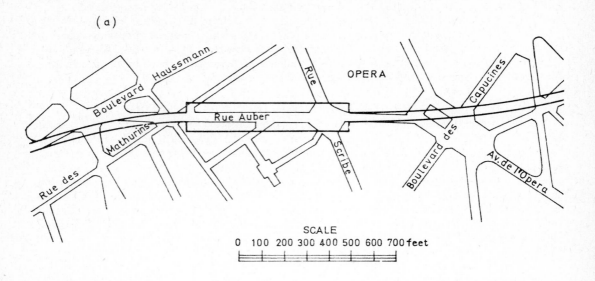

SCALE

0   100 200 300 400 500 600 700 feet

(b)

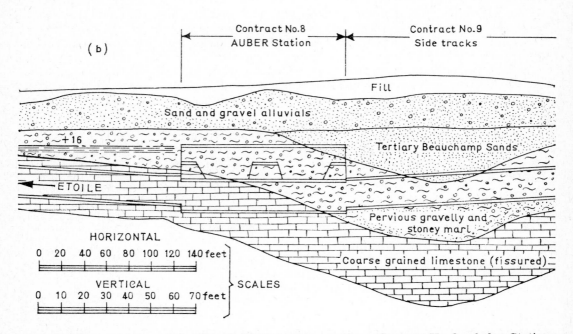

Fig. 21 (above and opposite). New E. W. Metro express line. Contract No. 8. Auber Station. Consolidation and watertightening grout works. (a) General lay-out. (b) Geological profile. (c) Grouting treatment of side galleries from upper gallery. Also grouting of sidewalls. (d) Grouting of invert and consolidation of arch

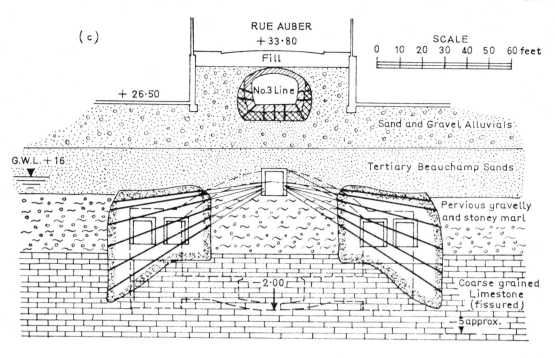

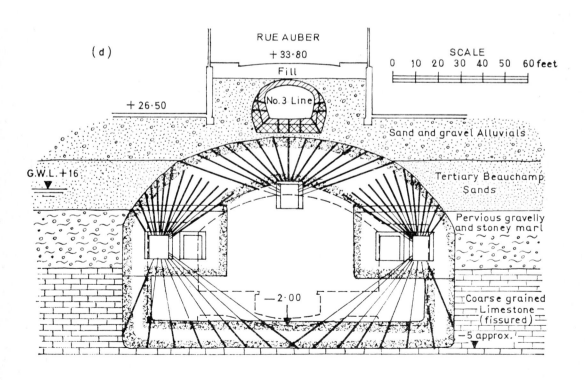

approach is alluvial grouting, for here the improvements have been the direct result of soil studies.   For example, theories of the flow of Newtonian and other fluids in granular media have led to the development of new grouts with a wide range of viscosities (Table 1), and have made possible the treatment of sands finer than before, and an appreciation of the complex structure of alluvial deposits has led to the invention of new devices for injection, such as the 'tube à manchette'.   Also methods have been devised for recording and controlling the injection pressures, the rate of grout acceptance, and the degree of ground heave, and from such records the spread of the fluid in the ground can be followed, and hence the degree of consolidation achieved assessed (Ischy & Glossop, 1962).

As a result of these improvements grouting is now looked upon as a normal part of engineering practice, and many examples of its use in cut-offs for dams, in tunnelling, in underpinning foundations, and to protect open excavations, have recently been described.

A remarkable instance of its use is to be found on an extension to the underground railway system of Paris, which is now under construction (Janin, 1967).   This project is for an east-west line, with running tunnels 8·7 metres in diameter, passing beneath the centre of the city and intended for traffic with a maximum speed of 100 km. per hour.

A station has been built beneath the rue Auber (Figure 20, page 240) and immediately adjacent to the foundations of the Opera House.   This is a very large excavation, 750 feet long, 128 feet wide, and 62 feet high.   Its invert is 115 feet below street level, and groundwater stands 56 feet above invert.   The geological section is complex, and includes three principal soil types, with the following succession from the surface: sand and gravel (Seine alluvials), Beauchamp sands (fine grained tertiary sands), marl with concretions and fissured limestone. Apart from the proximity of existing foundations, it will be seen (Fig. 21) that the station tunnel is located immediately beneath the tunnel of an existing line which has been kept in operation.   The construction of this station, which is obviously a work of exceptional difficulty, has been done with the help of alluvial grouting.   The upper sands and gravels have been treated with a grout based on sodium silicate of a type which acquires considerable strength on hardening.   The Beauchamp sands have been treated with a pheno-plastic resin, and the lower marl and limestone with clay-cement mixtures.

The main grouting was carried out from three headings: one beneath the crown of the arch, and one near the springing on either side.   Preliminary grouting was necessary before these access headings could be driven.

RECENT DEVELOPMENTS

Never has there been more interest in the borderland of civil engineering with the earth sciences than there is today.   Research in Classical Soil Mechanics remains vigorous, as, for example, in the work at Cambridge University, which includes a detailed examination of the stress–strain behaviour of soils so that a structure and its foundations can be treated as a unit (Roscoe, 1964).

As said earlier, an important feature of modern work is the strong influence of geological thinking, including the study of the fine structure of soils, and of the small scale geological structure of masses of soil or rock.

As regards the former, it is a noteworthy feature of Classical Soil Mechanics and proof of the genius of Terzaghi, that such an effective body of knowledge was built up on such relatively simple principles: Coulomb's equation, the concept of effective stress, and the theory of consolidation, concepts which owe very little to any detailed knowledge of the microstructure and mineralogy of soils.   Terzaghi was, of course, aware that the intimate structure of soils must in the long run control their properties, and said so, but in those early days he was too wise to be diverted from his well chosen point of attack.   Arthur Casagrande in 1932 put forward a

Fig. 22. Landslide in quick clay

hypothesis for the structure of clay which was illuminating, but the subject was not then pursued. Nowadays problems arise from time to time which require a knowledge of the structure of soils, and much work is in progress on the effect of the mineralogy and micro-structure of soils on its mechanical properties.

The first effective work in this field was carried out at the Geotechnical Institute at Oslo which under its Director, Laurits Bjerrum, remains pre-eminent in this field, as can be seen from the Proceedings of the Conference held there in 1967. Early work by Rosenquist at Oslo was concerned with the structure of the quick clays which occur on the shores of the Baltic (Rosenquist, 1953). These have unusual properties, for their natural moisture content is invariably above the liquid limit, and although when undisturbed they are firm, or even stiff, they become virtually liquid when remoulded. They were known to be marine clays of Post-Glacial age, elevated with the Isostatic rise of the land following the retreat of the ice sheet, but Rosenquist showed that they had subsequently been leached, either by rainwater percolating downwards, or by artesian water percolating upwards through them. This leaching reduced the salt concentration in the pore water and left them in a metastable condition, which explained the catastrophic landslides to which they are subject (Figure 22, page 247).

Quick clays are an example of the effect of microstructure; as an example of the effect of mineral composition certain residual soils, usually described as Halloysite soils, are referred to.

The only material available for the construction of the Sasamua Dam, near Nairobi, was a residual soil formed from Phonolite, with a liquid limit of 85, plastic limit of 55, and plasticity index of 30. Since the optimum Proctor dry density was only 70 lb/cu. ft at 50% optimum moisture content, and the natural moisture content in the borrow pit was well above this value, it appeared that as a material of construction it was wholly unsuitable when compared with soils in the normal range of experience (Dixon, 1958). However, examination under the electron microscope showed it to be composed of Halloysite with subsidiary Geothite and Gibbsite. The Halloysite occurs as small tubular structures 0.5μ long and 0.08μ in diameter. It was found that over 20% of the natural moisture content of the clay was held in the pore spaces of the mineral aggregates and within the Halloysite tubes. This water, being essentially a part of the minerals themselves, was inert as regards the plasticity and mechanical properties of the clay. This suggested a method of working with such a soil.

Borrow pits with an area of thirty acres were established to accelerate drying, and the fill was taken off by skimming the soil to a depth of four inches over an area of six acres each day. Heavy compaction equipment was used with excellent results.

Another example of this new approach to soil mechanics is found in the work now proceeding both at the Road Research Laboratory and at Birmingham University on the nature of the Keuper marl. Within the Keuper marl a number of rock types occur, including evaporites, sandstones, shales and mudstones, of which the latter are the more important. When conventional tests are made on them the scatter of the results is so great as to make them useless as a basis for design. The reason for this scatter is being examined in the belief that when its cause is known it will be possible to arrive at results of practical value. At Birmingham the microstructure of the shales and mudstones has been investigated (Davis, 1967), using not only the optical microscope, but the more advanced techniques of X-ray refraction and the electron probe, and it has been shown that the percentage of clay fraction estimated by standard tests at about 20% is quite misleading, and that the actual clay content is in the neighbourhood of 80%, and this in a material which shows a high value for ϕ' and a relatively high permeability. This anomaly has been explained by the observation that the clay minerals are aggregated into silt sized particles which control the geotechnical properties of the rock. Work is now in progress on methods for testing these materials, and it is intended to combine them with field observations, such as plate bearing tests.

As a final example work on the effect of shear strain on the microstructure of clay, which has followed from the original discovery of the orientation of particles on the slip surfaces at Waltons Wood, is mentioned. The results so far published by Morgenstern and Tchalenko of Imperial College (1967) and by Kenney of Toronto University (1967), suggest that it will lead to a better understanding of the fundamental mechanical properties of clay, and in particular of the residual strength, and indeed, it may also make an important contribution to geology.

The second feature of recent work is the recognition of the importance of the small scale geological structure of a site. Although an appreciation of the significance of minor geological details has been a basic doctrine in Classical Soil Mechanics, it is one which has not always been observed, perhaps because research on the shear strength of clay, which has been pursued for many years, has, since results must be reproducible, often used remoulded material. This may have deflected attention from the complexity of most soil profiles. One might almost say that some have subconsciously come to define clay as a substance which obeys Terzaghi's consolidation theory, and Horslev's modification of the Coulomb equation of shear strength, and have overlooked the fact that sediments are rarely homogeneous for any great depth. This heresy is now being corrected. For example, the recent Flandrian deposits found in most British estuaries, although dominantly of soft clay, also contain thin beds of silt and of peat, and horizons filled with fossil rootlets. These may act as drainage paths, and Rowe, at Manchester (1968) has shown that the 'real drainage behaviour of such a deposit as a whole, depends upon the geological details of its formation,' and that the index properties of the clay may give no indication of these properties. Thus a coefficient of consolidation of a thick bed of recent clay may be many times greater than that suggested by tests on specimens of the clay portion itself. This has led him to develop methods of procuring and testing large diameter samples following a preliminary exploration by means of continuous cores taken with the Delft sampler. This work has practical importance, for it suggests that in many cases in the past money has been wasted on sand drain installations to accelerate consolidation which were, in fact, unnecessary and ineffective.

These small scale structures are, of course, not limited to minor variations in a sedimentary cycle, but include, for example, the joints in fissured clay. In the case of stiff fissured clays it has been found that the strength of the clay in mass is significantly less than the values obtained from laboratory tests. An extreme example is, of course, the residual strength on pre-existing slip surfaces, which may be many times lower than that of the intact parent clay.

From fissures in clay one passes without a break into faults and joints in rock, but here one enters the allied subject of rock mechanics, and indeed it has been said that the only distinction between soil mechanics and rock mechanics is that in rock the effect of discontinuities is more important than are the properties of the rock itself.

CONCLUSION

In preparing this Paper I have become very conscious that Soil Mechanics means different things to different people. To a purist it may mean a branch of physics or of applied mechanics dealing with the behaviour of aggregates of small particles; to others it is a quantitative branch of engineering geology; and yet to others it is a branch of engineering science devoted to the theory of foundation engineering and strongly influenced by geology. I myself would say that the boundary of Classical Soil Mechanics is the field of homogeneous soils, and that the subject which I have been considering is better termed 'geotechnology,' of which an essential and basic discipline must be Classical Soil Mechanics.

This raises the question of training. To work in this field should the basic course be in civil engineering, but with less electricity and less advanced structural theory, together with a good deal more geology and theoretical soil mechanics, and above all as much experience as possible of geological mapping in the field? Or should the training be basically a course in geology, with emphasis on physical geology and structural geology, relatively little palaeontology and mineralogy (other than that of the rock forming minerals), and some civil engineering subjects such as elementary theory of structures and elementary hydraulics, and certainly a thorough course in theoretical soil mechanics, leading not to a nodding acquaintance, but to a good working knowledge of the subject? In any case, I feel that soil mechanics should be the key discipline for any course.

Personally, I lean to the first alternative, for the end product must be an aid to the design and construction of public works, but one thing is certain: the education of an engineer in this branch of science is incomplete until he has had much experience of geology in the field. In the recent past—perhaps because the demand for soil engineers has been greater than the supply—there has been a tendency for graduates to be given responsibilities beyond their powers, and if trouble has ensued it has been attributed to a weakness in the subject, rather than to inexperience in the practitioner.

This state of affairs has been commented on more than once, and is well described by M. Henri Lossier, who is known to many of us as the author of a monograph on 'The pathology of reinforced concrete.' In an article called 'La crise de confiance dans le méchanique des sols,' he says:

'. . . cette science, l'une des plus attrayants et des plus importantes de l'art de l'ingénieur, est de par sa nature même trop complex et d'une application trop delicate pour pouvoir être utilisée sans risques graves, par des techniciens encore inexperimentés ou d'une culture simplement livresque.'

. . . 'En tous cas la méchanique des sols n'est par, elle meme, pour rien dans la crise de confiance qu'elle subir injustement. Elle n'est alors victime que de ses apprentis-sorciers.'

('. . . this science, one of the most attractive and important in the art of engineering, is by its nature so delicate and so complex that it can be dangerous if left in the hands of technicians who lack experience or who depend upon book learning. . . . However that may be, the science itself is in no way responsible for any lack of confidence which it may have unjustly inspired. It is simply and solely the victim of its own apprentice-sorcerers.')

To conclude, in 1945 I gave a lecture to the Institution of Civil Engineers on the wider aspects of soil mechanics, as it then existed, and ended by saying 'we can see a new and broad subject emerging . . . and I believe that the time has come to recognize it under the name of "Geotechnology."'

With this quotation I conclude a Rankine Lecture which has undeniably been sponsored by the British Geotechnical Society.

ACKNOWLEDGEMENTS

I should like particularly to record my thanks to my colleagues, Mr B. O. Corbett, Mr K. R. Early, and Mr N. B. Hobbs for their useful advice in preparing this Paper and to Mr I. K. Nixon for drawing up the tables. I should also like to thank many friends with whom I have had discussions, and in particular Dr Laurits Bjerrum, for his hospitality during a most interesting visit to the Geotechnical Institute at Oslo.

APPENDIX

Table 2. Boreholes, pits, trenches and adits

Method	Geology	Technique	Application in civil engineering
Boreholes	Clays, silty clays and peats	Hand or power auger (single blade or continuous spiral)	Shallow reconnaissance Power operation fast Limited to non-caving ground except for hollow continuous augers
	As above, also silts, sands and gravels	Wash boring	Inexpensive equipment Unsatisfactory for precise investigation
	As above with occasional cobbles and boulders also decomposed rocks	Percussion cable tool boring with casing	Standard for soil exploration Water added below water table to stabilize base of boring Clean out with auger before core sampling cohesive soils
	As above and soft rocks	Pneumatic chisel, rotary tricone bit	Fast, unsatisfactory for precise investigation Limited to location of hard ground (Check for presence of boulders)
	All rocks	Rotary core drilling	Standard for rock exploration Reliability depends on correct selection of core barrels (see Table 4) Water table observations difficult
Pits	Clays and peats	Excavation by hand or power grabs, with support as required	Direct access gives best opportunity for detailed studies of ground in situ, presence of stratification and thin clay layers
	Silts, sands and gravels	Close timbering ground water lowering essential below water table	Depth usually limited by problems of ground water lowering
	Soft and medium hard rocks	Hand excavation with support as required	Detailed study of local variations, bedding, fissures and joints
Trenches	Clays, silts, peats and sand and gravel above water table	Excavation usually by machine such as hydraulic powered excavators	Direct access with extended inspection of lateral variations Exploration of borrow areas
Adits	All soils and rocks	Appropriate forms of hand excavation and timbering as for tunnelling	Established method for detailed exploration of dam abutments and underground structures Sub-surface exploration of steeply inclined rock strata

Table 3. Sampling

Source	Geology	Sampling technique and application in civil engineering	
		Disturbed	Undisturbed
Boreholes	Clays, silty clays and peats	*Hand auger* Normally representative of composition, but unreliable for examination of structure *Clay cutter* As above, but liable to more mixing	*Open drive samplers* (area ratio not exceeding 25%) Standard usually 4 in. dia. × 18 in. occasionally 1½ in. dia. × 6 in. long. Suitable for local stratigraphical identification and soil mechanics testing excluding pore water pressure measurement
	As above, also silts and sands	*Shell* Standard for non-cohesive strata to examine composition. Best when whole contents of shell is emptied into tank and allowed to settle before taking representative sample from sediment *Power auger* Liable to considerable disturbance and mixing except when conditions in depth are uniform *Water flush* Liable to serious disturbance and mixing *Standard penetration test sampler* Provides small specimens of both cohesive and non-cohesive soils for classification purposes but is not normally suitable for retaining structural features	*Piston samplers* Less disturbance and better recovery than for open drive samplers. Non-cohesive strata only retained within mud filled borehole. Improved quality helpful when testing soft recent clays and for effective stress analyses. Reliability aids studies of specific horizons. Sample diameters range from 2½ to 10 in. and lengths up to 3 ft *Continuous samplers (usually begun from ground surface)* (a) Delft 29 mm dia. (Nylon stocking).† Rapid method with individual samples up to 25 m long in recent alluvium (Dutch cone resistance below 200 kg/sq. cm) for stratigraphical identification (b) Delft 66 mm dia. (Nylon stocking).† As for 29 mm sampler, also all standard soil mechanics testing (c) Swedish 68 mm dia. (Steel foils).‡ Individual samples up to about 20 metres in soft recent alluvial clays and laboratory strength tests correspond to in situ vane results. Can also be used in silts and sands of medium to low density *Compressed air sampler* (60 mm dia.)* For recovery of silt and sand strata from above or below water table without use of mud, to study laminar structure and composition, density and permeability
	Gravel, cobbles and boulders	*Shell* *Power auger* Standard for gravel, but grading may be unreliable. Specimens up to gravel size may be recovered without reliance on source	No common method in use
	Soft rocks (including hard clays)	*Auger* Sample identification generally misleading due to remoulding which produces a weaker material *Air flush (vacuum recovery)* Possible for study of mineral composition above water table	*Driven samplers* Shatter during driving causes serious structural disturbance which can affect results of soil mechanics tests

Boreholes (cont'd)	All rocks	Rotary core barrels§	Single tube. Simplest type suitable only for massive uniformly hard rock
			Double tube types support and protect core during drilling
			Inner tube rigid:
			  Least likely to jam but liable to cause serious sample disturbance in variable and broken rock
			Inner tube swivel:
			  Internal discharge adversely affects core recovery in variable and broken rock which is minimized when discharge is below core lifter
			  Face discharge although expensive is considered the best method to minimize losses in variable and broken rock
			Triple tube types provide extra split inner tube which assists in removal of core from barrel with least disturbance. Other special barrels include spring loaded inner barrel which extends to protect core in weak layers
			Wire line barrels provide facility to withdraw and return inner barrel and core from bottom of hole independently of outer barrel and bit
			Water flush is generally used to cool bit and remove cuttings. Air flush requires special equipment to maintain air speeds, can have advantages when coring above the water table. Mud flush can be helpful to reduce erosion of core
			Rock cutting is usually with diamond bits but tungsten carbide inserts are applicable for uniform soft rocks. Chilled steel shot is used only for large diameter cores (over 6 in. dia.) when some loss is acceptable
			Fissures must be grouted to prevent loss of shot
			Suitable ancillary equipment as well as skilful operation are essential for good core recovery and the greater the complexity in ground conditions the higher the degree of skill required. The more broken the ground is the shorter each drill run should be to ensure good recovery

		Water flush	Rock sludge samples provide opportunity for identification by microscope if no core is recovered when conditions are uniform
Pits, trenches and adits	Clays and peats, silts, sands and gravels, and soft and medium hard rocks	Hand excavation	For identification purposes particularly useful to study local variations and anomalies. Ensure fresh in situ surface is exposed before sampling
		Open drive and piston samplers	See notes under boreholes. Offers opportunity for horizontal and inclined as well as vertical tube samples, silts and sands as well as clays. Ensure fresh surface is exposed before sampling
		Block samples	Hand cut specimens of self supporting soil or soft rock, carefully cut and trimmed in situ to provide undisturbed sample with minimal disturbance Samples, often 6 in. cube, are coated in wax reinforced with muslin as each face is exposed
Ground-water	—		Bale out borehole or pool and sample after the water has returned to its former level. Rinse the container thoroughly beforehand, preferably using water from test source. Ensure surface or rain water has not diluted water to be tested

* *British Standard Code of Practice*, CP 2001, 1957. Site investigations.
† *Laboratorium voor Grondmechanica Paper No. 4*, 1966. A new apparatus for taking a continuous soil sample.
‡‡ *Royal Swedish Geotechnical Institute Proc. No. 1*, 1950. Soil sampler with metal foils. Device for taking undisturbed samples of very great length.
§ *British Standards 4019, Part 1*, 1966. Specification of Rotary core drilling equipment.

Table 4. In situ testing and field instrumentation

Nature of works	Geology	Technique	Application in civil engineering
Foundations for static loads	Soft recent clay	Vane test. Direct penetration from surface and in borehole or pit	Undrained shear strength, particularly for sensitive clays
	Soils	Simple probe. Driving usually by drop hammer or pneumatic hammer	Location of hard ground beneath weak strata. Beware of boulders
		Cone penetration. Probing with standardized dynamic driving procedure. Dutch deep sounding test. Standardized test with shielded rod and constant rate of penetration. Adaptable for piston sampling	See remarks for simple probe. Bearing value and length of piles in silts and sands. Relative densities. Location of weak zones
		Standard Penetration Test (Raymond). Important always to maintain positive head in borehole. Provides small sample (See Table 4)	Bearing values of non-cohesive soils. Relative densities. Unreliable in gravel. Correction to be applied to tests in fine grained soils
		Piston loading test. Plate loading test on base of borehole. Pile tests. Loading, pulling and lateral as required	In situ bearing value of sands (Niebuhr) and clays (Butler). Pile design. Ratio of settlement in sands between individual test and group suggested by Skempton
		(i) Maintained load method (M.L.) (ii) Constant rate of penetration method (C.R.P.) (iii) Equilibrium load method (E.L.). Requires fairly even temperatures and leak proof ram	M.L. method represents conventional technique. C.R.P. method is very quick for load carrying behaviour. E.L. method is compromise for determining load carrying behaviour quickly
	Soils and particularly stony clays, soft and weathered rocks	Plate bearing tests (at surface). Prevent plate from tilting and ensure test load is carried well clear of plate	Bearing value for foundation design. Test by boring for softer deposits at depth. Special tests (e.g. *Géotechnique*, 1955) for coefficients of subgrade reaction applicable to raft design. In situ C.B.R. tests are subject to climatic changes
		Borehole loading test (e.g. Menard pressure meter). Radial compression test on wall of borehole. Above or below water table	Modulus of elasticity, creep limit and shear strength up to 10 tons/sq. ft
	Rocks	In situ shear strength. Normally a direct shear test across a predetermined plane, with or without normal loading	Rock strength parameters and modulus of elasticity
		Drillhole loading test (Centex cell). Expansion of two halves of cylindrical shell in truly drilled hole. Drillhole dilatometer with flexible membrane	Modulus of elasticity of strong rocks; directional pressure
		Plate jacking test. Usually carried out between two sides of pit or adit	Modulus of elasticity of weak to strong rocks; all-round pressure. Modulus of elasticity and bearing value involving maximum volume of rock to take account of discontinuities
		Seismic measurements. Determination of seismic velocities in various modes	Modulus of elasticity and indirectly strength. Preferably confined to extension of direct measurements. Field delineation of low velocity areas can indicate fractured rock
		Stress measurements: (i) Overcoring methods. A device is fixed in place (drill hole or surface) and observations are made before and after overcoring. Types include stress plugs, discs or meters; utilizing transducers, strain gauges or birefringent elements (ii) Flat jack methods. A strain gauge is fixed on rock surface and observations are made before and after a slot is cut, and again after a flat jack is grouted into slot and pressurized to restore ground stress to unrelieved state (iii) Seismic methods. Velocity of propagation is a function of stress. Field and laboratory test comparisons indicate in situ stress levels	Absolute stresses in rock masses. All methods require measurements in three planes for complete stress ellipsoid

Application	Material	Method	Purpose / Remarks
Foundations for dynamic loads	Soils and rocks	Static loading test. Extra sensitive plate test cycled over expected stress range to give a modulus of reaction	'Spring constant' for foundation design
		Dynamic loading test. Small vibrators mounted on soil to give resonance response	Values of elastic moduli, Poisson's ratio and damping
		Seismic velocity measurements. In various modes	Elastic moduli (See note above opposite Seismic measurements)
Earthworks, soil and rock slopes	Soils	In situ shear strength. Normally undrained direct shear test	Undrained in situ shear strength having regard to structure and orientation of failure plane particularly for slope design
		Sand replacements (also water balloon device). Calibrate sand at natural humidity	Bulk density during construction
		Nuclear devices at surface. Radioactive sources and counting unit	Bulk density (preferably by attenuation method) and in situ moisture content
		Nuclear density probe. Usually back-scatter method with radioactive isotopes	Bulk density measurements above and below water table, with casing if required
		Proctor needle. In earthwork construction	Field control of consistency of fine grained soils
		Piezometers. High air entry value in partially saturated soils	Pore water pressure instrumentation
		Total pressure cells. Require very careful positioning	Total earth pressures against substructures
		Settlement and heave instruments. Types: water, mercury, magnetic ring, buried plates, rods and notched tubes	Total and relative settlement
	Soils and rocks	Inclinometers and deflectometers. Portable and installed	Creep and slip detection
		Extensometers. Various types	Expansion due to relief of stress and across tensile zones arising from differential settlement
Groundwater, permeability, etc.	Soils and rocks	Observation wells or piezometers or Dutch pore water pressure device. Use effective filter, test regularly and seal from extraneous infiltration	Level of water table, artesian and sub-artesian conditions
		Rapid response recorders. Transducer type	Tidal measurements, effect of surges, rainstorms and earthquakes
	Clays and silts	Constant head seepage tests. In situ measurement of permeability	Coefficient of consolidation (certain advantages over laboratory tests)
	Sands and gravels	In situ permeability. Careful shelling beforehand. Make both rising and falling head tests	Local measurement of in situ permeability either through base of borehole or after placing coarse filter and withdrawal of casing. Treat results with caution
		In situ permeameter (Menard). Careful installation inside special slit casing	Measurement of local horizontal permeability
		Pumping tests. Pump to equilibrium conditions measuring transients during drawdown and recovery. Use at least two lines of observation wells	Best form of test for natural permeability measurement. Transient measurements provide storage coefficient
		Two well pumping test. Established technique	Estimation of difference between horizontal and vertical permeability
		Radioactive tracers. Various	
		Electrical resistivity. Four electrodes. Wenner or Schlumberger configuration	Extension of direct measurements of porosity, degree of saturation, and permeability
	Rocks	Formation tests. Expanding packers isolate zone under test	Joint seepage and condition of joints by measuring flow under varying pressures, rising and falling
Miscellaneous, corrosion, etc.	Soils	Thermocouples and thermisters	Ground temperature of coal tips on fire, beneath boilers and refrigeration plant
		Electrical resistivity. Four electrode system. Wenner configuration or two electrode probe	Electrical resistivity for corrosion survey
		Corrosion probe. Short circuit current between magnesium iron cell and earth	Depolarizing ability of soil for corrosion survey
		Stray current measurement	For corrosive effect
	Soils and rocks	Periscopes and borehole cameras	Defining cavities, fractures, etc.
	Rocks	Noise detectors. Considerable amplification required	Incipient ground movement at faults, slopes, tunnels

Table 5. Photographic techniques

Photography	Technique	Application in civil engineering	Notes
Aerial vertical monochrome (normally panchromatic)	Mosaics (assembly of matched series of prints)	Preliminary planning	(i) Least expensive (ii) Basically a diagram with variable scale (iii) Most reliable when it is 'controlled' mosaic of flat areas
	Photogrammetry	(a) Maps and plans for final design and construction, roads, railways, urban and industrial development (b) Volumetric assessment of stockpiles, reservoir projects, embankments (c) Representation by spatial co-ordinates for computational services, such as cut and fill information, setting out data and projectional planning	(i) Scales generally range from about 1:500 down to 1:25 000 (ii) Accuracy depends upon the 'contact scale' of the photographic negative. Typical accuracies with modern equipment: *Contact* *Assumed* *Contour* *Spot* *Plan* *scale* *mapping* *height* *scale* 1/3000 1:500 ±6 in. ±3 in. ±6 in. 1/20 000 1:10 000 ±5 ft ±2 ft ±4 ft (iii) Areas per photograph (acres): *Mapping* *Contact* *Whole* *Overlap* *scale* *scale* 1:500 1/3000 117 32 1:10 000 1/20 000 5200 1400 (iv) Photographs 9 in. square Overlap forward 60% Overlap lateral 30%
	Photo-interpretation	Basic for terrain evaluation including: (a) geology; rock outcrops, structural details, soils (b) drainage patterns and hydrographic features (c) mass and character of the vegetation (d) land classification (e) human development	Prints should have good definition of details and be free from cloud *Contact scale* *Minimum length of object* *perceived* (F. L. 6 in.) 1:20 000 6 ft e.g. cattle 1:12 000 4 ft e.g. sheep 1:8000 2 ft e.g. poultry 1:5000 1 ft e.g. ploughing
Aerial vertical colour	False colour (infra-red Ektachrome)	(a) Delineation of water course and areas of standing water, particularly in forests and shorelines	(i) Developed for camouflage detection (ii) Also of use in ecological studies
	Natural colour	(a) Of assistance in photogrammetry mainly for differentiation of details (b) Superior to monochrome for photo interpretation of geology and landforms studies	Until recently colour emulsions have only been coated on non-stable film and the resultant distortion has restricted use in photogrammetry
Aerial vertical	Infra-red	Detection of areas of bedrock below overburden	Method relies upon the interpretation of thermal images
Aerial oblique	Oblique photography	Pictorial representation, record purposes and job progress	(i) Shows ground relief and general development to maximum advantage in single prints (ii) Natural colour film of considerable advantage
Terrestrial monochrome	Photogrammetry	(a) Surveys of cliffs, gorges, steep slopes and architectural features (b) Measurement records of complex shapes pipework, joint distribution in rock faces and structural movements	(i) Use of photo-theodolite or stereocameras (ii) Interval between successive photo stations about 2 to 25 metres (iii) Typical camera for civil engineering purposes: Focal length 150 mm Plates 13 × 18 cm Variable base 2–3 metres

Table 6. Geophysical methods

Method	Principle	Application in civil engineering
Electrical resistivity	The form of flow of an induced electric current is affected by variations in ground resistivity, due mainly to the pore or crack water Current is passed through an outer pair of electrodes while the potential drop is measured between the inner pair	Simplest and least expensive form of geophysical survey Exploration of simple geological features, stratigraphy and irregularities in soils, rocks and groundwater (subsurface saline bodies) 'Expanding' electrode technique for changes in depth 'Constant separation' technique for lateral delineation of soil boundaries, e.g. sand and gravel. Location of faults Extension of direct measurements of porosity, saturation and permeability Analysis is often done by theoretical curve-fitting techniques
Seismic	The speed of propagation of an induced seismic impulse or wave is affected by the elastic properties and density of the ground	Most highly developed form of geophysical survey Can be quite accurate under suitable conditions, particularly for horizontally layered structures Also for ground vibration problems and estimation of Young's modulus of elasticity and Poisson's ratio
	Refraction technique with single shots concerns travel times of refracted waves which travel through sub-strata and are rebounded to the surface Valid only when seismic velocities increase with depth Short separate traverses used to check this	Determination of depth to bedrock, including horizontal and inclined surfaces, also buried channels and domes Direct evidence of seismic velocities in refracting strata For checking effectiveness of cement grouting of rock
	Reflection technique with single shots concerns the directly reflected impulses from horizons of abrupt increase in seismic velocity	Interpretation generally possible only for depths greater than is normally required for civil engineering
	Continuous seismic profiling systems concern the reflected wave trace from a regular series of low frequency acoustic (sonar) impulses of ultra short period for high resolution	Submarine exploration of general stratigraphy, also possible beneath lakes and rivers Seismic velocities are not normally calculable and the pattern of the records has to be calibrated with drillhole data
Gravitational	The earth's natural gravitational field is affected by local variations in ground density Measurements are made of differences between stations in the vertical component of the strength of gravity, which is then corrected for latitude, height and topography to reflect only changes due to sub-surface geology Careful topographical survey of stations is necessary to obtain reliable results as differences are small	The interpretation of regional geology, without depth control, mainly where some geological information is already available For distinguishing anomalies such as rock ridges, large domes, faults, intrusions and steeply inclined strata. Also for positioning buried channels, cavities and old shafts Fitting techniques based on simplified structures can be applied for studying anomalies
Magnetic	Many rocks are weakly magnetic and the strength varies with the rock type depending upon the amount of ferromagnetic minerals present. This modifies the earth's field Surveys are similar to those for gravity measurements Although the field work is simpler the interpretation is more difficult	Mainly qualitative assessment of regional structures For locating the hidden boundaries between different types of crystalline rock and positions of faults, ridges and dykes
Borehole logging	The application of geophysical methods in boreholes	Electrical and sonic methods to distinguish between strata especially where core recovery is difficult

Quality of the interpretation is very dependent upon the experience used in the analysis and the amount of geological knowledge that is available.

Whenever possible carefully link the results with drill hole data or rock outcrops.

Table 7. Laboratory tests

Category	Test (Description)	Symbol	Foundations – Bearing capacity C	BC NC	BC R	Foundations – Settlements C	Set NC	Set R	Slopes C	Slopes NC	Dams and embankments C	Dam NC	Earth pressure C	EP NC	Water flow C	WF NC	Roads and runways C	RR NC	RR R	RR S
Identification	Visual inspection	—			2			2					2							
	Density	γ	2	2	2	2	2	2	*	*	2	*	*	*	2	2	2	2	2	2
	Moisture content	w	2			2					2		2		2		2	2		
	Atterberg limits	LL, PL	2			2					2		2		2		2			
	Shrinkage limit	SL				2					2									
	Limiting densities	γmax., min.		2			2			2		2		2			3	3		
	Particle size	Grading curve		2			*			2		2		2		2	2	3			3
	Particle shape	Roundness, sphericity		3						3		3		3							
	Specific gravity of particles	G_s			2	2	2	2			2						2		2	
Shear strength total	Unconfined compression	q_u	(*)						*											
	Triaxial (Undrained)	$c\phi$	*		*				2											
	Shearbox (Undrained)	$c\phi$		*					2											
	Shearbox (12 in. square)	$c\phi$		(*)																
Effective	Triaxial with pore pressures	$c'\phi'$							*	*	*	*	*	*						
	Special T.X.L.	K_0							*		*		*							
	Special T.X.L.	$\bar{B}$									*	2	*	2		*				
Residual	Shearbox, drained multi-reversal	$c_r'\phi_r'$							*	2	*		*	*						
Compressibility and permeability	Oedometer consolidation	$m_v c_v$				*					*	*								
	Triaxial consolidation	$c_v k$						*			2	2								
	Young's modulus and Poisson's ratio	$E\mu$					*	*	2	2	2	2								
	Triaxial permeability	k									2	2			*					
	Permeameter (constant and falling head)	k									2	2				*				
Construction	Compaction	O.M.C., γ_p							*		*	*					*	*		*
	C.B.R.	C.B.R.															*	*	*	*
	Traditional empirical tests	Puddle clay									3									
	Freeze and thaw	Soundness																	*	*
	Chemical	pH, SO_3	3	3							3						3	3		3

C   Cohesive soils   R   Soft rocks   *   Fundamental values   3   Additional useful data

NC   Non-cohesive soils   S   Stabilized soil   2   Other essential data   (*)   Alternative tests

REFERENCES

BELL, A. L. (1915). Lateral pressure and resistance of clay and the supporting power of clay foundations. *Min. Proc. Instn civ. Engrs* **199**, 232–272. (See also: SKEMPTON, A. W. (1958). Arthur Langry Bell (1874–1956) and his contribution to soil mechanics. *Géotechnique* **8**, No. 4, 143–152.)

BÉRIGNY, C. (1832). *Mémoire sur un procédé d'injection propre à prévenir ou arrêter les filtrations sous les fondations des ouvrages hydrauliques.* Paris. (See also: GLOSSOP, R. (1960). The invention and development of injection processes. Part 1: 1802–1850. *Géotechnique* **10**, No. 3, 91–100.)

BINNIE, G. M. et al. (1967). Mangla. *Proc. Instn civ. Engrs* **38**, November, 337–575.

BISHOP, A. W. (1954). The use of pore-pressure coefficients in practice. *Géotechnique* **4**, No. 4, 148–152.

BJERRUM, L. (1967). Engineering geology of Norwegian normally-consolidated marine clays as related to settlements of buildings. Seventh Rankine Lecture. *Géotechnique* **17**, No. 2, 81–118.

BJERRUM, L. & EIDE, O. (1956). Stability of strutted excavations in clay. *Géotechnique* **6**, No. 1, 32–47.

BJERRUM, L. & FLODIN, N. (1960). The development of soil mechanics in Sweden, 1900–1925. *Géotechnique* **10**, No. 1, 1–18.

BLACKALL, T. E. (1952). A. M. Atterberg, 1846–1916. *Géotechnique* **3**, No. 1, 17–19.

BOUISSINESQ, J. (1885). *Application des potentiels à l'étude des solides élastiques.* (See also: MAYER, A. (1954). Joseph Bouissinesq: 1842–1929. *Géotechnique* **4**, No. 1, 3–5.)

BOYD-DAWKINS. (1898). On the relation of geology to engineering. James Forrest Lecture, March 1898. Quoting from Robert Stephenson's 2nd Report to the Directors of the London, Westminster and Metropolitan Water Company, London, 24 August, 1841.

BUISMAN, A. S. (1934). Détermination expérimentale de la courbe de Mohr pour un échantillon quelconque de terre sous l'influence de différentes pressions principales. *Sci. Ind.*, Paris, April, 149–153.

CAROTHERS, S. D. (1924). Test loads on foundations as affected by scale of tested area. *Proc. Int. Math. Congr.*, Toronto.

CASAGRANDE, A. (1947). Classification and identification of soils. *Proc. Am. Soc. civ. Engrs* **73**, 783–810. (See also discussion.)

COCHRANE, Sir Thomas (1830). Cochrane's Specification, A.D. 1830, No. 6018. Apparatus for excavating, sinking and mining. (See also: THOMAS, Tenth Earl of Dundonald. (1860). *The autobiography of a seaman*, 2nd ed., 2 vols. London: Richard Bentley.)

COLLIN, A. (1846). *Recherches expérimentales sur les glissements spontanés des terrains argileux accompagnée de considération sur quelques principes de la méchanique terrestre.* Paris: Carilion-Goeury. English translation by Schriever, W. R. (1956). University of Toronto Press. (See also: SKEMPTON, A. W. (1949). Alexandre Collin. A note of his pioneer work in soil mechanics. *Géotechnique* **1**, No. 4, 216–222.)

COLLINGWOOD, R. G. (1939). *An autobiography.* Oxford University Press.

COOLING, L. F. & GOLDER, H. Q. (1942). The analysis of the failure of an earth dam during construction. *J. Instn civ. Engrs* **19**, No. 1, 38–55.

COOLING, L. F. & SKEMPTON, A. W. (1941). Some experiments on the consolidation of clay. *J. Instn civ. Engrs* **16**, No. 7, 381–398.

COULOMB, C. A. (1773). Essais sur une application des règles de maximis et minimis a quelques problèmes de statique relatifs à l'architecture. Mémoires de mathématique et de physique presenté a l'Académie Royale des Sciences par divers savants et lus par ses assemblées. (See also: GOLDER, H. Q. (1948). Coulomb and earth pressure. *Géotechnique* **1**, No. 1, 66–72.)

COULOMB, S. A. de. (1779). *Recherches sur les moyens d'exécuter sous l'eau toutes sortes de travaux hydrauliques sans employer aucun épuisement.* Paris.

CRONEY, D. & LISTER, N. W. (1965). Research into the design of flexible road pavements. *Proc. 6th Int. Conf. Soil Mech.* **2**, 36–40.

CRUTTWELL, G. E. W. (1893). The foundations of the river-piers of the Tower Bridge. *Min. Proc. Instn civ. Engrs.* **113**, 117–150.

DAEHN, W. W. & HILF, J. W. (1951). Implications of pore pressure in design and construction of rolled earth dams. *Trans. 4th Congr. Large Dams* **1**, 259.

D'APPOLONIA, E. R. A. & D'APPOLONIA, D. J. (1967). Behaviour of a colluvial slope. *J. Soil Mech. Fdns Div. Am. Soc. civ. Engrs* **93**, No. S.M.4, July.

DARCY, H. P. G. (1856). Les fontaines publiques de la ville de Dijon. Exposition et application des principes a suivre et des formules a employer dans les questions de distribution d'eau. Paris: Victor-Dalman. (See also: ROUSE, H. & INCE, S. (1957). *History of Hydraulics.* Iowa Institute of Hydraulic Research.)

DAVIS, A. G. (1967). The mineralogy and phase equilibrium of Keuper marl. *Q. Jl Engng Geol.* **1**, 25–38.

DEPARTMENT OF SCIENTIFIC AND INDUSTRIAL RESEARCH (1952). *Soil Mechanics for road engineers*, 7th impression, pp. 416–418. H.M.S.O.

DIXON, H. H. (1958). Moisture control and compaction methods used during the construction of the Sasamua Dam, Kenya. International Commission on Large Dams, 6th International Congress, New York.

DOWLING, J. W. F. & WILLIAMS, F. H. P. (1964). The use of aerial photographs in materials surveys and classification of land forms. *Conf. civ. engng problems overseas*, paper 9. London: Institution of Civil Engineers.

FELLENIUS, W. (1927). *Erdstatische-Berechungen mit Reibung und Kohäsion und unter Annahme Kreiszylindtische Gleitflächers.* Berlin: Ernst & Sons.

GLOSSOP, R. (1961). The invention and development of injection processes. Part II: 1850–1960. *Géotechnique* 11, No. 4, 255–279.

GLOSSOP, R. & SKEMPTON, A. W. (1945). Particle size in silts and sands. *J. Instn civ. Engrs* 25, No. 2, 81–105.

GOLDER, H. Q. (1941). The ultimate bearing pressure of rectangular footings. *J. Instn civ. Engrs* 17, No. 2, 161–172.

GOLDER, H. W. (1953). The history of earth pressure. *Arch. Int. Hist. Sci.*, 23–24.

HENKEL, D. J. & SKEMPTON, A. W. (1954). A landslide at Jackfield, Shropshire, in a heavily over-consolidated clay. *Proc. European Conf. Stability Slopes* 1, 90–101.

HILF, J. W. (1948). Estimating construction pore pressures in rolled earth dams. *Proc. 2nd Int. Conf. Soil Mech.* 3, 234.

HUDSON, P. G. (1948). The development and construction of airfields and runways for the Royal Air Force, 1939–1945. *The Civil Engineer in war*, vol. 1, pp. 4–48. Institution of Civil Engineers.

ISCHY, E. & GLOSSOP, R. (1962). An introduction to alluvial grouting. *Proc. Instn civ. Engrs* 21, 449–474 and 23, 705–725.

JACOB, A. (1866). On the designing and construction of storage reservoirs. *J. Trans. Soc. Engrs.*

JANIN, J. (1967). Problemi tecnica della construzione a Parigi delle nouve linee metropolitaine. *Riv. Ing.*, No. 2.

JÜRGENSEN, L. (1934). The application of theories of elasticity and plasticity to foundation problems. *J. Boston Soc. civ. Engrs* 21, 206–241.

KÉLSO, A. E. (1936). The construction of Silvan Dam, Melbourne Water-Supply. *Min. Proc. Instn civ. Engrs* 239, 403–446.

KENNEY, T. C. (1967). The influence of mineral composition on the residual strength of natural soils. *Proc. Geotechnical Conf.*, Oslo.

KERISEL, J. (1956). Historique de la méchanique des sols en France jusqu'au 20e siècle. *Géotechnique* 6, No. 3, 151–166.

McILDOWIE, G. (1935). The construction of the Silent Valley Reservoir, Belfast Water Supply. *Min. Proc. Instn civ. Engrs* 239, 465–516.

MAYER, A. (1963). Recent work in rock mechanics. Third Rankine Lecture. *Géotechnique* 13, No. 2, 97–120.

MIDDLEBROOK, T. A. (1948). Seepage control for large dams. *Trans. 3rd Int. Conf. Large Dams* 2.

MILLARD, R. S. (1962). Road building in the tropics. *J. appl. Chem.* 12, 342–357.

MORGENSTERN, N. R. & TCHALENKO, J. S. (1967). Microscopic structures in kaolin subjected to direct shear. *Géotechnique* 17, No. 4, 309–328.

PENMAN, A. D. M. & WATSON, G. H. (1967). Foundations for storage tanks on reclaimed land at Teesmouth. *Proc. Instn civ. Engrs* 37, May, 19–42.

PORTER, O. J. (1938). Studies of fill construction over mud flats including a description of experimental construction using vertical sand drains to hasten stabilisation. *Proc. 18th Annual Meet.*, 129–141. Highway Research Board.

PROCTOR, R. R. (1933). Fundamental principles of soil compaction. *Engng News Rec.* 31 August, 7, 21 and 28 September.

RANKINE, W. J. M. (1857). On the stability of loose earth. *Phil. Trans. R. Soc.* 147, 9–27. (See also: COOK, Gilbert (1951). Rankine and the theory of earth pressure. *Géotechnique* 2, No. 4, 271–279.)

ROSCOE, K. H. (1964). A brief introduction to soil mechanics and an outline of recent work at Cambridge. Cambridge Conference of International Study Group on Soils.

ROSENQUIST, I. Th. (1953). Considerations on the sensitivity of Norwegian quick-clays. *Géotechnique* 3, No. 5, 195–200.

ROWE, P. W. (1968). The influence of geological features of clay deposits on the design and performance of sand drains. *Proc. Instn civ. Engrs*, Suppl., 1–72.

RUFFLE, N. J. (1965). Derwent Reservoir. *J. Instn Wat. Engrs* 19, No. 5, 361–408.

SCHMIDT, M. F. (1895). L'emploi de la congélation pour l'exécution de travaux dans les terrains aquifères. *Bull. Soc. Ind. Miner. St. Etienne* 9, 3e serie.

SCHULTZE, E. (1954). Hans-Detlef Krey and the experimental approach to soil mechanics. *Géotechnique* 4, No. 3, 93–96.

SKEMPTON, A. W. (1942). An investigation of the bearing capacity of a soft clay soil. Fourth Rankine Lecture. *J. Instn civ. Engrs* 18, No. 7, 307–321.

SKEMPTON, A. W. (1954). The pore-pressure coefficients A and B. *Géotechnique* 4, No. 4, 143–147.

SKEMPTON, A. W. (1957). Stability of natural slopes in London Clay. *Proc. 4th Int. Conf. Soil Mech.*, London 2, 378–381.

SKEMPTON, A. W. (1958). *Arthur Langtry Bell 1874–1956 and his contribution to soil mechanics.*

SKEMPTON, A. W. (1964). Long-term stability of clay slopes. *Geotechnique* 14, No. 2, 77–101.

SKEMPTON, A. W. & LAROCHELLE, P. (1965). The Bradwell slip: a short-term failure in London Clay. *Géotechnique* 15, No. 3, 221–242.

STRANGE, W. L. (1898). Reservoirs with high earthen dams in Western India. *Min. Proc. Instn civ. Engrs* 132, 130–199.

TELFORD, Thomas (1838). *Life of Thomas Telford, etc.* pp. 58–61. London. (See also: TOMLINSON, M. J. (1956). Telford and soil mechanics. *Géotechnique* 6, No. 3, 99–105.)

TERZAGHI, K. VON. (1913). Beitrag zur Hydrographie und Morphologie des Kroatischen Karstes. *Mitt. Jb. K. ung. geol. Anst.* 20, No. 6, 256–374. (For English translation see: *From theory to practice in soil mechanics.* John Wiley & Sons.)

TERZAGHI, K. VON. (1925). *Erdbaumechanik auf bodenphysikalischer Grundlage.* Leipzig und Wien : Franz Deuticke. (See also: CASAGRANDE, A. (1960). *From theory to practice in soil mechanics. Selections. from the writings of Karl Terzaghi.* New York, London : John Wiley & Sons.)

TERZAGHI, K. VON. (1936). Stability of slopes of natural clay. *Proc. 1st Int. Conf. Soil Mech.*, Harvard **1**, 161–165.

TERZAGHI, K. VON. (1929). *Effect of minor geologic details on the safety of dams.* American Institute of Mining and Metallurgical Engineers. Technical Publication 215, 31–44.

TRIGER (1841). Mémoire sur un appareil à air comprimé, pour le percement des puits de mines et autre travaux, sous les eaux et dans les sables submergés. *C. r. hebd. Seanc. Acad. Sci., Paris*, July–December.

WALKER, F. C. (1948). Experience in the measurement of consolidation and pore pressure in rolled earth dams. *Trans. 3rd Int. Congr. Large Dams* **2**.

WALKER, F. C. & DAEHN, W. W. (1948). Ten years of pore pressure measurements. *Proc. 2nd Int. Conf. Soil Mech.* Rotterdam.

YATES, E. M. & MOSELY, F. (1958). Glacial lakes and spillways in the vicinity of Madeley, North Staffordshire. *Q. Jl geol. Soc., London* **113**, 409–428.

ADVANTAGES AND LIMITATIONS OF THE OBSERVATIONAL METHOD IN APPLIED SOIL MECHANICS

R. B. Peck, C.E., D.C.E.

INTRODUCTION

Observational methods have always been used by engineers working in the fields now included in applied soil mechanics, but 'the observational method' is a term having a specific restricted meaning. In its complete and ultimate form the observational method provides a distinct and possibly novel approach to design. I believe we owe its formulation and development as a systematic procedure to Karl Terzaghi.

During the five years in which *Soil mechanics in engineering practice* was being written, Dr Terzaghi and I experienced the greatest of difficulties with Part C, which dealt with applied soil mechanics. These difficulties came as an unpleasant surprise, because our consuming interest in the practical applications of our subject had induced us to believe that dealing with applied soil mechanics would be the easiest portion of our task. Gradually we realized that Terzaghi's enormous experience had not led him consciously to a deliberate methodology in solving his problems; each problem was attacked as a new entity. Indeed, early in our association he advised me that on every new job I should start without any preconceptions and that it would be well to get all the facts by vigorous probing, quite as if soil mechanics did not exist, before attempting to make any interpretations.

Out of the necessity for writing a book that should contain a consistent method of attack on practical problems, Terzaghi began deliberately to examine and reflect on his instinctively developed methods. He made little progress until the chapters on piping and dam foundations. Here the unavoidable shortcomings in knowledge of the subsurface conditions and their influence on the porewater pressures drew his attention to the necessity for a substantial element of empiricism in design, and he realized the undercurrent of observation common to all his work. He then so quickly organized his conceptions that in 1945 he wrote, for one version of the Introduction to the book:

'In the engineering for such works as large foundations, tunnels, cuts, or earth dams, a vast amount of effort and labor goes into securing only roughly approximate values for the physical constants that appear in the equations. Many variables, such as the degree of continuity of important strata or the pressure conditions in the water contained in the soils, remain unknown. Therefore, the results of computations are not more than working hypotheses, subject to confirmation or modification during construction.

'In the past, only two methods have been used for coping with the inevitable uncertainties: either to adopt an excessive factor of safety, or else to make assumptions in accordance with general, average experience. The designer who has used the latter procedure has usually not suspected that he was actually taking a chance. Yet, on account of the widespread use of the method, no year has passed without several major accidents. It is more than mere coincidence that most of the failures have been due to the unanticipated action of water, because the behavior of water depends, more than on anything else, on minor geological details that are unknown.

'The first method is wasteful; the second is dangerous. Soil mechanics, as we understand it today, provides a third method which could be called the experimental method. The procedure is as follows: Base the design on whatever information can be secured.

Make a detailed inventory of all the possible differences between reality and the assumptions. Then compute, on the basis of the original assumptions, various quantities that can be measured in the field. For instance, if assumptions have been made regarding pressure in the water beneath a structure, compute the pressure at various easily accessible points, measure it, and compare the results with the forecast. Or, if assumptions have been made regarding stress-deformation properties, compute displacements, measure them, and make a similar comparison. On the basis of the results of such measurements, gradually close the gaps in knowledge and, if necessary, modify the design during construction.

'Soil mechanics provides us with the knowledge required for practical application of this "learn-as-you-go" method.'[1]

To save space, this was replaced by another, shorter introduction in the published book. Statements of comparable clarity did not appear until about 1960, when Bjerrum so remarkably caught the essence of Terzaghi's method of working in the Anniversary Volume (Bjerrum et al., 1960), and when Terzaghi himself devoted attention to the method while he discussed the past and future of applied soil mechanics (Terzaghi, 1961). The latter statements were more complete and detailed than the one quoted here.

In Terzaghi's hands the observational procedure led to significant and even spectacular successes, yet I have the impression that such consistent and successful use has not been the experience of many other engineers. This Paper examines whether this impression is correct and, if so, why Terzaghi was so notably successful. Can the conditions for successful use of the method be defined? Are there conditions under which the observational method cannot or should not be used?

To the last question at least one categorical answer can be given. If the character of the project is such that the design cannot be altered during construction, the method is inapplicable. Otherwise, it may have the potential for great savings in time or money, or for providing needed assurance of complete safety. The possibilities for obtaining these attractive benefits are worth considering.

REVIEW OF METHOD

In brief, the complete application of the method embodies the following ingredients.

(a) Exploration sufficient to establish at least the general nature, pattern and properties of the deposits, but not necessarily in detail.

(b) Assessment of the most probable conditions and the most unfavourable conceivable deviations from these conditions. In this assessment geology often plays a major rôle.

(c) Establishment of the design based on a working hypothesis of behaviour anticipated under the most probable conditions.

(d) Selection of quantities to be observed as construction proceeds and calculation of their anticipated values on the basis of the working hypothesis.

(e) Calculation of values of the same quantities under the most unfavourable conditions compatible with the available data concerning the subsurface conditions.

(f) Selection in advance of a course of action or modification of design for every foreseeable significant deviation of the observational findings from those predicted on the basis of the working hypothesis.

---

[1] Terzaghi's original drafts were in a somewhat cryptic, abbreviated form. I have taken the liberty of editing his notes in accordance with the procedures followed in preparation of the final manuscript of the book as published.

(g) Measurement of quantities to be observed and evaluation of actual conditions.

(h) Modification of design to suit actual conditions.

The degree to which all these steps can be followed depends on the nature and complexity of the work. We can readily distinguish between projects, on the one hand, in which events have already set the stage for the observational method as being almost the only hope of success, and those, on the other hand, in which use of the method has been envisioned from the inception of the project. Applications of the first type are much the more familiar.

BEST-WAY-OUT APPLICATIONS

Conditions for suitability of method

Whenever construction has already started and some unexpected development has occurred, or whenever a failure or accident threatens or has already taken place, an observational procedure may offer the only satisfactory way out of the difficulties. Under these circumstances perhaps most engineers would instinctively adopt such a procedure. The mere observation of events, such as the measurements of settlements or lateral movements, often suggests remedial measures that prove to be successful. Yet the results are sometimes disappointing and occasionally disastrous because the observations do not constitute part of a well-considered programme encompassing all the applicable steps in the complete learn-as-you-go procedure.

Cleveland Ore Yard

A classic example of the application of the method is the Republic Steel ore yard in Cleveland, Ohio, well-known to those who have read Terzaghi's report in the Anniversary Volume (Bjerrum et al., 1960). The example is familiar and so only the aspects most significant to this discussion are mentioned: the location, general layout and dimensions of the ore yard had been fixed before Terzaghi came to the job; the exploration was limited to four borings, which were sufficient to establish the likelihood of foundation failure but not to disclose all the variability in subsurface conditions; the observational programme was rather elaborate, planned with the greatest of care and conscientiously executed; the results were studied and interpreted without delay, on a weekly or sometimes daily basis; the ore load could at any time or place be held constant, or even rather quickly decreased, if necessary to prevent failure. Thus the maximum possible utilization of the ore yard was assured, but at the same time the possibility of failure was eliminated. Had the actual capacity of the ore yard been less than the requirements of the blast furnace, the steel company would have faced an economic penalty for shipping part of the ore to the furnace by railroad as needed, but they did not face the far greater penalty of a failure of their dock or their loading and storage facilities. In this instance the observational procedure certainly falls into the 'best-way-out' category.

Cape Kennedy Causeway

A more recent illustration involving quite different physical phenomena concerns a causeway at Cape Kennedy to permit transport of Saturn rockets from the Vertical Assembly Building to one of the launching pads, a distance of about four miles. The rockets, each about as high as a 35-storey building, are transported in a vertical position on a platform carried in turn on four track-type crawlers resembling huge bulldozers. The crawlers operate on a compacted 'limerock' surface about 3 ft thick resting on hydraulically placed uniform fine sand overlying similar natural sand. The general ground surface is only a few feet above sea level.

The first of two such causeways was constructed and used without difficulty except for a few zones of minor settlement where the subsoil contained lenses of clay. Accordingly the second was built like the first, on the basis of preliminary exploratory borings that disclosed similar sands but only minor inclusions of clay. Construction was started while exploratory studies were still being made because of the accelerated pace of the space programme. Most of the studies consisted of dynamic penetration tests similar to the standard penetration test

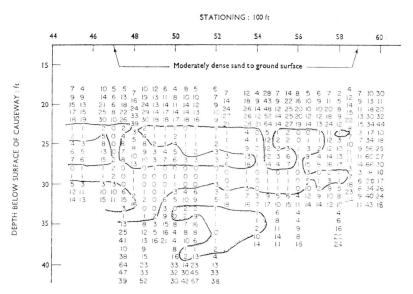

Fig. 1. Penetration resistance record showing zone of extremely loose sand beneath causeway. Numbers indicate blows per foot on two-inch o.d. sampler weighing 300 lb and falling 18 in.

except that a 300 lb weight was allowed to fall 18 in. The number of blows was counted for each foot of penetration. The results disclosed several zones in which the resistance was consistently less than 2 blows/ft. One of these (Fig. 1) near station 52 was much deeper and looser than any that had been encountered beneath the first crawlerway, and suggested the possibility of liquefaction and sudden failure under the passage of the fully loaded transporter. It was concluded that the degree of danger could not be assessed reliably by any known procedure using the results of laboratory tests, but that positive steps were nevertheless required to assure that no accident could possibly lead to overturning the transporter while it was carrying a Saturn vehicle.

Among the positive steps considered were the injection of chemicals to provide stabilization, densification by vibroflotation, removal of the loose sands and their replacement by stable fill, and dewatering or surcharging to produce at least some breakdown of the structure of the loose sand. The great expense of any of these measures made them unattractive but, more important, the time required for the operations would have disrupted the entire Saturn programme. Finally, in the interests of safety, each method would have been applied to many areas where it might not have been needed at all.

An observational procedure was worked out that would avoid all the serious disadvantages of the 'positive' methods and that instead would have several inherent advantages. It would consist essentially of traversing the causeway with the unloaded transporter, and then by the transporter plus larger and larger fractions of the design load. At each stage of loading some alteration of structure of the sand could be expected on account of the shearing stresses induced by the load; any such alteration would be beneficial. The alteration would presumably be accompanied by an increase in porewater pressure. If the pore pressure were to exceed a certain amount liquefaction would develop, but if the maximum pore pressure could be kept below this limiting value the deposit could be progressively densified by successive passages of the transporter and any appropriate fraction of the full load. As the sand was fairly pervious excess pore pressures were thought likely to dissipate rapidly.

Accordingly the following observational devices were set up: settlement reference points at the surface along and beside the entire causeway; settlement observation plates at the top and bottom of the loose zone; slope indicator casings alongside the zone; and porewater-pressure measuring devices (quick-acting and automatically recording) at the upper and lower quarter points in the thickness of the loose sand zone. The unloaded transporter, constituting about one third of the design loading, was slowly advanced over the causeway.

Porewater pressures, equal to about one third of the increase of stress calculated on the basis of the theory of Boussinesq, were observed in the loose sand. These dissipated rapidly whenever the transporter was stopped. A small but significant decrease in thickness was observed in the sand, even after a single passage of the unloaded transporter. These observations were considered favourable because they demonstrated that the structure of the sand could be altered at relatively low loads, if necessary by repeated loadings, and that the rise of pore pressure could be reduced by slowing down the transporter.

At this stage the results were available of studies of the ability of the transporter to carry loads, such as boxes of earth or tanks of water, equal to such fractions as 50 or 75% of the design load. The studies showed that the required structural modifications could not be made quickly or at reasonable cost. Due to the details of the structural framing of the transporter, the next practical increment of load would be the weight of the launcher-umbilical tower (LUT). The load of transporter plus LUT would constitute roughly 90% of the design load including the weight of the rocket.

The favourable results with the unloaded transporter were felt to justify the conclusion that it would be safe to subject the causeway to the transporter and LUT, since the transporter could if necessary be made to operate at an extremely slow speed and the porewater

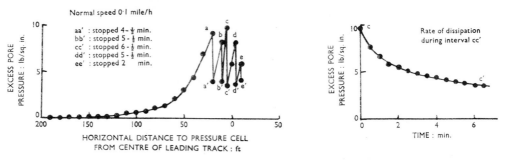

Fig. 2.   **Typical pore–pressure observations during first passage of transporter and LUT, Saturn causeway.   The pressure cell is located at a depth of 19·2 ft**

pressure thus kept under control.   The only drawback appeared to be the possibility that the advance might have to be so slow that the space programme would be delayed.   This risk was judged to be slight and was accepted.

It proved possible to control the pore pressure within close tolerances by reasonable adjustments in the rate of advance of the load.   Typical results of the observations are shown in Fig. 2.   With each passage, densification occurred and in a general way the pore pressure under the next loading was smaller than before.   The loosest zones, by now clearly defined by the measured surface settlements, were traversed several times until their behaviour approximated that of the sand beneath satisfactory portions of the causeway.   Lateral displacements, indicating gradual shearing distortions of the mass of sand, were clearly shown by the slope indicators.   They did not exceed about 1·5 in.

After the combination of field measurements and 'proof testing', the causeway was felt to be conditioned to the point that it would be safe to operate the fully loaded transporter at its normal speed, with the only restriction that the pore pressures should be observed and controlled.   If these pressures should exceed a predetermined amount that had in fact already been exceeded during the previous tests, the rate of advance of the transporter should be reduced as necessary.

This programme was followed with the greatest success.   No restrictions on rate of travel were found necessary in routine operation of the transporter, and with each passage of the load the safety improved.

AB INITIO APPLICATIONS

Harris Trust excavation support

Although the observational method often offers the best way out of difficulties that have already developed, its intended use from the inception of a project offers even more opportunity for imaginative planning and may lead to the best possible design from the points of view of safety, economy and time.[2]   For example, the bracing system for support of the sides of the excavation for the Harris Trust building in Chicago was designed to take advantage of knowledge of the actual conditions at the site.   A cross section through the proposed excavation, indicating the levels of bracing as determined by the requirements of the permanent substructure, is shown in Fig. 3(a).   The contractor had at his disposal the results of

---

[2] One of the earliest and best examples of the use of the method from the beginning of a project was to ensure the verticality of the turbine shafts at the Svir III hydroelectric project (Graftio, 1936; Terzaghi and Peck, 1948).   Since Terzaghi was a consultant on the work, it is more than likely that he was responsible for the approach.

THE INFLUENCE OF STRAINS IN SOIL MECHANICS

K. H. ROSCOE

INTRODUCTION

I greatly appreciate the honour of being invited to give the Tenth Rankine Lecture personally but more as a tribute to the work of all the past and present members of the team that I represent. I thank Sir John Baker for his kind remarks and because working under his leadership I have benefited greatly as a person and as an engineer. The first day I met him in 1945 he asked me if I had ever heard of soil mechanics. When I answered 'no' he gave me Terzaghi's (1943) textbook and said, 'Come back in two months' time and tell me if you'd like to start work in soil mechanics here'. Shortly after returning to Cambridge Sir John advised me to visit the Building Research Station for a fortnight to discover what soil mechanics was about. There I met Dr L. F. Cooling who both then and since has given me much sound advice, and Professor A. W. Skempton who introduced me to the penetrating writings of Hvorslev (1937) and Rendulic (1938). I still think that Terzaghi's book is one of the best I have read in soil mechanics, but even it, like its many successors, provided a great challenge in that the approach to this material called soil was concerned only with its behaviour at failure. Load-deformation curves were never discussed, except, of course, in the section on long term, one-dimensional settlements or when the soil was assumed to be a bed of elastic springs.

I was made fully aware of the limitations of this type of approach to the subject when Sir John Baker asked me in 1951 to design foundations that would fail when the steel portal frames that they supported were loaded to collapse. The designers of the portals (span 6 m) told me the moment M, the vertical force V and horizontal force H that the portals when collapsing would impose on each foundation, provided that the foundations either did not move or behaved as perfect pin joints which were not displaced. Ideally I should then have been able to design foundations under these loads and tell the structural designers what displacements and rotations they might expect for the feet of their portal frames. They could then modify their estimates of M, V and H and by a process of trial and error we could together arrive at a reasonable solution to the problem (see Roscoe, 1958). However, the soil mechanics theories that were then in use did not contain any mention of displacements, except for vertical settlements. They were restricted to predicting the forces that the soil would impose on the foundation when the soil failed. Presumably the designer was meant to assume that the foundation did not move until the soil failed, and then the movements were catastrophic. Even for failure conditions the current theories (which are still in use) were lamentably restricted. In the portal frames the eccentricity of loading M/V was so great that excessively large pad footings were required when designed according to Meyerhof (1951, 1953). Eventually, short pier foundations were selected which were constrained to rotate about ground level as described by Roscoe (1957). The forces that were assumed to act on these footings when the soil failed are shown in Fig. 1. The weight of the pier is W, but to determine the soil forces P_1, P_2 and P_3 it was first necessary to reduce the problem to two dimensions by assuming that the forces per unit length of an infinite strip foundation were identical to those on the piers. The methods currently available for assessing the magnitudes of P_1, P_2 and P_3 are discussed in detail later, but before any use could be made of them in the portal frame problem it was necessary to know or estimate the magnitudes of the angles of wall friction δ_1, δ_2 and δ_3 as well as of the positions of the forces $\bar{z}_1$, $\bar{z}_2$ and $\bar{z}_3$. Details of the methods of making guesses of the magnitudes

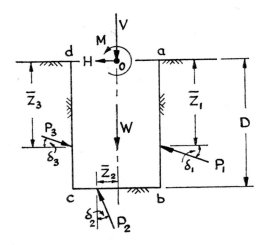

Fig. 1.   Two-dimensional system of forces assumed to act on pier

of these nine quantities have been discussed by Roscoe and Schofield (1956). It is not surprising that any agreement between prediction and observation for the large-scale portal tests was entirely fortuitous. After collapse of the portal frames, during which none of the piers failed, the problem was slightly simplified by removing the tops of the frames and then testing each pier in turn to failure by applying a horizontal load to the top of the stanchion to which it was attached. The experimental results were compared with the predictions of seven different theories, but again the necessary assumptions were so numerous and based on a negligible quantity of reliable relevant data that any agreement between prediction and observation was a matter of chance.

Current theoretical methods of assessing the failure values of P, z and δ are discussed later. The soil mechanician should not be interested only in failure; he should be concerned with being able to predict the movements of a foundation when subjected to given working loads. It will then be possible to design a foundation and its superstructure as a unit. Before this can be done a detailed study of the stress–strain behaviour of soils must be made. We have been concentrating attention on such a study at Cambridge for the past two decades and some of this work has been summarized by Roscoe (1969).

OBJECTIVES OF CAMBRIDGE RESEARCH

The immediate aims of the Cambridge work have been to

(a) work with soils in their simplest possible states (e.g. well graded sands and saturated remoulded clays) so that their properties can be defined by the minimum possible number of parameters—these parameters are associated with the critical state as indicated by Roscoe (1969) or in more detail by Schofield and Wroth (1968)

(b) prepare soil samples in initially uniform states (e.g. see Roscoe, 1967)

(c) devise test equipment which will enable fundamental soil parameters to be measured under as wide a variety of imposed stress and/or strain paths as possible (e.g. simple shear, biaxial and true triaxial apparatus, see Report on specialty session 16, Mexico Conference, 1969)

(d) develop non-destructive (e.g. X- and γ-ray) methods of checking the uniformity of the behaviour of the soils at all stages of these tests (see Coumoulos, 1968)

(e) develop scanning electron microscopy methods of studying the change of soil fabric during mechanical deformation

(f) develop stress–strain theories for these soils in terms of the fundamental soil parameters (e.g. see Roscoe and Burland, 1968)

(g) carry out model tests on mixed boundary value problems in which all boundary stresses, internal strains and pore pressures within the soil are measured so that their observed values can be compared with those predicted from the stress–strain theories (e.g. see James and Bransby, 1970a)

(h) develop centrifugal model test methods so that prototype problems can be studied at reduced scale (e.g. see Roscoe, 1968a)

(i) carry out controlled field tests to check the theories at full-scale.

Our ultimate objective is to develop simple methods for the practising engineer which will enable him to predict, with confidence, either the movements of a foundation, wall and so on when subjected to a given load, or the forces imposed on the foundation when it is subjected to known displacements relative to the soil.

We have made considerable progress with the immediate aims and are about to embark in limited fields upon our ultimate objective.

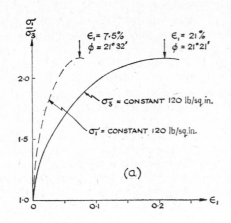

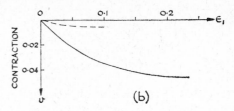

Fig. 2. Influence of stress path on strains to develop peak stress ratio during triaxial tests on identical samples of normally consolidated Weald Clay. Continuous curves for constant cell pressure at 120 lb/sq. in. and axial stress increased. Dashed curves for constant axial stress at 120 lb/sq. in. and cell pressure reduced

Need for versatility in shear testing soils

We have concentrated at Cambridge on developing a wide range of shear test equipment because our knowledge of the stress–strain behaviour of soils will be seriously restricted if we only do tests such as the axisymmetric triaxial test in one type of apparatus. The need for this versatility can best be shown to those familiar with the axisymmetric triaxial test by considering Fig. 2. This shows the relationship between the stress ratio σ_1/σ_3, where σ_1 is the major and σ_3 is the minor principal effective stress, and the axial strain ϵ_1 and volumetric strain v during two conventional axisymmetric triaxial compression tests by Parry (1956) on initially identical samples of Weald Clay. In one test (represented by the continuous curves) the cell pressure ($\sigma_2 = \sigma_3$) was maintained constant at 120 lb/sq. in., while the axial stress σ_1 was increased. In the other test (represented by the dashed curves) the axial stress σ_1 was maintained constant at 120 lb/sq. in. while the cell pressure was reduced. Both samples attain the same peak stress ratio and therefore have the same limiting angle of internal friction $\phi = 21\cdot5°$, but the first sample required an axial strain of $\epsilon_1 = 21\%$ to develop this ϕ while the second only required a strain of $\epsilon_1 = 7\cdot5\%$. The first test corresponds to soil failure under passive, and the second under active, conditions. When taking ϕ as the same at all points on a failure surface, such as in a stability of slope problem or in the stability of a retaining wall, is it not relevant that even according to the triaxial test the strains required to develop ϕ are three times as much in the passive as in the active region, especially if the ultimate strength is less than the peak strength?

The stress and/or strain paths imposed in conventional triaxial tests are rarely, if ever, strictly applicable to an element of soil in the field. In research laboratories it is therefore imperative that soils are tested under as wide a range of stress and strain paths as possible. Hambly and Roscoe (1969) describe a new biaxial test machine, which is shown in Fig. 3. The rectangular sample P is constrained between two glass plates (the top plate is removed in Fig. 3(b)). The four platens A, B, C and D can change the dimensions of the sample to any magnitude between 13 cm and 7 cm as shown in Fig. 3(a) under stress or strain-controlled conditions. The biaxial apparatus is limited to testing under plane–strain conditions and in the light of experience with it J. A. Pearce has recently built a true triaxial machine according to principles laid down by Hambly (1969). This apparatus, shown in Fig. 4, operates in the same manner as the biaxial apparatus but also permits independent variation of the third dimension of a cube-shaped sample. In both the biaxial and true triaxial apparatus each platen can contain load cells to measure the boundary contact stresses. A typical load cell for the true

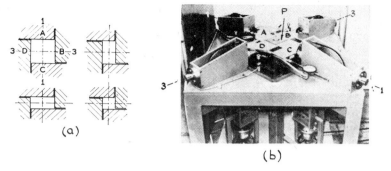

Fig. 3.   Biaxial apparatus: (a) schematic diagram, (b) with top glass
plate removed showing sample P

Fig. 4.   Overall view of true triaxial
apparatus

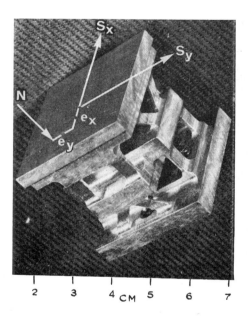

Fig. 5.   Load cell for measuring magnitudes of shear forces S_x and S_y and
magnitude N and eccentricities e_x
and e_y of normal force

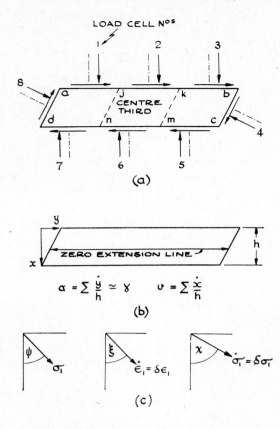

Fig. 6. Schematic diagram of Mks 4–8 of
the simple shear apparatus showing
(a) load cells, (b) strains with horizontal
line of zero-extension, (c) definitions of
the angles ψ, ξ and χ

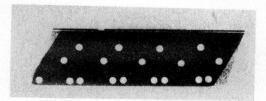

Fig. 7. Two superimposed radiographs
of dense sand containing lead shot
after increment of shear strain under
post-peak stress ratio conditions.
Black rupture zone between lower
two rows of shot shows failure zone
is along a line of zero-extension

triaxial is shown in Fig. 5.   We have developed at Cambridge a range of load cells for a variety of purposes and in particular a special model for use in the field; twelve such load cells have been operating satisfactorily for more than three years under an embankment in Canada.   The smallest load cells we have yet made are pore pressure probes about 4 mm long and 3 mm in diameter.

All these types of shear test apparatus suffer from the limitation that they compel the principal axes of stress and of strain to coincide at all times on the boundaries of the soil sample.   The data obtained from them will therefore not necessarily be of general application in field problems.   This is because these principal axes frequently rotate on an element of soil in the field as it is subjected to load from, say, a footing.   I know of only two types of laboratory shear test equipment that cause the principal axes to rotate during the test.   The first type applies torsion to a hollow thin cylinder of soil which is subjected to internal and external radial pressures (e.g. see Saada, 1968); such a test is complicated to carry out and samples are difficult to prepare.   The second type is the simple shear apparatus in which the test procedure and sample preparation is as simple as in a standard shear box test.   Eight different models of the simple shear apparatus have been developed at Cambridge.   In all models subsequent to the Mk 4 the boundaries of the sample abcd are surrounded by at least eight load cells as indicated in Fig. 6(a).   The shear strain at any stage of a test is denoted by $\alpha = \Sigma(\dot{y}/h)$ where $\dot{y}$ is a small increment of y and h is the height of the sample as shown in Fig. 6(b).   If the sample dilates h will depend on y.   When testing sands and clays it has always been found that α is approximately equal to the maximum shear strain γ.   (In fact $\alpha = \gamma \cos \nu$ and ν is generally small.)   From the evidence of X- and γ-rays it has been found that the shear strain is most uniform in the central third jkmn of the sample.   From the load cell readings it is possible, as described by Roscoe et al. (1967), to determine the magnitudes and directions of the principal stresses, and therefore of stress increments (or stress rates as they will be called) in the central third at any stage of a test.   The corresponding data for strains and strain rates can be determined from the shear strain α and the vertical strain $\Sigma(\dot{x}/h)$ which is also equal to the volumetric strain v.   The directions of these principal axes of stress, strain rate (increment) and of stress rate (increment) are defined as shown in Fig. 6(c) in which ψ, ξ and χ are the angles with the vertical made by the directions of the major principal stress σ_1, major principal strain rate $\dot{\epsilon}_1$, and major principal stress rate $\dot{\sigma}_1$, respectively.

One of the main features of the simple shear apparatus, the importance of which is emphasized, is that there can be no linear strain in the horizontal y-direction, i.e. horizontal lines are lines of zero-extension in the sample.   The failure planes are always observed to be horizontal in the simple shear apparatus as can be seen in Fig. 7, which is a typical photograph of two superposed successive radiographs of an initially dense sand sample, taken before and after a small increment of shear strain at a late stage of a test when post-peak strength conditions prevailed.   The white spots are images of the lead shot, and the radiographs have been superposed so that the images of the top row of shot in each radiograph are coincident.   If the sample had strained uniformly during the increment of shear distortion then two images of each of the shot in the middle and bottom rows should be visible.   This is only true for the bottom row and hence all the increment of shear distortion has taken place between the middle and bottom rows of shot, as is confirmed by the horizontal dark band on the radiograph between these two rows.   This dark band represents the rupture surface, in which the sand has dilated to the critical state.   It is evident that once a rupture surface has formed all the subsequent shear strain occurs within it and the soil on either side behaves as a solid body.   The important deduction to draw from Fig. 7 is that the rupture surface develops along a line of zero-extension and not along a plane on which the ratio of the shear stress τ to the normal stress σ is a maximum.

The mechanical behaviour of sand is discussed in detail later.

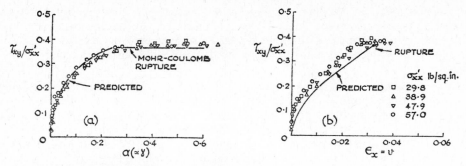

Fig. 8. Curves giving stress–strain relationships for normally consolidated kaolin in simple shear apparatus as predicted by Roscoe and Burland (1968) from soil constants determined in axisymmetric triaxial compression tests. Points represent data actually observed in the simple shear apparatus

Further points concerning immediate aims

A number of stress–strain theories have been developed and in all any fundamental soil parameters that have been used have been related to the critical state.   Recently Roscoe and Burland (1968) initiated the development of a generalized three-dimensional stress–strain theory for soils which are initially looser than critical so that they tend to contract when sheared at constant mean normal stress.   Since dry sands usually exist in states denser than critical they will tend to expand under these conditions, hence the Roscoe and Burland theory is predominantly relevant to normally consolidated and lightly over-consolidated clays or to loose damp sands.   This theory has so far only been successfully confirmed by using it to predict, from the fundamental soil parameters as determined in a conventional triaxial axisymmetric compression test, what happens in the biaxial and simple shear plane–strain types of apparatus.   The work with the biaxial apparatus was particularly interesting in that a wide range of different stress and strain paths were imposed on the samples (Hambly and Roscoe, 1969).   The excellent agreement between prediction and observation in the simple shear tests is shown in Fig. 8(a), where the continuous line gives the relationship between the stress ratio on horizontal planes in the simple shear apparatus τ_{xy}/σ_{xx} and the shear strain α as predicted from soil constants determined by conventional triaxial axisymmetric tests, while the points are as actually observed during simple shear tests.   Fig. 8(b) gives the corresponding information for predicted and observed relationships between τ_{xy}/σ_{xx} and the volumetric strain v.   The real check on this theory will come when the data become available from the true triaxial apparatus and also from a relatively large model apparatus, designed by S. C. Dick, in which fully instrumented model walls and footings can be tested in clays.   This model apparatus can be attached to the new 5 m radius centrifuge that is being built at Cambridge; it is similar to, but larger than, that described by Burland and Roscoe (1969).   The corresponding apparatus for sands is briefly described later.

It is the purpose of this Paper to illustrate the need for this type of fundamental research by considering only one example of how the Cambridge concepts may be used to obtain a new insight into almost every soil mechanics problem.   The example will be that of a vertical retaining wall which is either rotated about its toe, rotated about its top or translated horizontally into a uniform mass of well graded sand with a horizontal free surface.   The cases of rotation about the toe and of translation are usually regarded as the classic passive earth pressure problem in textbooks and are treated as identical; only rarely is mention made in these books of the case of a wall rotating about its top.

In the experimental work attention is restricted to sands because the Cambridge model test work has been far more extensive in sands than in clays.   Since failure surfaces in our models

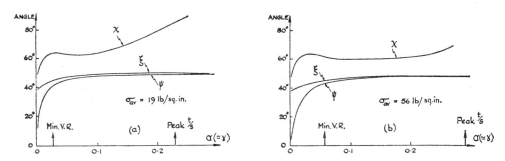

Fig. 9. Curves showing angles made with the vertical of directions, ψ of σ_1, ξ of $\dot{\epsilon}_1$ and χ of $\dot{\sigma}_1$ (see Fig. 6(c)) during simple shear tests on medium dense ($e_0 = 0.64$) sand at $\sigma_{av} = $ constant: (a) 19 lb/sq. in., (b) 56 lb/sq. in.

are of the order of ten grains thick they can readily be seen to develop during tests by non-destructive X-radiographic methods when dealing with sands, whereas a scanning electron microscope is required to study them properly in clays.

BASIC PROPERTIES OF SAND AS DETERMINED IN THE SIMPLE SHEAR APPARATUS

The particular sand used at Cambridge has been Leighton Buzzard rounded sand which passes the 14, but is retained on the 25, BS sieve. It has maximum and minimum voids ratios of 0.79 and 0.49 respectively as determined by methods recommended by Kolbuszewski (1965). Unfortunately, when dry this sand cannot be set up in a state looser than critical and consequently will always expand when sheared sufficiently to reach the critical state. The denser the sample the greater this expansion and the larger will be the peak strength compared to the ultimate (critical state) strength. While in the condition between peak and critical states the sand is unstable and will tend to fail on the thinnest possible zone, band or surface, which is approximately ten grains thick. Once these rupture bands have formed the strains become concentrated within them and the neighbouring material on either side behaves as a rigid body as indicated in Fig. 7. Cole (1967) made an extensive series of tests on this sand in the Mk 6 simple shear apparatus. Some typical results have been described by Roscoe et al. (1967) which showed that for monotonically increasing stresses the principal axes of strain rate (increment) and of stress coincided as the sand was sheared, except for the earliest stages of the test before the sample developed its minimum voids ratio. The results of two such tests are shown in Fig. 9 in which ψ is the angle that the major principal stress σ_1 makes with the vertical, while χ and ξ are the corresponding angles for the major principal stress rate $\dot{\sigma}_1$ and for the major principal strain rate $\dot{\epsilon}_1$ respectively (see Fig. 6(c)). This coincidence of axes of strain rate and of stress corresponds to the behaviour expected of a plastic material and it was noted that at no stage of a test did the axes of strain rate and of stress rate coincide as would be expected of an elastic material. However, if after monotonic increase of the shear stress it was reduced and then increased again the sand did behave elastically. In Fig. 10(a) the shear stress τ_{xy} and the normal stress σ_{xx} are acting on horizontal planes in the central third of the sample (see Fig. 6(a)), while α denotes the shear distortion. The α axis in Fig. 10 starts with a false origin and is broken in two places so that the end of the initial virgin loading process AB can be separated from the unloading BC and the reloading CD; in reality ABCD is a continuous curve. It can be seen from Fig. 10(b) that during the virgin loading AB the axes of strain rate ξ and of stress ψ coincide (since $\psi = \xi$) indicating plastic behaviour, while during unloading BC the axes of stress rate χ and strain rate ξ coincide (since $\chi = \xi$). They continue to coincide (so that $\chi = \xi$) during reloading CD until the stress ratio corresponding to the previous value at

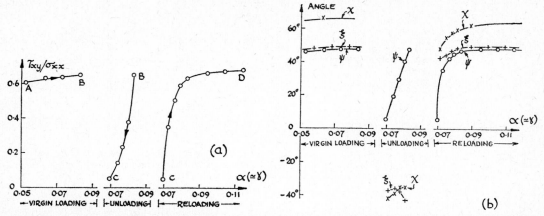

Fig. 10.   (a)   **Stress ratio on horizontal plane in central third against shear strain during unloading and reloading of the shear stress τ_{xy} in a σ_{av}=constant (19 lb/sq. in.) simple shear test on
sand (e_0=0·64).   (b) Curves showing coincidence of principal axes of stress ψ and strain
rate ξ during plastic yield and of stress rate χ and strain rate ξ during elastic behaviour.
(For definitions of ψ, ξ and χ see Fig. 6(c))**

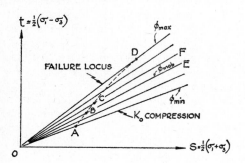

Fig. 11.   **Typical family of successive yield loci
for given initial voids ratio of Leighton Buzzard sand in the Mk 6 simple shear apparatus**

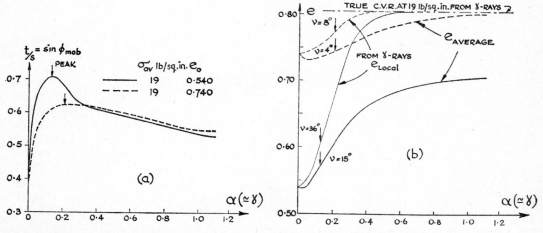

Fig. 12.   (a)   **Typical stress ratio t/s in central third versus average shear strain α curves for dense
(full line) and loose (dashed line) sand in the Mk 6 simple shear apparatus.   (b) Voids ratio
e versus average shear strain α relationships for tests in (a)**

B is reattained, when the sample begins to yield once more and again $\psi = \xi$. This result is of immediate practical importance in that it permits interpretation of data from tests on this sand made in less sophisticated models of the simple shear apparatus in which the average normal σ_{av} and shear τ_{av} stresses on horizontal planes are recorded. In all models of the simple shear apparatus the linear strain rate is zero in a horizontal direction so that only the vertical linear strain rate $\dot{\epsilon}_x$, and the shear strain rate with reference to the horizontal and vertical planes $\dot{\alpha}$, have to be measured. Consequently Mohr's circle of strain rate can be drawn and the angle ξ can be determined. Since $\psi = \xi$ it is now possible to determine the corresponding Mohr's circle of stress by merely knowing τ_{av} and σ_{av}. Hence the principal stresses σ_1 and σ_3 and the invariants of stress can be calculated, and data from the simple shear apparatus can be compared with those from other types of test equipment (such as the conventional triaxial axisymmetric apparatus) in which the principal stresses are recorded.

From an extensive series of tests on the Leighton Buzzard sand in the Mk 6 simple shear apparatus, Cole (1967) concluded that up to and including the development of peak stress ratio $(t/s)_{max}$, where $t = \frac{1}{2}(\sigma_1 - \sigma_3)$ and $s = \frac{1}{2}(\sigma_1 + \sigma_3)$, the sand behaved as an elastic plastic anisotropic work hardening material with a family of yield loci below the failure locus as shown in Fig. 11. These loci are approximately straight lines through the origin but their slopes diminish slightly as s increases. Each of these lines can be considered to correspond to a mobilized angle of friction ϕ_{mob} since

$$\frac{t}{s} = \frac{\frac{1}{2}(\sigma_1 - \sigma_3)}{\frac{1}{2}(\sigma_1 + \sigma_3)} = \sin \phi_{mob} \qquad \qquad \text{. . . . . (1)}$$

with the maximum value ϕ_{max} corresponding to Mohr–Coulomb rupture. In Fig. 11 the curve ABCD is a typical stress path during a test. Point A corresponds to the initial K_0 condition, where K_0 is the coefficient of earth pressure at rest. If the stress ratio t/s is increased monotonically along AB so that B is the largest stress ratio the sample has experienced, then line OBE is the current yield locus, i.e. if the stress ratio is reduced below that corresponding to OBE then the sample behaves elastically but if the stress ratio is increased above OBE then plastic irrecoverable strains will occur. The sample work hardens during this plastic deformation in the sense that when, for example, a stress ratio corresponding to C has been attained the current yield locus will be OCF. Finally at D the sample fails on as thin a band as possible; thereafter the strains as determined from measurements of the movements of the boundaries of the sample are likely to have little meaning and to be gross underestimates of what is really happening in the failure bands. Cole also plotted strain rate vectors and found they were not normal to the actual yield loci of Fig. 11. He determined the components of these vectors by carrying out a small stress probe cycle at constant t/s; since the stresses were identical before and after the probe, the strains observed should have been entirely plastic. It would therefore appear that the concept of normality of theoretical plasticians is not relevant to sand, but this remark must be tempered by the knowledge that Cole was determining strains by measuring movements of the boundaries of the sample so that he was making the assumption that the whole sample was deforming uniformly. After developing a special theory of the attenuation of γ-rays by granular materials, which takes account of the fact that such rays can never be truly collimated, Coumoulos (1968) was able to show that the voids ratio changes, and hence volumetric strains in local regions of Cole's samples were underestimated to the extent that they might be recorded as half their true magnitudes. (This work has been briefly reported by Roscoe (1967).) In Fig. 12(a) the relationships between the stress ratio t/s and the shear distortion α are shown for two typical tests of Cole's on initially dense (full line) and initially loose (dashed line) samples of sand all subjected to a constant average vertical stress $\sigma_{av} = 19$ lb/sq. in. The corresponding void ratios e at all stages of these tests are shown in Fig. 12(b) where the thick lines refer to the average voids ratio of the whole sample and the thin lines to local voids ratios as measured by Coumoulos with γ-rays at the points within the samples that first began to dilate. These points had been previously determined by X-radiographs.

A parameter is now introduced called the angle of dilation ν which was first drawn to the attention of soil mechanicians by Hansen (1958). It is a parameter that is as significant as ϕ and is defined by the equation

$$-\frac{\dot{v}}{\dot{\gamma}} = -\frac{\dot{\epsilon}_1 + \dot{\epsilon}_3}{\dot{\epsilon}_1 - \dot{\epsilon}_3} = \sin \nu \qquad \ldots \ldots \ldots \quad (2)$$

where $\dot{\epsilon}_1$ and $\dot{\epsilon}_3$ are the major and minor principal compressive strain rates respectively. The slopes of the curves in Fig. 12(b) may be used to determine the value of ν at any stage of a test. Cole's average curves in Fig. 12(b) give dilation rates at conditions of peak stress ratios (vertical arrows) of $\nu_{max} = 15°$ (dense) and $4°$ (loose), respectively. Coumoulos's curves, based on the correct local value of $\dot{v}$ but only the average value of $\dot{\gamma}$ (which will be an underestimate of the local value of $\dot{\gamma}$ in the deforming zone), give gross overestimates of the values of ν_{max}, namely $36°$ (dense) and $8°$ (loose). No proper assessment of Cole's values can yet be made, since, although Coumoulos showed that Cole was grossly underestimating $\dot{v}$, he did not show to what extent Cole was underestimating $\dot{\gamma}$.

It is essential that correct values of dilation rates and the associated stresses are determined because in developing a stress–strain theory for any type of elastic-plastic work-hardening material such as sand appears to be, two basic requirements are a yield surface and a flow rule. The successive yield surfaces as a sample of sand hardens are given in Fig. 11.

A yield surface is a curve or surface in stress space (e.g. the t–s space in Fig. 11) such that if the soil is subjected to stresses represented by a point within that surface then the soil will deform elastically, whereas if the point is outside it yields plastically. The flow rule can be obtained either from the normality concepts of the theory of plasticity (which does not appear to be relevant to sand) or by some energy equation which will relate stresses and strain rates, i.e. it will relate ϕ_{mob} and ν_{mob}, where ν_{mob} is the current mobilized dilation rate. There is also a third basic requirement in developing a stress–strain theory for a material such as sand: a work-hardening law. Such a law relates some invariant strain parameter such as volumetric strain with the stresses as the current yield locus of a soil changes as it hardens. Roscoe and Burland (1968) were able to develop a simple hardening law for wet clays, but it is difficult to obtain an equally simple law for sands. We believe that such a law should be related to critical state parameters but even this concept has only recently been confirmed for sands (Roscoe, 1967). Pending the development of a simple hardening law the difficulty can be evaded by assuming that one can, for a sample of sand at a given initial voids ratio e_0 and mean stress level s_0, always revert to the t/s–γ relationship for that sand in the simple shear apparatus. Stroud (1970) is now completing a further detailed study of the sand in the Mk 7 simple shear apparatus in which he is endeavouring to develop a work hardening law for the sand. He is paying particular attention to the behaviour of the sand at small mean stress levels ($s < 5$ lb/sq. in. or 35 kN/m^2). His results will be required especially when the model wall apparatus is used to study the onset of active failure, since then the mean stress levels are of the order of 1 lb/sq. in. (or 7 kN/m^2). He has improved the apparatus and also the test technique, in particular the measurement of internal shear and volumetric strains. Stroud placed a regular pattern of lead shot (1 mm dia.), spaced at approximately 4 mm intervals within the central plane of shear in dense samples, in the simple shear apparatus and was able to calculate from their displacements the local strains at about 60 points (each at the centre of a triangle formed by three neighbouring lead shot) uniformly distributed throughout the bulk of the sample. He found that the volumetric v and shear γ strains were remarkably uniform throughout the sample from the start of the test to the attainment of peak stress ratio. After peak stress ratio all the deformation took place within a horizontal zone with its centre at the mid-height of the sample. This zone contained about 30 of the lead shot triangles and the

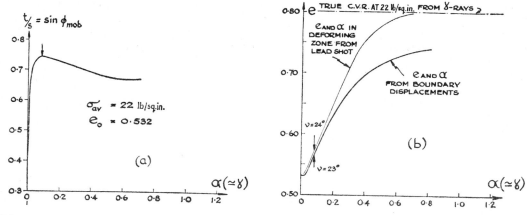

Fig. 13. (a) **Typical stress ratio** t/s **in central third versus average shear strain** α **for dense sand in the Mk 7 simple shear apparatus.** (b) **Voids ratio** e **versus shear strain** α **relationship**

strains within them were uniform. The t/s–α curve for Stroud's test is shown in Fig. 13(a). The thick curve in Fig. 13(b) gives the e–α relationship, where e and α are the averages for the whole sample as determined from measurements of the movements of the boundaries of the sample. The thin curve in Fig. 13(b) relates average values of the local voids ratio e and of the local shear strain γ as determined from the mean of their values in the central 30 triangles. It can be seen that the final critical voids ratio in the deforming zone is identical to that obtained from γ-rays by Coumoulos. Although Stroud's test was at $\sigma_{av} = 22$ lb/sq. in. and initial voids ratio $e_0 = 0.53$, whereas Cole's was at $\sigma_{av} = 19$ lb/sq. in. and $e_0 = 0.54$, the value of $(t/s)_{max}$ obtained by Stroud corresponded to $\phi_{max} = 48°$, whereas Cole's dense test only gave $\phi_{max} = 43°$. The slopes of the e–α or γ curves at peak stress ratio in Fig. 13(b) give dilation rates for the dense sand of $\nu_{max} = 23°$ (thick line) and $\nu_{max} = 24°$ (thin line). The latter is likely to be the more correct since it is based on local values of both volumetric strain and of shear strain. They may be compared with the corresponding value of $\nu_{max} = 15°$ obtained by Cole.

Finally Cole, and this is confirmed by Stroud, found that the stress ratio against shear distortion curve was sensitive to mean stress level. Without a computer attached on line to the load cells of the simple shear apparatus it is not possible to run tests at constant mean stress s. However, the variation of the (t/s)–α relationship during tests on virtually identical samples of dense sand but with different values of the average vertical stress σ_{av} ranging from 6 to 57 lb/sq. in. lay between the continuous curves in Fig. 14(a). The corresponding trend for tests on samples of loose sand is shown by the dashed curves. The mean stress level evidently has some effect on the stress ratio t/s and hence on ϕ_{mob}, but as can be seen in Fig. 14(b) has an even more marked effect upon the dilation rate $\dot{v}/\dot{\gamma}$ and hence upon ν_{mob}. In Fig. 14(b) the relationships between t/s or ϕ_{mob} and $\dot{v}/\dot{\gamma}$ or ν_{mob} are shown for the same tests depicted in Fig. 14(a). The continuous and dashed curves again relate to tests on dense and loose samples respectively. For intermediate values of the initial voids ratio the data lie within the limits specified by the outer curves. The results of seven tests on identical dense samples at constant $\sigma_{av} = 19$ lb/sq. in. showed scatter which nearly covered the whole range between the upper and lower curves in Fig. 14(b). When inspecting Fig. 14(b) it should be noted that negative values of $\dot{v}/\dot{\gamma}$ correspond to expansion of the sample while the positive values refer to contraction, which for dense samples only occurs over very small strains in which elastic effects may be significant. It must also be recalled that Cole's average values of $\dot{v}/\dot{\gamma}$ will, according to Stroud's results, underestimate the true values. Any satisfactory stress–strain

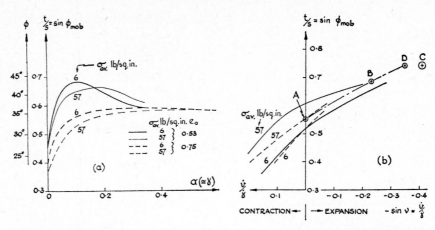

Fig. 14. Effect of average vertical stress σ_{av} on the relationships between stress ratio $t/s=(\sigma_1-\sigma_3)/(\sigma_1+\sigma_3)=\sin\varphi$ and (a) shear strain $\alpha\simeq\gamma$, (b) dilatancy rate $\dot{v}/\dot{\gamma}$ or v for dense (full lines) and loose (dashed lines) sand in the central third of the Mk 6 simple shear apparatus

theory for sands must take account of the variation of stress ratio, and of the even greater variation of dilation rates, with mean stress level and with initial voids ratio at all stages of shear strain.

Cole investigated several theoretical ways of predicting the relationship between t/s or ϕ_{mob} and $\dot{v}/\dot{\gamma}$ or v_{mob} as observed in his tests. He came to the conclusion that the stress–dilatancy rule of Rowe (1962) could be made to give a reasonable first approximation to the data shown in Fig. 14(b). Rowe's rule can be expressed in the form

$$\frac{t}{s} = \frac{(K-1)-(K+1)\dot{v}/\dot{\gamma}}{(K+1)-(K-1)\dot{v}/\dot{\gamma}} \qquad \cdot \quad \cdot \quad \cdot \quad \cdot \quad \cdot \quad \cdot \quad (3)$$

where $K=\tan^2[45+(\phi_f/2)]$ and Cole suggested that K and ϕ_f could be treated as constants. This is equivalent to replacing the data of Fig. 14(b) by a single curve. By inserting the value of $t/s=0.55$ at $\dot{v}/\dot{\gamma}=0$, corresponding to point A in Fig. 14(b), into equation (3) Cole obtained $K=3.445$. This value of K was then used to plot the relationship between t/s and $\dot{v}/\dot{\gamma}$ as predicted by equation (3); it is represented by the chain dotted curve AB in Fig. 14(b) and the point B corresponds to the maximum value of t/s observed by Cole in tests on dense samples at the low stress level of $\sigma_{av}=6$ lb/sq. in. This value of $(t/s)_{max}=0.682$ corresponds to $\phi_{max}=43°$. At B the maximum dilation rate predicted from equation (2) with $t/s=0.682$ and $K=3.445$ is $\dot{v}/\dot{\gamma}_{max}=0.228$ or $v_{max}=13°$, whereas Cole actually observed an average value of $v_{max}=15°$. On the other hand Stroud obtained $(t/s)_{max}=0.741$, corresponding to $\phi_{max}=47.8°$ at an average value of $v_{max}=23°$ and locally of $v_{max}=24°$. The point C in Fig. 14(b) corresponds to the latter. The point D is considered later.

It is evident from Fig. 14(b) that the assumption that there is a unique relationship between t/s and $\dot{v}/\dot{\gamma}$ for all samples in all states is more likely to be true while they are expanding than while contracting. Further the variation in the possible values of t/s for a given negative value of $\dot{v}/\dot{\gamma}$ in this region of expansion is far less than the corresponding possible variation in $\dot{v}/\dot{\gamma}$ for a given value of t/s. The data for the loose tests do not extend far into this region of expansion which is therefore predominantly relevant to dense samples between the point of minimum voids ratio and peak stress ratio conditions. It is seen later when discussing Bransby's (1968) model wall tests that, in his early attempts to predict stress patterns near the wall from the strain patterns he had experimentally observed, he only used the stress–

dilatancy rule when referred to dense tests by extrapolating the curve AB to point D in Fig. 14(b). This was because Bransby observed higher dilation rates in his wall test than Cole had observed in the Mk 6 simple shear apparatus; the detailed results of Stroud's work with the Mk 7 apparatus are still unavailable and had scarcely begun when Bransby was analysing his wall data. Further discussion of the results from the simple shear apparatus is deferred until the data from some model wall tests are given.

THEORETICAL METHODS FOR SOLVING PASSIVE PRESSURE RETAINING WALL PROBLEMS

No attempt is made here to go into details of the methods that are currently used to solve passive earth pressure retaining wall problems since they can be found in textbooks. However, it is desirable to consider the underlying assumptions upon which they depend and to state what each theory considers to be the answer to the problem.

As a basis for discussion consider the wall AB of height D in Fig. 15(a) which is being pushed in some, as yet unspecified, way into a mass of initially uniform sand with a horizontal surface. Most theories assume that the wall rotates about its base B (which is not subjected to any horizontal or vertical displacement, i.e. remains fixed in space) or is translated horizontally (with no vertical movement) into the sand. No attention is paid to the extent of this rotation or horizontal movement, it is merely assumed to be sufficient to generate failure of the sand on a rupture surface that passes through the base of the wall B and extends to the free surface of the sand as represented by BC in Fig. 15(a). At this instant of failure the sand everywhere along BC, whatever the shear strain it is actually experiencing, is presumed to develop its largest stress ratio τ/σ, where τ is the shear stress along an element of BC at any arbitrary point E and σ is the normal stress across that element. This value of τ/σ is not exceeded on any other plane through the arbitrary point E and is independent of the intermediate principal stress acting perpendicular to the plane of Fig. 15(a). For a dense sand this is equivalent to assuming that its stress ratio–shear strain relationship corresponds to OD_1D_2 in Fig. 15(b),

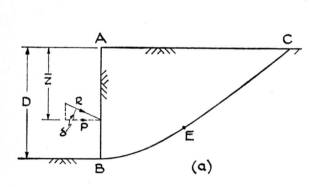

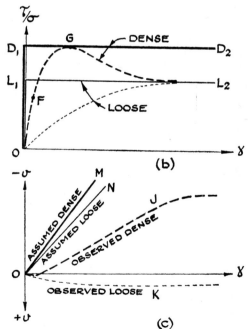

Fig. 15. (a) Typical assumed failure surface BC for determining passive force R on wall AB. Comparison of assumed (full lines) and observed (dashed lines) relationships between shear strain γ, (b) stress ratio τ/σ, (c) volumetric strain v for sand on arc BC or in sector ABC

i.e. the sand is taken to be rigid, perfectly plastic material. If the sand is loose the relevant stress ratio–shear strain curve is taken to be OL_1L_2. The more familiar way of stating these assumptions is that ϕ is constant round the arc BC and its magnitude depends on the initial density of the sand.

The next step in such theories is to assume a shape for the rupture surface BC in Fig. 15(a). If it is straight then the magnitude of the resultant force R (but not its location $\bar{z}$) can be determined by simple resolution of forces for the triangle ABC provided the direction of R (namely the overall angle of wall friction δ) is assumed to be known. There is no need to assume any value of the magnitude of σ at all points such as E on BC in Fig. 15(a). Concerning the magnitude of $\bar{z}$ most textbooks imply that $\bar{z} = \frac{2}{3}D$ and some base this on the concept that, if the sand in the triangle ABC had everywhere failed on straight lines parallel to BC, then by finding the horizontal component P of the force R on various depths z and by calculating dP/dz the pressure distribution is hydrostatic. Alternatively if the users of this theory had made the assumption that the distribution of σ on the straight rupture line BC was hydrostatic, then they could locate R by simple statics since R must pass through the intersection of the weight of the sector ABC and the resultant force on rupture line BC. Only if $\delta = 0$ is $\bar{z} = \frac{2}{3}D$ and if $\delta > 0$ then $\bar{z} < \frac{2}{3}D$. Other commonly assumed shapes for BC are that it is, at least in part, a circle or a logarithmic spiral. Restriction is usually placed on the centre or pole of these curves. If a circle is used it is necessary to estimate a distribution of the normal stress σ across it and then P and $\bar{z}$ can be found by simple statics provided a value of δ is assumed. If a logarithmic spiral is used it is not necessary to estimate the distribution of σ but the magnitude of P can then only be obtained if values of both $\bar{z}$ and δ are assumed.

Usually textbooks ignore the passive problem of the wall rotating about its top A (see Fig. 15(a)) into the sand, although most discuss the active case of the wall rotating about its top away from the sand. This is generally catered for by imposing a different restriction on the centre of the circle or pole of the spiral than was assumed for rotation about the toe B or for horizontal translation of the wall. To obtain a solution for the passive pressure problem the reader is left to make some such additional assumption or to presume that the answer to the problem of rotation about the top is the same as about the bottom of the wall. One notable exception to this is discussed by Harr (1966, pp. 217–225). Harr outlines a method developed by Dubrova for assessing the pressure distributions at soil failure on walls which rotate about their toe, oi top, or are subjected to horizontal translation. She assumes for the walls that rotate that the full value of the angle of internal friction ϕ_{max} only develops along a straight failure surface which rises from the point of maximum displacement of the wall and makes an angle of $[45° - (\phi_{max}/2)]$ to the free surface of the sand. At the axis of rotation the value of ϕ_{mob} is zero and this value is relevant along a straight line that passes through this axis and makes an angle of 45° with the sand surface. At any intermediate point between the axis of rotation and the point of maximum wall displacement the relevant value of ϕ_{mob} is obtained by linear interpolation between $\phi = 0$ and $\phi = \phi_{max}$. Again the corresponding straight line on which the soil is failing at this intermediate value of ϕ_{mob} makes an angle of $[45° - (\phi_{mob}/2)]$ with the sand surface. Dubrova can also take account of the fact that the local angle of wall friction δ' at any depth on the wall varies and is not equal to the overall average value δ. To obtain the pressure distribution at failure on the wall when it is translated horizontally she assumes that the pressure at any depth z is the mean of the two values obtained for the wall rotating about its top and its toe. While Dubrova's work represents a significant improvement on the previous methods it takes no account of the actual magnitudes of the displacements since they do not appear in her equations. Her method provides no means of assessing the pressure distribution for any conditions other than when the soil first begins to fail over one of the assumed straight rupture surfaces. With a wall rotating about its top this definition of failure might approximate to the development of the maximum force on the wall, but when the wall rotates about its toe the full value of ϕ_{max} is only developed along a straight line of zero length from the top of the wall to the sand surface. The predicted resultant force on the wall will be much less than the maximum that can ultimately be developed. Dubrova's method of predicting the stress distribution at failure of a translating wall is therefore open to criticism.

Before discussing more sophisticated methods of solving the general problem it is desirable to consider further the quandary in which the reader of textbooks will find himself. In some other section of these books he will be told that the stress ratio–shear strain relationships for the dense and loose sand are of the types shown by the dashed curves $OFGL_2$ and OL_2 respectively in Fig. 15(b), and that the sand is not incompressible but dilates as represented by curves OJ (dense) and OK (loose) as shown in Fig. 15(c), at least up to the development of peak stress ratio. All the theories discussed so far make the assumption that in a dense sand the curve $OFGL_2$ can be replaced by OD_1D_2. If we think of strains, can this assumption be valid even to the crudest of approximations? Suppose the point B in Fig. 15(a) is displaced into dense sand by translation or rotation of the wall about its top sufficiently for the shear strain at E to be enough to generate the maximum stress ratio corresponding to G in Fig. 15(b). Is it not likely that, as suggested by Rowe and Peaker (1965), the strains at B at a given instant will be much larger and correspond to a stress ratio given by L_2 while those at C will be much smaller and correspond to point F? It would suggest that gross overestimates of the magnitude of P would always be made for dense sands from the theories discussed if the real values of ϕ_{max} are used rather than those allowed by the Code of Practice. An improvement in accuracy of the predictions might be expected in loose sands since at large strains the curve OL_2 coincides with OL_1L_2 and the peak stress ratio remains constant. Consider the problem of a wall rotating about its toe B into the sand in Fig. 15(a). Intuitively one would expect the strains near the top A of the wall to be far greater than at the toe B and that the angle of wall rotation required to develop ϕ_{max} near B would be much larger than that required to produce the peak force R_m on the wall. It is debatable whether the bottom rupture surface would ever pass through B for angles of rotation of the wall that are small enough to be of practical value. It is interesting to recall that an angle of wall rotation of $\theta = 5\frac{1}{2}°$ about the toe is equivalent to a horizontal displacement of the top of a 20 ft high wall of 2 ft.

The second type of approach that has been developed to retaining wall problems, which is sometimes used but is often regarded as too sophisticated, is that in which it is assumed that the whole mass of sand near the wall (in a sector such as ABC in Fig. 9(a)) is simultaneously failing according to some assumed failure criterion. This criterion and two equations of equilibrium give three equations relating the three components of stress that fully define conditions in a plane–stress type of problem. Sokolovski (1965) assumed the Mohr–Coulomb failure criterion and then developed a finite difference method of solving these equations which is tedious unless done by computer. Sokolovski's method can only be applied to the wall problem if a small surcharge of known magnitude and direction is applied to the free sand surface (AC in Fig. 15(a)), and if the local angle of wall friction δ' is known at every point on the wall. Since he ignores deformations his solutions to the problems of the wall rotating about top, toe or translating will be identical unless he assumes different δ' distributions on the wall for these three different cases. No information was available to assist him in the estimation of such distributions and when applying Sokolovski's method it is usual to assume that $\delta' = \delta = $ constant at all points on the wall. Thinking again of strains, the possibility of developing ϕ_{max}, corresponding to point G for dense and L_2 for loose sand in Fig. 15(b), simultaneously at all points within sector ABC in Fig. 15(a) when the wall rotates about its top or toe is extremely unlikely. One might expect the Sokolovski solution to be more relevant to the stress distribution on the wall when it translates into the soil. It will be important to recall later that the stress characteristic field of Sokolovski consists of two families of curves and/or straight lines which everywhere make angles of $[45° - (\phi_{max}/2)]$ with the direction of the major principal stress and which represent surfaces on which the maximum stress ratio $(\tau/\sigma)_{max}$ is attained.

They are often assumed to be slip lines, but as will be shown later this could never be true in practice for a real soil.

Hansen (1953) makes an alternative use of the three basic equations of the Mohr–Coulomb failure criterion and two of equilibrium in that from them he derives Kötter's equation which gives the variation of normal stress on a rupture surface. If the stress is known at one point on the surface then it can be found from Kötter's equation at all points on such a surface whose shape is known. Hence the magnitude, location and direction of the force across the rupture surface are known and when combined in the three equations of equilibrium with the other known forces on the block (ABC in Fig. 15(a)) they give P, δ and $\bar{z}$. Unfortunately the shape of the rupture surface is not usually known, although Hansen selects suitable rupture patterns by considering the compatibility of the movement of the sand and of the wall. When doing this he assumes the sand is non-dilatant and that the rupture surface can be made up of combinations of straight lines and circular arcs. This means that frequently his rupture surfaces do not meet the boundaries at the statically correct angles, which is a problem that he does not resolve satisfactorily.

Extensive research was carried out in the 1950s by workers in the theories of plasticity to extend the concepts they had developed for metals to materials which failed according to the Mohr–Coulomb criterion. Some of these concepts are discussed after the experimental data are presented later. It will then be even more apparent how extensively they need adapting by methods of the type now being developed at Cambridge if they are to provide a reasonably reliable means of predicting the observed behaviour. The main objection to these theories is that they require excessive dilation of the sand as shown by lines OM and ON in Fig. 15(c) for which $\nu = \phi_{max}$.

MODEL WALL TEST RESULTS

Apparatus and test technique

The versatile model test apparatus used for testing walls or foundations which rotate about any desired centre is shown in Fig. 16. The wall face AB 13 in. high was originally designed as shown to contain 18 of the Cambridge pattern of load cells which measure the magnitude and eccentricity of the normal load and at the same time the shear load on their active faces (see Arthur and Roscoe, 1961). The load cells are arranged in three vertical columns and sometimes the central bottom load cell is replaced by six smaller cells so that more detailed information can be obtained concerning the contact stress distribution between the soil and the wall. The glass-sided sand container has internal dimensions of 8 ft × 5 ft × 7½ in., and the lateral deflexion of the ⅜ in. thick glass sides can be restricted by adjustable supporting pads. The width of 7½ in. permits radiographs to be taken with reasonable exposure times (usually less than 10 min) using a 150 kV X-ray apparatus of a pattern of lead shot (usually 2 mm dia. and a mesh size of about 2 cm) placed within the sand. The sand samples are placed by pouring from a hopper. For dense samples successive layers are poured and the lead shot can then be placed on the surface of the sand using a special template. When preparing loose samples the lead shot are first strung in position on fine wires made of an alloy of 70% silver and 30% copper. The sand is then poured as rapidly as possible and the wires are vaporized by applying 220 V d.c. mains electric supply. A radiograph is taken at the start of a test when the wall rotation θ is zero. The wall is then driven at slow speed through a torquemeter, the readings of which are compared with the net moment on the wall as computed from the load cell readings. At intervals during the test further radiographs are taken. The locations of all the shot are then determined on an automatic film measuring machine designed by Dr R. G. James. This punches out on paper tape the co-ordinates of each shot; the tape is then fed into the large store (128k) Titan computer of the Cambridge Mathematical Laboratory which automatically plots contours of any desired strain at any stage of a test. The strains are computed on the

Fig. 16. Model earth pressure apparatus and recording equipment
showing instrumented wall AB

Table 1. Main features of typical model wall tests

Test number	Initial voids ratio	Investigator	Wall movement	Type of failure
LE	0·52	James	Rotate about top	Passive
LF	0·53			
MB	0·73	Lord		
MD	0·70			
PE	0·51	Bransby	Rotate about toe	
PH	0·77			
NA	0·52	Lucia	Translate	
MC	0·69	Lord	Rotate about top	Active
MF	0·52			

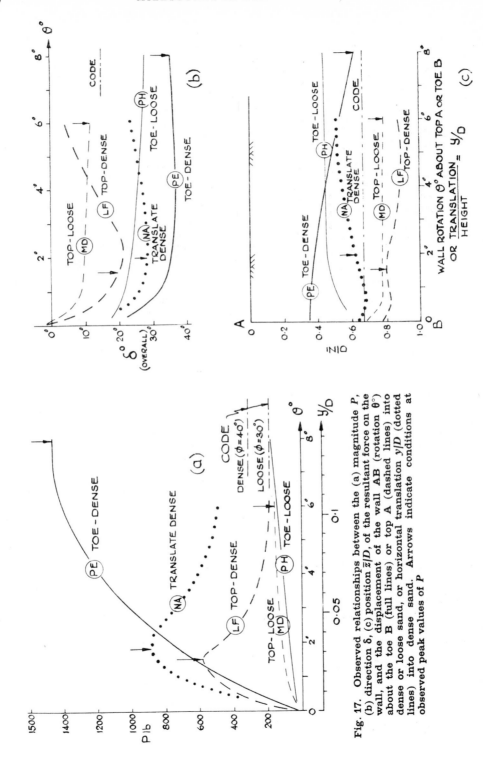

Fig. 17. Observed relationships between the (a) magnitude P, (b) direction δ, (c) position $\bar{z}/D$, of the resultant force on the wall, and the displacement of the wall AB (rotation θ°) about the toe B (full lines) or top A (dashed lines) into dense or loose sand, or horizontal translation y/D (dotted lines) into dense sand. Arrows indicate conditions at observed peak values of P

assumption that each triangle of soil formed by three neighbouring shot is straining uniformly (see Roscoe *et al.*, 1963). Dr James's machine can measure to the nearest micron but has only recently come into use; consequently many of the strain contours presented later in this Paper have been measured by cruder methods.

Arthur and Roscoe (1965) have shown that the glass sides have little influence on the plane strain of the sand mass. This was done by showing that the strain patterns obtained from the radiographs of lead shot were virtually identical with those obtained from camera photographs of markers placed on the inner surface of the glass sides. The glass sides were selected only after many other materials had been considered and a further check on their satisfactory behaviour with the Leighton Buzzard sand is the observation that at no stage in more than twenty tests have the three columns of load cells differed by more than 10% at any level when the stress exceeded 10 lb/sq. in. Usually the difference is much less.

Discussion of typical test results

Some typical results obtained by James (1965), Bransby (1968) and Lord (1969) from tests on the wall shown in Fig. 16 rotating about its toe (B) or top (A) into dense or loose sand are now presented. In all cases sand-paper (grade 2S) was glued to the wall face with a clearance of 0·002 in. between neighbouring load cells. Wherever possible these results are compared with those obtained by Lucia (1966) for a similar, but smaller, wall which was translated horizontally into the dense sand. First it is shown how the magnitude R, direction δ and position $\bar{z}$ of the overall force (see Fig. 15(a)) are greatly dependent on the mode of movement of the wall and that any correlation between these quantities when R is at its maximum value R_m and those predicted by the Code of Practice No. 2 is entirely fortuitous. Second the observed contact stress distributions, and third the observed strain patterns, are contrasted at different stages of rotation about the toe or top of the wall. Similar detailed information for a translated wall is not available but is now being obtained by Dr R. H. Bassett.

The main features of these typical tests are given in Table 1.

Dependence of overall force on wall displacement. The thick continuous curve in Fig. 17(a) gives the observed relationship between P, the component normal to the wall of the resultant force R on the wall (see Fig. 15(a)), and the angle of rotation θ of the wall about its toe into dense sand during test PE. The curve PE may be compared directly with the thick dashed curve LF for the wall when rotated about its top into the dense sand, and also with the heavy dotted curve NA when the wall of height D is translated horizontally a distance y into the dense sand. (The data for tests PE, LF and NA were obtained for walls of height $D = 12 \cdot 1$, 13 and 6 in. respectively; their breadths b varied slightly and consequently all the data in Fig. 17(a) have been scaled for comparison on the assumption that P is proportional to bD^2. The quoted magnitudes of P correspond to $D = 13$ in. and $b = 7 \cdot 60$ in.) The vertical arrows on each of these three curves for dense sand indicate the respective peak values P_m of the force P. When rotating about the top the peak value is 583 lb after a rotation of only 1·4°, whereas when translating the peak value is 885 lb after a horizontal displacement equal to the maximum displacement of the wall after rotation of 2° about either its top or bottom. If the same wall rotates about its toe the peak force is 1470 lb which is only attained after a rotation of 8°. All these observed values may be compared with that obtained from the Code of Practice (using the recommended values of $\delta = 15°$ and the maximum value of $\phi = 40°$ for dense sands) which gives a predicted value for P_m of 314 lb; it is implicit in the Code that this value should be the same for all the three cases, but the rotations or displacement required to attain this value are unspecified. (It is possible to interpret the Code so that for the case of the wall rotating about its toe the value of δ could be taken as 30°. This would lead to a predicted value of $P_m = 469$ lb which may be compared with the observed value in test PE of $P_m = 1470$

lb.) The gross under-prediction of the Code can almost entirely be ascribed to the fact that the maximum value of ϕ it allows is 40°, whereas it will be shown later that a reasonable value of ϕ_{max} for the dense sand is 49°. The tabulated values of the passive pressure coefficient K_p in the Code increase so rapidly with increase of ϕ at high values that few engineers would trust any extrapolation of the data. Whereas the maximum tabulated value of $K_p = 11 \cdot 4$ at $\phi = 40°$ and $\delta = 15°$, the values observed when $P = P_m$ in test PE are $K_p = 35 \cdot 7$ at $\phi = 49°$ and $\delta = 35 \cdot 5°$.

The other two curves in Fig. 17(a) refer to loose sands. The thin continuous line PH $(e_0 = 0 \cdot 77)$ refers to the wall rotating about its toe into the loose sand; it is virtually straight and continues so until the test was stopped at $\theta = 13°$ when $P = 270$ lb. No value of P_m can be quoted for this test since the rotation required for its development would be beyond the range of practical interest. The thin dashed line MD $(e_0 = 0 \cdot 70)$ refers to a wall rotating about its top into a moderately loose sand; the peak value $P_m = 160$ lb was attained at $\theta \simeq 6°$ and this may be compared with the Code value of 183 lb for $\delta = 15°$ and $\phi = 30°$. The Code value would appear to overpredict, i.e. is unsafe, for loose sand especially since such sands require larger wall displacements than can be tolerated in practice to develop the peak value of P.

Figure 17(b) shows the variation of the overall angle of wall friction δ with θ or y/D throughout the five tests and also the value recommended by the Code for peak load conditions, the observed values of which are indicated by the vertical arrows on the curves. The Code value of $\delta = 15°$ for tests LF and NA grossly underestimates, and for MD overestimates, the observed value, whereas the Code value of $\delta = 30°$ for walls rotating about their toe may be correct for the test PH on loose sand but is an underestimate by 5° for test PE on dense sand.

In Fig. 17(c) the curves show the variation of the depth $\bar{z}/D$ of the resultant force on the wall AB for all values of θ or y/D during the five tests. The chain dotted line labelled Code at $\bar{z}/D = 0 \cdot 67$ corresponds to the generally assumed hydrostatic pressure distribution at so-called failure when $P = P_m$. When the wall rotates about its top into moderately loose MD or dense LF sand the resultant force is always at greater depth, $\bar{z}/D > 0 \cdot 8$. On the other hand when rotating about its toe into loose sand PH the force rapidly moves up the wall and then remains at a value of $\bar{z}/D = 0 \cdot 42$, whereas for dense sand PE the force is very high in the early stages with $\bar{z}/D = 0 \cdot 35$, and then steadily descends to $\bar{z}/D = 0 \cdot 6$ when $\theta = 8°$ and $P = P_m$. It would seem that the pressure distribution might be approximately hydrostatic for the translating wall NA up to $P = P_m$, but thereafter changes steadily to a symmetric distribution about the mid-height of the wall.

Further discussion of the curves of Fig. 17 is deferred until the patterns of wall contact stress and of internal strains within the soil are presented.

Wall–soil contact stresses. The distribution of the normal σ_w and shear τ_w wall contact stresses with the sand, as measured by the load cells, is shown at three stages ($\theta = 1°$, 3° and 7° respectively) of wall AB rotating about its toe B into dense sand during test PE in Figs 18 (a–c). The continuous lines refer to σ_w and the dashed lines to τ_w. The length of the arrow representing the resultant force of the wall on the soil is proportional to the value of R/R_m and its position and direction are shown to scale. The conditions in Fig. 18(c) virtually correspond to failure in that $R/R_m = 0 \cdot 99$. The main features to notice concerning Figs 18(a–c) are

(a) the stresses are always negligible over the lowest fifth of the wall height

(b) for any given value of θ the largest values of σ_w and τ_w occur at approximately the same point on the wall, but this point moves down the wall as θ increases

(c) the magnitudes of σ_w and τ_w on the top third of the wall steadily increase up to $\theta = 3°$ but then drop significantly despite further strain as θ is increased to 7°

(d) the magnitudes of σ_w and τ_w on the middle third of the wall develop more slowly than for the top third but continue to increase much longer with increase of θ until they

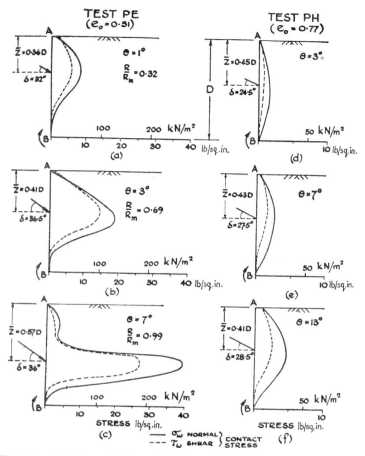

Fig. 18. Variation of stress distribution recorded by load cells as wall AB rotates about toe B into (a-c) dense, (d-f) loose, sand

attain their greatest magnitude of about 40 lb/sq. in. when $\theta=8°$ and $R=R_m$. Bransby (1968) carried out a similar test in which he continued rotation to $\theta=17°$ which also showed that $R=R_m$ when $\theta=8°$. For $\theta>8°$ the magnitudes of σ_w and τ_w reduce greatly in the middle third but slowly begin to build up in the lowest third. The magnitude of R does not change greatly but its point of application drops below $\bar{z}/D=0.8$. Bransby concluded from four tests on dense sand with the wall rotating about its toe that at any point on the wall the maximum value of σ_w is recorded when the horizontal displacement y of the wall at that point has attained a given value. This value of y is approximately the same for all points on the wall

(e) the overall angle of wall friction has attained a magnitude of $\delta=32°$ by the time $\theta=1°$ and thereafter only increases fractionally to $\delta=36°$ when $\theta=7°$

(f) the ratio of τ_w/σ_w is much greater near the top of the wall than the bottom.

The development of wall contact stresses as measured by the load cells during test PH in which the wall rotates about its toe into a loose sand is shown in Figs 18 (d–f) for $\theta=3°$, $7°$ and

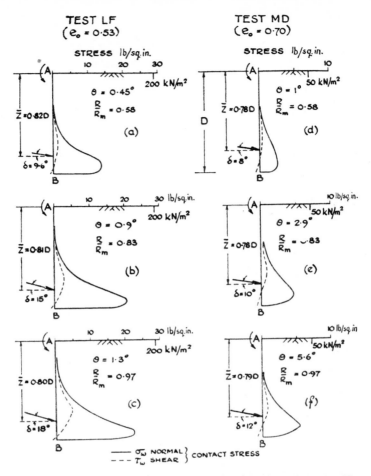

Fig. 19. Variation of stress distribution recorded by load cells as wall AB rotates about top A into (a-c) dense, (d-f) loose, sand

13°. The scale for the stresses in test PH is double that used for test PE, and the maximum recorded stress in test PH on loose sand was only about one tenth of that recorded in test PE on the dense sand. It will be recalled that the magnitude of R was still increasing steadily even when $\theta = 13°$. Throughout the range from $\theta = 3°$ to $\theta = 13°$ the distribution of σ_w is approximately parabolic, but the resultant force moves up the wall as $\bar{z}/D$ decreases from 0·45 to 0·41 and δ increases from 24° to 28° approximately. The shear stress is again zero on the lowest fifth of the wall and the ratio τ_w/σ_w at any point decreases as that point moves down the wall. The magnitudes of σ_w and τ_w build up more quickly on the top half than the bottom half of the wall and at any instant the largest value of τ_w occurs higher up the wall than does the largest value of σ_w.

The distribution of σ_w and τ_w for a wall AB rotating about its top A into a dense sand is shown in Figs 19 (a–c) and into a moderately loose sand in Figs 19 (d–f). The three stages of each test correspond to $R/R_m = 0.58$, 0·83 and 0·97 respectively. Again the stress scale for the loose sand is double that for the dense. The greatest value of σ_w observed in test LF on

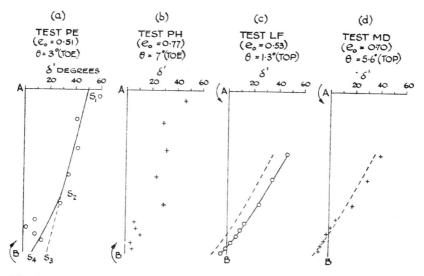

Fig. 20. Variation of δ′ as recorded by load cells as wall AB rotates about
(a) and (b) the toe B, (c) and (d) the top A into dense or loose sand

dense sand was 22·5 lb/sq. in. whereas in test MD on the loose sand it was only 5·5 lb/sq. in. In both cases the normal stresses σ_w are negligible on the top third of the wall even when $R = R_m$, but develop predominantly in the lowest third. At any instant the largest shear stress is considerably higher up the wall than the largest normal stress and at the toe B of the wall the shear stress is at all times acting downwards, rather than upwards, on the wall. In both cases the pattern of stress distribution is developed rapidly, e.g. $\theta = \frac{1}{2}°$ dense and $\theta = 1°$ loose, and thereafter changes little until $R = R_m$ at $\theta = 1·3°$ dense and $\theta = 5·6°$ loose. It is important to notice how small the overall angle of friction δ is at all stages of these tests and how in the dense sand LF it nearly doubles in value (from 9·6° to 18°), while in the loose sand MD it increases considerably (from 8° to 12°) as R/R_m increases from 0·58 to 0·97. It is shown later when considering the prediction of the contact stresses on the wall that it is much more important to know the variation of the local angle of wall friction δ′ over the wall height than to know the average overall value δ.

Variation of local angle of wall friction δ′ over height of wall. The variations of the local angle of wall friction δ′ as measured on each load cell for the wall AB rotating about its toe B into dense sand (test PE at $\theta = 3°$ when $R = 0·69\ R_m$) and into loose sand (test PH at $\theta = 7°$) are represented by the points in Figs 20(a) and (b) respectively. (The curves in Fig. 20(a) should be ignored for the moment.) The development of this pattern of δ′ decreasing for points lower down the wall and becoming virtually zero at the toe B is clearly defined after the first increment of rotation of the wall and remains virtually the same for all values of θ in the test. The scatter in the points at the toe B of the wall is due to the extremely small stress levels in this region (see Fig. 18). The patterns for loose and dense sand are similar but the value of δ′ on the top half of the wall is about 10° less for the loose than for the dense sand.

The corresponding data for walls that rotate about their tops are represented by the points for dense (test LF at $\theta = 1·3°$ when $R \simeq R_m$) and for moderately loose sand (test MD at $\theta = 5·6°$ when $R \simeq R_m$) in Figs 20(c) and (d) respectively. The dashed curves in both these diagrams are the mean values observed in tests on looser samples ($e_0 \simeq 0·75$). The continuous line curve in Fig. 20(c) is the mean for several dense samples with e_0 ranging from 0·52 to 0·57

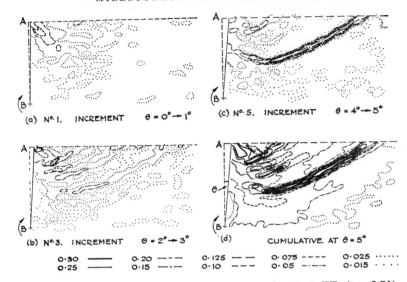

(a) Nº. 1. INCREMENT $\theta = 0° \rightarrow 1°$

(c) Nº. 5. INCREMENT $\theta = 4° \rightarrow 5°$

(b) Nº. 3. INCREMENT $\theta = 2° \rightarrow 3°$

(d)   CUMULATIVE. AT $\theta = 5°$

| 0·30 —— | 0·20 – – – | 0·125 — — | 0·075 – – – – | 0·025 ······ |
| 0·25 —— | 0·15 –·–·– | 0·10 – – – | 0·05 –·––·– | 0·015 · · · · |

Fig. 21. Contours of maximum shear strain, test PE ($e_0 = 0·51$).
(a–c) Contours of shear strain increment $\dot\gamma$ during three typical
increments of rotation of wall AB about its toe B into dense sand
during test PE. (d) Contours of cumulative shear strain γ at peak
load on wall

and all the data for samples of intermediate initial voids ratio lay between these two curves.
No data have been presented in Figs 20 (c) and (d) for the top third of the wall where the
stresses were virtually zero, but the recorded values of δ' always lay within 40° and 60° with
considerable scatter for individual tests.   Perhaps the most striking feature of the information
provided in Fig. 20 is the unexpected similarity in the patterns of distribution of δ' when the
wall rotates about the toe and the top.

Strain patterns.   Figures 21(a–c) show contours of maximum shear strain increment $\dot\gamma$ as
obtained from the measured displacements of the lead shot for three of the five increments of
wall rotation θ required to obtain failure in test PE.   In this test the wall AB was rotating
about its toe B into dense sand.   It is evident that during the first increment ($\theta = 0–1°$) the
strains develop at the top A of the wall and begin to spread downwards from A along a radius
at an angle of about 45° to the horizontal into the sand.   By the third increment (Fig. 21(b)
with $\theta = 2–3°$) the strains are beginning to develop tangentially across and symmetrically
about this radius.   In the fifth increment ($\theta = 4–5°$) approaching peak load ($R = R_m$) the
lowest transverse contours extend to the surface as shown in Fig. 21(c).   If all five increments
of strain are added vectorially the cumulative maximum shear strain γ at failure ($\theta = 5°$) is
obtained as shown in Fig. 21(d).   The similarity between this cumulative strain diagram and
the previous incremental strain diagrams implies that the principal axes of strain rate were not
rotating to any great extent; from the curves shown in Fig. 9 it is expected that all such rotation of principal axes occurred in the earliest stages of the first increment.   The contours of
volumetric strain rate $\dot v$ or cumulative volumetric strain v (compression positive) at the same
stages of test PE are shown in Fig. 22.   It must be remembered that the contours in Figs 21 and
22 are as plotted by the computer from information obtained from about a thousand triangles
in the lead shot mesh.   Bransby (1968) estimated that the maximum likely error is 0·006 for $\dot\gamma$
or γ and 0·008 for $\dot v$ or v; this error would occur in only one of twenty values and usually the

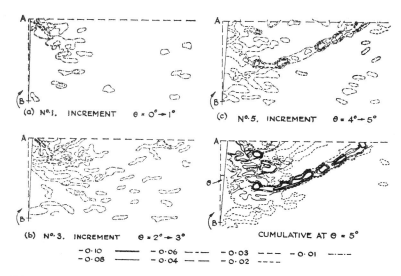

Fig. 22. Contours of volumetric strain (compression positive), test PE ($e_0 = 0.51$). (a–c) Contours of volumetric strain increment $\dot{v}$. (d) Contours of cumulative volumetric strain v at same stages of test PE as Fig. 21

error would be much less. It can be seen that these errors approach the orders of magnitude of the lowest contours of 0·015 for $\dot{\gamma}$ and 0·01 for $\dot{v}$; hence the true contours should be smoother curves than those actually shown. In Fig. 22 no contraction is recorded in this dense specimen. It is evident that the dilation (expansion) is a consequence of the shear strain and the relationship between v and γ when $\theta = 5°$ for all the sand in the deforming zone is represented by the curve PE in Fig. 27.

The dark bands on the radiograph, taken at $\theta = 5°$ in test PE (see Fig. 23(b)), show where the soil has dilated (the small white spots are the images of the lead shot). Along the centre line of these dark bands I believe that the soil will have dilated sufficiently to have attained the critical state, when the dilation rate has dropped to zero. They will also be the rupture surfaces which are displacement or velocity discontinuities. On such a discontinuity it is to be expected that the gradient (with respect to distance across it) of the shear strain contours would be greatest and this can be seen to be the case when comparing Figs 23(a) and (b) (the former is the same as Fig. 21(d)). It must be emphasized that this does not imply that the rupture planes coincide with those planes which are associated with the maximum shear strain, as will be made clear later when discussing Fig. 34(b).

In Fig. 23(c) the observed trajectories of the α and β zero-extension lines are plotted (to the same scale as Figs 23(a) and (b)) as dashed lines, while the continuous lines represent the directions η of the major principal compressive strain ϵ_1. (η is the angle ϵ_1 makes with the vertical.) All these data are obtained from the measured displacement of the lead shot and are based on the cumulative strains at $\theta = 5°$. (Strictly they should be based on the incremental strains at $\theta = 5°$.) This procedure is justified only if the principal axes of strain and of strain increment are not rotating throughout the test as was found to be the case. James (1965) was the first to show experimentally that rupture surfaces (i.e. velocity discontinuities) coincide with the directions of zero-extension in sands. Geiringer (1930) had first shown theoretically that this should be the case for a perfectly plastic non-dilatant material; Shield (1953) had

(a)

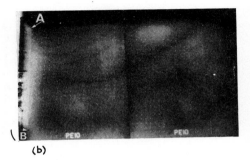

(b)

Fig. 23. Coincidence of rupture surfaces as (a) obtained from observed
contours of maximum shear strain
γ, (b) seen by dark bands on radiographs, (c) the observed α and β zero-
extension lines and directions η of ϵ_1.
All data obtained from radiographs
and refer to same rotation of wall AB
about its toe B into dense sand

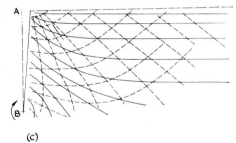

(c)

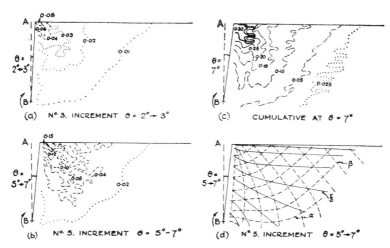

Fig. 24. Typical contours of incremental or cumulative shear strain and zero-extension line mesh at various stages of rotation of wall AB about its toe B into loose sand.   Test PH ($e_0 = 0.77$).   (a) and (b) Contours of maximum shear strain rate $\dot{\gamma}$, (c) contours of maximum shear strain γ, (d) α and β zero-extension lines and directions ξ of $\dot{\epsilon}_1$ during $\theta = 5° \rightarrow 7°$

extended this concept to ideal sand with a constant angle of internal friction ϕ_{max} which dilated at a rate such that $\nu = \phi_{max}$ corresponding to lines OM and ON in Fig. 15(c).   James's work, which has been confirmed subsequently by all the tests in the earth pressure models and in the simple shear apparatus at Cambridge, shows that this postulate is true for Leighton Buzzard sand which dilates so that ν is always less than ϕ.   It can be seen in Fig. 23 that the α–zero-extension lines coincide remarkably well with the observed rupture surfaces.   This concept, which was first appreciated by Hansen (1958), has very important but simple implications concerning the current method of using the Mohr–Coulomb criterion.   This is fully discussed later.

The development of the contours of maximum shear strain during test PH, in which the wall AB was rotated about its toe B into a loose sand, is shown for two increments of wall rotation in Figs 24(a) and (b) and the cumulative value at $\theta = 7°$ is shown in Fig. 24(c).   It will be recalled that in this test the peak load had not been developed even when $\theta = 13°$.   It is evident from Fig. 24(c) that when $\theta = 7°$ there is no sign of the development of a rupture surface. However, the zero-extension line trajectories for the increment $\theta = 5° \rightarrow 7°$ shown in Fig. 24(d) clearly intersect everywhere approximately at right angles indicating that the dilation rate $\nu = 0$ and that the sand is shearing at constant volume.   In this diagram the ξ lines give the direction of the major principal compressive strain rate $\dot{\epsilon}_1$.   (ξ is the angle $\dot{\epsilon}_1$ makes with the vertical.)   The α and β zero-extension lines both make angles of $[45° - (\nu/2)]$ with the ξ lines.   For previous increments to that shown in Fig. 24(d) the zero-extension line pattern had revealed contraction of the sand and during the first increment this corresponded to $\nu = -30°$.

The strain patterns for tests PE and PH have been presented in detail not only because they represent what is regarded as the classic passive retaining wall problem but also because they clearly show how far from the truth is the conventional assumption that the rupture surface passes through the toe when the peak load is developed.   Further information concerning these tests has been presented by James and Bransby (1970a) and in greater detail by Bransby (1968).

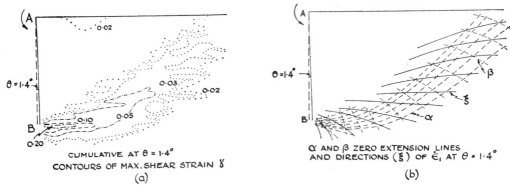

CUMULATIVE AT $\theta = 1\cdot4°$
CONTOURS OF MAX. SHEAR STRAIN γ

(a)

α AND β ZERO EXTENSION LINES
AND DIRECTIONS (ξ) OF $\dot{\epsilon}_1$ AT $\theta = 1\cdot4°$

(b)

**Fig. 25.   Strain patterns developed just before attainment of peak load on wall AB as it
was rotated about its top A into dense sand.   Test LE ($e_0 = 0\cdot52$)**

For the case of a wall rotating about its top into the sand the rupture surface always starts
to form at the toe and subsequently develops progressively up towards the free sand surface.
The cumulative maximum shear strain contours in test LE on a dense sand are shown in
Fig. 25(a) when the angle of rotation of the wall AB about its top A was only $\theta = 1\cdot4°$ but the
resultant force had nearly attained its maximum since $R/R_m = 0\cdot97$.   (The tests LF and LE
carried out by James (1965) were almost identical in their behaviour up to peak load.)   The
development of this strain pattern had been quite a continuous process during the three increments preceding peak load that were investigated by James.   However, it is interesting to
note, by referring to Fig. 12 or Fig. 13, that the peak stress ratio will only have been attained in
the region within the $\gamma = 0\cdot10$ contour when the peak force acts on the wall.   The α and β
zero-extension line trajectories shown by the dashed curves in Fig. 25(b) refer to the incremental strains observed as θ increased from $0\cdot95°$ to $1\cdot4°$.   These trajectories were clearly
defined only in the region within the contours shown in Fig. 25(a)—elsewhere the directions
were random.   The continuous line curves ξ in Fig. 25(b) are directions of the major principal
compressive strain rate $\dot{\epsilon}_1$.

Figures 26(a) and (b) show the corresponding information when $R = 0\cdot95\,R_m$ in test MD,
carried out by Lord (1969), on a moderately loose sand.   The peak load condition was only
attained after a rotation of the wall AB about its top A of $\theta = 6°$.   As for the dense sand in test
LE the development of the strain pattern was a continuous process starting at the toe of the
wall.   In Fig. 26(a), representing conditions at $\theta = 5°$, the peak stress ratio had been fully
developed only within the $0\cdot20$ contour.   The trajectories of the α and β zero-extension lines,
and of the directions of the major principal compressive strain, based on the cumulative
strains at $\theta = 5°$ are shown in Fig. 26(b).   In these diagrams the failure zone at peak load
moves closer to the wall and is of larger extent as the initial voids ratio increases.   The dilation pattern in test MD on loose sand is more complex than for test LE on dense sand.   The
loose sand initially contracts over a large region as shown by the shaded area in Fig. 26(c),
which gives contours of volumetric strain at $\theta = 2°$ in test MD.   In this diagram positive
values of v correspond to compression while negative values represent expansion.   Fig. 26(d)
indicates that virtually all the compression has taken place when $\theta = 2°$, but it should be
borne in mind that any region showing expansion has previously been compressed.

The relationships between the volumetric strain v and shear strain γ within all the lead shot
triangles throughout all the tests discussed are shown in Fig. 27.   Three additional curves are
shown in this diagram.   The first is for test MF which was a test in which the wall AB was
rotated about its top A away from the dense sand thereby corresponding to active rather than

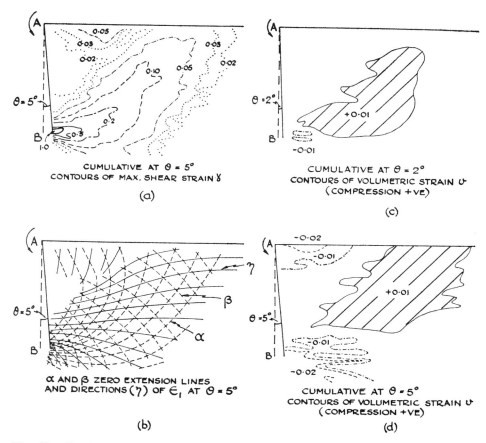

CUMULATIVE AT $\theta = 5°$
CONTOURS OF MAX. SHEAR STRAIN γ

(a)

CUMULATIVE AT $\theta = 2°$
CONTOURS OF VOLUMETRIC STRAIN υ
(COMPRESSION +VE)

(c)

α AND β ZERO EXTENSION LINES
AND DIRECTIONS (η) OF ϵ_1 AT $\theta = 5°$

(b)

CUMULATIVE AT $\theta = 5°$
CONTOURS OF VOLUMETRIC STRAIN υ
(COMPRESSION +VE)

(d)

Fig. 26. Strain patterns developed as wall AB was rotated about its top A into moderately loose sand. Peak load observed at $\theta = 6°$. Test MD ($e_0 = 0·70$)

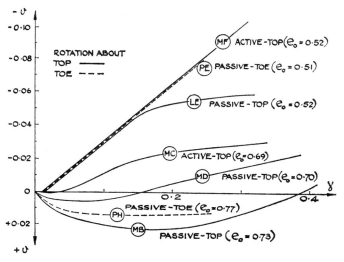

Fig. 27. Curves showing mean υ-γ relationship for the deforming lead shot triangles during all stages of each test

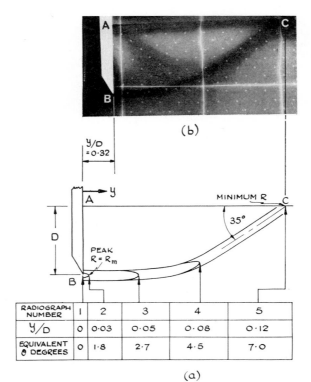

(b)

(a)

Fig. 28.   (a)   Curves showing extent of rupture surface visible on radiographs as wall **AB** of height
D is translated horizontally a distance **y** into
dense sand ($e_0 = 0.51$).   Peak load occurred at y/D
$= 0.03$ and then fell to a minimum at $y/D = 0.12$.
(b) Radiograph   taken   at $y/D = 0.32$ showing
development of secondary rupture surfaces

passive conditions. This curve, for a test in which the maximum normal stress on the wall never exceeded 1 lb/sq. in., is identical to that in test LE when this stress was 23 lb/sq. in. and also to that in test PE when this stress rose to 40 lb/sq. in. It would therefore seem reasonable to assume for these tests on dense sand that, for values of γ between 0·01 and 0·15 and for all stress levels, the sand dilated at a constant rate $\dot{v}/\dot{\gamma}=0·346$ (given by the slopes of these curves) corresponding to a value of $\nu=20·2°$. The second additional curve is for test MC which is also for an active test with the wall rotating about its top away from moderately loose sand ($e_0=0·69$) with the normal stress level never exceeding 1 lb/sq. in. When this is compared with the corresponding passive test MD ($e_0=0·70$), in which the normal stress level rose to 6 lb/sq. in., it is evident that stress level has a significant effect on the dilation behaviour of moderately loose sand. The third additional curve in Fig. 27 refers to a passive test MB with the wall rotating about its top into a loose sand ($e_0=0·73$) in which the normal stress level rose to about 4·5 lb/sq. in. When this is compared with the curve for test PH with the wall rotating about its toe into an even looser sand ($e_0=0·77$) and in which the normal stress rose to the same value of 4·5 lb/sq. in., it is also apparent that initial voids ratio has a profound effect on the dilation behaviour of loose sand. The curves in Fig. 27 become important when attempting to relate stresses and strains in the soil mass.

As previously explained no detailed strain patterns are available for model walls that have been translated horizontally into the sand. However, series of radiographs are available which show how the rupture surfaces develop in dense sand ($e_0=0·51$). The first rupture surface BC is formed progressively from the toe B of the wall AB as indicated in Fig. 28(a). This type of failure is similar to that formed when the wall rotates about its top. The peak load R_m on the wall of height D was observed after a horizontal displacement y such that $y/D=0·03$ (which corresponds to an angle of rotation of the wall about its top of $\theta=1·8°$, see curve NA in Fig. 17(a)). The extent of the rupture zone which was then visible as a dark band on the radiograph, within which the sand had attained the critical state, corresponds to radiograph No. 2 in Fig. 28(a) and was of negligible proportions. As y/D increases the rupture zone grows progressively as shown in Fig. 28(a), while the force on the wall diminishes as shown in Fig. 17(a) until finally when $y/D=0·12$ (corresponding to $\theta=7°$) the rupture zone extends to C on the free surface of the sand and the force on the wall has decreased to its minimum value. Thereafter sliding continues on this primary rupture surface BC while the force slowly increases to a second peak value (much smaller than the first) and then diminishes to a second minimum when $y/D=0·32$ (equivalent to $\theta=20°$). The radiograph shown in Fig. 28(b) was taken at this stage and clearly shows that the radial and transverse rupture surfaces, corresponding to those seen at failure for a wall rotating about its toe (see Fig. 23(b)), are at last beginning to develop. Subsequent radiographs, after further translation of the wall, show that these transverse secondary rupture bands never extend to the free surface. Instead another rupture surface, similar to BC, develops to the right of BC after a large horizontal displacement corresponding to y/D attaining a value of approximately unity.

This work on a translating blade is part of a project on the cutting of soils which was initiated by Major J. May and Mr J. B. J. Lucia and is now being continued by Dr R. H. Bassett. The early work has been summarized by Roscoe (1968b).

PREDICTION OF CONTACT STRESS AND FORCES ON A WALL

It is desirable at this stage to recall one of the two aspects of the main purpose of all this research, namely to be able to predict the contact stress distribution for any assumed displacement of a wall in a soil whose fundamental stress–strain parameters have been determined in some laboratory or field test apparatus. If a method could be developed to do this for the three cases of wall movement discussed in the previous section, then considerable confidence could be placed in the same method when predicting the contact stress distribution for any type of wall movement.   Further, little extension of the method would be required to obtain a solution to the second aspect of the main purpose of this research, namely to be able to predict the displacement of the wall when subjected to some externally imposed load of known magnitude, position and direction.

When considering stresses I always recall a statement made by Burland (1965) at the beginning of his thesis: 'Stress is a philosophical concept—deformation is a physical reality'. We cannot measure stress but only the deformations caused by a force.   In the tests described in the previous section the deformations of the sand have been observed and the boundary stresses recorded by measuring the deformations of the load cells.

Stresses obtained from observed strain fields and stress–strain relationship

Since the observed strain fields in the model wall tests are more reliable before the onset of rupture surfaces the most reliable comparisons, between the wall stresses as measured by the load cells and the predicted stresses in the neighbouring sand, will be those made at stages of tests in which serious discontinuities have not yet developed.   At the same time the strains should be sufficiently large to ensure that the errors in their measurement are not of the same order.   A typical appropriate case is to consider test PH after the wall AB has been rotated through $\theta = 7°$ about its base into a loose sand.   The most dependable strain recorded in the model wall tests is the cumulative maximum shear strain γ.   Hence Bransby (1968) elected to assume that the observed stress–strain relationship that was most appropriate to adopt was the t/s–γ relationship obtained in the simple shear apparatus for the same initial voids ratio and mean stress level as in the model test.   The t/s against γ curve selected by Bransby for use with test PH was the dashed curve for $\sigma_{av} = 6$ lb/sq. in. in Fig. 14(a).   It is now possible to replace the observed value of γ at the centre of each triangular mesh of the lead shot network (see Fig. 24(c)) by a stress ratio t/s.   Further, from the observed strain data the direction ξ of $\dot{\epsilon}_1$ is known in each mesh and if it is assumed that axes of strain rate and of stress coincide then $\psi = \xi$ and therefore the direction of σ_1 is also known.   A knowledge of the value of t/s and of ψ everywhere throughout the sand is all that is required to be able to use the method of Arthur et al. (1964) to predict the magnitude of any desired stress at any point within the sand mass. This is done by a finite-difference method starting from the free surface of the sand.   The chain dotted curve in Fig. 29 is the value of the horizontal stress σ_y on a vertical plane 1 in. in front of the 12·1 in. high wall as obtained by the Arthur et al. method from the measured displacements of the lead shot.   It may be compared with the continuous line curve in this diagram which represents the normal stress on the wall σ_w as measured by the load cells at the same

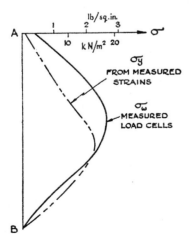

Fig. 29. Comparison of normal stress σ_w on wall AB as measured by load cells after rotation about toe B into loose sand with the normal stress σ_y on a vertical plane 1 in. in front of the wall predicted from the observed strain field and an observed t/s-γ relationship.   Test PH ($e_0 = 0·77$), $\theta = 7°$

stage ($\theta = 7°$) in test PH. The latter curve is identical to that in Fig. 18(e) but to a larger scale. There is good agreement in the lower half of the wall where the rate of change of stress with distance y from the wall is much lower than at the top. As the top is approached there is an expected significant difference in the stresses on the two vertical planes which are 1 in. apart. It is interesting that the normal stress σ_w recorded over the bottom inch of the wall diminished from its at rest value of approximately $\frac{1}{2}$ lb/sq. in. to virtually zero. The relatively large displacements at the top compared to the toe of the wall were causing reduction of the compressive stresses in the soil near the toe.

An alternative to considering only the single t/s–γ relationship already assumed would be, as suggested by Arthur *et al.*, to use a range of t/s–γ curves each depending on the mean value of s during the test. Yet another possibility tried by Bransby was to assume that Rowe's stress–dilatancy rule, as given by equation (3), could be used to obtain t/s from the observed value of the dilatancy rate $\dot{v}/\dot{\gamma}$ in each triangle of the lead shot network. However, he found the observed values of $\dot{v}/\dot{\gamma}$ were less reliable than γ, and consequently abandoned the use of the dilatancy rule. It is evident that it will merit further attention when Stroud's more reliable stress–strain data for the sand at mean stress levels of less than 5 lb/sq. in. become available and also when the accuracy of measuring the lead shot displacements is increased by the use of Dr James's automatic film measuring machine.

In the next section the prediction of strain fields is considered and since a number of unfamiliar concepts are introduced the presentation is as simple as possible. If a satisfactory strain field can be predicted then the method already outlined for predicting stresses from the observed strain field can be applied to the predicted strain field.

Introduction to prediction of strain fields

A simple method of predicting a strain field from known boundary conditions is outlined. The known boundary conditions are the known displacements of the wall and the known stress conditions on the free surface of the sand. In this simple method it is necessary to assume a shape for the rupture surfaces. Perhaps the most important fundamental error made in conventional methods of analysis, in which a shape is assumed for the rupture surface, is that the limiting maximum value of the stress ratio acts on that surface. The fundamental difference in the proposed method is to assume that the rupture surfaces are lines of zero-extension. Now instead of assuming that ϕ is constant at all points along the rupture surface BC (and sometimes at all points within sector ABC) in Fig. 15(a) it is only necessary to assume that v is constant at all such points. As can be seen in Fig. 15(b) the assumption that ϕ is constant in a dense sand is equivalent to assuming that all the sand has been subjected to the shear strain γ corresponding to point G. Any variation in γ will cause large reductions of ϕ. On the other hand v is given by the slopes of the curves OJ for dense or OK for loose sand in Fig. 15(c). These slopes are approximately constant over large ranges of shear strain γ. Hence the assumption that v is constant at all points in the deforming sand is likely to be much more relevant than that ϕ is constant throughout.

The first step in this simple method of predicting a strain field is to assume a shape, built up of simple curves or straight lines, for the zero-extension line field. A typical example for the case of $v = 20°$ is shown in Fig. 30(a). The α and β lines are straight in sector AEC in Fig. 30(a) while sector ABE is a radial fan with pole A through which the straight β lines pass, while the α lines are logarithmic spirals. The fact that the radial fan extends back to the wall AB implies that the wall is a zero-extension line. This is equivalent to assuming that the sand does not slip on the wall, which in the light of the experimental data seems to be a reasonable presumption. (If the wall were smooth so that the sand did slip upon it this would entail reducing the size of the radial fan and placing another straight line zone between it and the wall.) The fact that the wall has been assumed to be a β zero-extension line implies that the

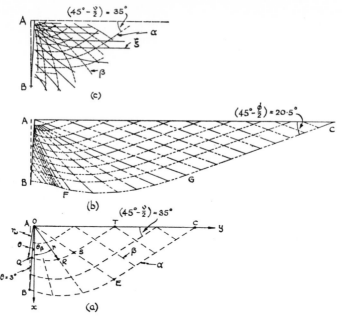

Fig. 30. Simultaneous field of characteristics for wall AB after rotating ($\theta = 3°$) about toe B into dense sand ($e_0 = 0.51$) during test PE: (a) simple assumed velocity characteristics for $\nu = 20°$, (b) Sokolovski (1965) stress field for $\varphi = 49°$ and δ' distribution given by S_1S_3 in Fig. 20(a), (c) observed zero-extension line field (velocity characteristics)

direction of the α lines, and hence ξ_w the direction of $\dot{\epsilon}_1$ at the wall, is fixed near the wall since the α lines must make an angle of $90° \pm \nu$ to this β line. The question of whether to take the positive or negative sign is solved by knowing that the shape of the zero-extension lines must be similar to any rupture surface that might develop. It is important to realize that all the zero-extension lines do not have to be rupture surfaces simultaneously but that if a rupture surface develops it should coincide with one of these lines or lie between two neighbouring lines. The boundary condition near the free surface of the sand is that the direction of the major principal stress σ_1 should be horizontal so that $\psi = 90°$. Since axes of strain rate and of stress are assumed to coincide the direction ξ of the major principal strain rate $\dot{\epsilon}_1$ is also horizontal so that $\xi = 90°$. The directions of the zero-extension lines always make angles of $[(\pi/4) - (\nu/2)] = 35°$ with the direction of $\dot{\epsilon}_1$ and hence the directions of both the α and β lines are fixed on the boundary AC.

Before any use can be made of this zero-extension line field to predict strains within the sand it is necessary to show that these zero-extension lines coincide with the velocity characteristics in a material dilating at a rate ν. One important feature of velocity characteristics is that if there is any curve within the sand such that there is a sudden change in the velocity of the sand as the curve is crossed, then that curve is a velocity characteristic (for a mathematical proof see Davis, 1968, pp. 370–371). Such a sudden change is often called a jump or discontinuity of velocity and hence a velocity discontinuity must be a velocity characteristic. It is evident that a rupture surface is a velocity discontinuity since the velocity of the material on one side of the rupture surface is different to that on the other. Hence a rupture surface is a velocity characteristic and, since it has been shown that rupture surfaces can only develop

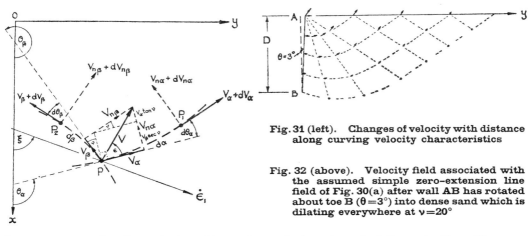

Fig. 31 (left). Changes of velocity with distance along curving velocity characteristics

Fig. 32 (above). Velocity field associated with the assumed simple zero-extension line field of Fig. 30(a) after wall AB has rotated about toe B ($\theta = 3°$) into dense sand which is dilating everywhere at $\nu = 20°$

along zero-extension lines, it is evident that velocity characteristics coincide with zero-extension lines. (A mathematical proof of this is given by Poorooshasb *et al.* (1967) in deriving their equation (63).)

The basic equations of the velocity characteristics, i.e. curves of the zero-extension line field, are

$$\frac{dy}{dx} = \tan\left[\xi \pm \left(\frac{\pi}{4} - \frac{\nu}{2}\right)\right] \quad \ldots \ldots \ldots \quad (4)$$

If the positive sign is taken as relevant and this first order differential equation is integrated then it will represent a family of curves in x, y space; each curve corresponds to a particular value of the arbitrary constant of integration. The negative sign provides a second family of characteristics. They are called velocity characteristics because it is more tedious to call them by their proper name which should perhaps be incremental displacement or displacement-rate characteristics. The main use of these velocity characteristics is that if their shapes are known it is possible, from the fact that they are zero-extension lines, to derive simple equations which give the changes of velocity (displacement increment) as one proceeds along them. To determine these equations consider the point P in Fig. 31 in a sand dilating at a rate ν under conditions of plane strain. Let the velocity of the sand at P be of magnitude V making an angle ϵ with the tangent to the α line at that point. V_α and V_β are the projections of V on the tangents to the α and β lines respectively at P (note that their vector sum does not equal V), while $V_{n\alpha}$ and $V_{n\beta}$ are the corresponding projections on to the normals to the characteristics at P. At point P the tangent to the α line makes an angle θ_α to the vertical axis Ox. If the corresponding angle for the tangent at another point P_1 on the α line is $(\theta_\alpha + d\theta_\alpha)$ and the velocity along this tangent at P_1 is $V_\alpha + dV_\alpha$ then, since PP_1 is a line of zero-extension, it can readily be shown by simple geometry that

$$dV_\alpha + V_{n\alpha}\, d\theta_\alpha = 0$$

and since $V_{n\alpha} = V_\alpha \tan \nu + V_\beta \sec \nu$

$$dV_\alpha + (V_\alpha \tan \nu + V_\beta \sec \nu)\, d\theta_\alpha = 0 \quad \ldots \ldots \ldots \quad (5)$$

Similarly as one moves from P to P_2 along a β line

$$dV_\beta - (V_\alpha \sec \nu + V_\beta \tan \nu)\, d\theta_\beta = 0 \quad \ldots \ldots \ldots \quad (6)$$

(It should be noted that if ν is constant everywhere then during any single movement $d\theta_\alpha$ and $d\theta_\beta$ will always equal $d\xi$, but this is not the case if ν varies throughout the sand mass.) Equations (5) and (6) can be used, when combined with the boundary conditions for the velocities, to determine what is called the velocity field which is the velocity at the nodes of the zero-extension line (i.e. velocity characteristic) mesh. Unfortunately the boundary condition imposed at the wall, namely that the velocity of the sand near the wall is the same as that of the wall is not on its own sufficient to be able to determine the velocities (displacement increments) throughout a velocity characteristic field such as in Fig. 30(a). An additional velocity boundary condition is required. This is usually provided by making the soil rigid outside one zero-extension line, e.g. below BEC in Fig. 30(a). From these two boundary conditions it is now simple to determine the velocity (displacement increment) at each node of the zero-extension line (velocity characteristic) mesh from merely a knowledge of the wall velocity (displacement increment) and using equations (5) and (6). This pattern of velocities is called a velocity field. Fig. 32 shows the velocity field (obtained from the zero-extension line field of Fig. 30(a)) for a wall after rotation about its toe through $\theta = 3°$ in a sand dilating everywhere at $\nu = 20°$. This would be a good approximation, except near the bottom of the wall, to conditions in test PE when $\theta = 3°$ as can be seen by comparing the observed zero-extension line field in Fig. 30(c) with the assumed field of Fig. 30(a).

Once the predicted velocity field at any given instant of a particular type of wall displacement has been obtained it is simple to calculate the corresponding strain–increment (rate) field. (Strain rates are merely spacial derivatives of velocities, e.g. $\dot{\epsilon}_x = \partial u / \partial x$ if u is the component of the velocity in the direction x.) If the predicted velocity field is as simple as that shown in Fig. 32 it is possible, as shown by James and Bransby (1970b), to derive simple equations for predicting any desired component of strain rate throughout the radial fan.

To obtain the predicted cumulative strain field of any desired component of strain, such as the maximum shear strain γ, after any given displacement of the wall it will in general be necessary to determine the incremental strain field for each preceding increment of wall displacement and then add the increments vectorially. Strictly speaking there will be a different zero-extension line field for each increment.

Knowing the predicted values of the shear strain γ and the direction ξ of the major principal strain rate throughout the sand, it is possible to predict the distribution of any desired stress throughout the sand and in particular the contact stress σ_w and τ_w on the wall at any stage of a test. The procedure is the same as outlined in the section on predicting stresses from observed strains, namely to use the relevant (t/s)–γ relationship obtained in the simple shear apparatus and the Arthur et al. (1964) method of calculation. Once the stresses have been predicted at all stages of wall movement it is simple to obtain the predicted relationships of the type required by an engineer, namely the P–θ, δ–θ and $(\bar{z}/D)$–θ relationships.

This method of tackling the problem by assuming a simple shape for the zero-extension line field is tempting since it can be based on commonsense and experience. Once the basic program has been written any number of variations on the simple theme outlined can be played rapidly on a small computer with an 8k storage. One of several more accurate methods by which we are attempting to make more reliable predictions than by the simple one outlined takes account of the fact that the soil near the wall is not uniform but dilates at different rates at differing points. Whereas the simple method entails an understanding of velocity characteristics the more accurate method also makes use of the concept of stress characteristics.

Introduction to stress characteristics

In soil mechanics the application of the method of stress characteristics has as yet been restricted to an ideal rigid plastic material which is everywhere failing according to the Mohr–Coulomb criterion. When applied to problems such as those already discussed this is equivalent to assuming that the soil everywhere in the deforming zone is of constant density ρ and is developing simultaneously at all points the maximum angle of internal friction ϕ_{max}. The basic equation of the stress characteristics (i.e. the curves on which the stress ratio τ/σ is a limiting maximum) in such an idealized material is

$$\frac{dy}{dx} = \tan\left[\psi \pm \left(\frac{\pi}{4} - \frac{\phi}{2}\right)\right] \qquad \ldots \ldots \quad (7)$$

This gives two families of stress characteristics each curve everywhere being inclined at $[(\pi/4) - (\phi/2)]$ to the direction ψ of the major principal stress σ_1. If at a point in the sand mass the soil is dilating at an angle ν and is subjected to a stress ratio corresponding to a mobilized angle of internal friction ϕ then, provided the directions of the major principal stress σ_1 and strain rate $\dot{\epsilon}_1$ coincide so that $\psi = \xi$, it is apparent from equations (4) and (7) that the stress characteristics always make an angle of $\frac{1}{2}(\phi - \nu)$ with the velocity characteristics. The other relevant equation for the change of stress along a stress characteristic is obtained by applying the equations of equilibrium and the Mohr–Coulomb failure criterion (see e.g. Sokolovski (1965) or for a more lucid description de Jong (1959))

$$ds + 2s \tan\phi \, d\psi = \rho(dy + \tan\phi \, dx) \qquad \ldots \ldots \quad (8)$$

where $s = \frac{1}{2}(\sigma_1 + \sigma_3)$ and $d\psi$ is the change of direction of either stress characteristic or of σ_1. Equation (8) may be compared with equations (5) and (6) for the velocity characteristics when $d\theta_\alpha = d\theta_\beta = d\xi$. It can be seen that, whereas for the stresses there are two equations and two unknowns (s and ψ), for the strains there are two equations and three unknowns (V_α, V_β and ξ). This means that if the values of s and ψ are known on a portion of a boundary (say on AB in Fig. 30(b)) then the directions of the stress characteristics are defined within a region contained by the boundary and the first characteristic through one end BF and the second characteristic through the other end AF. The point F is located by inserting the values of s and ψ at A and B into equation (8), as are also the magnitudes of s and ψ along AF and BF. Knowing the values of s and ψ at other points on AB it is possible to determine s and ψ at all other points within sector ABF. Unfortunately a knowledge of V_α, V_β and ξ at all points on the wall AB is not sufficient to determine their value at points near the boundary unless the shape of the zero-extension line field (velocity characteristics) is assumed (or determined from some extra information) and also the velocity conditions are known along one of the bounding velocity characteristics. One way in which the shape of the velocity characteristics can be determined is from the stress characteristics, provided the latter are known, since the stress and velocity characteristics always intersect at angles of $\frac{1}{2}(\phi - \nu)$ and it has been presumed that ϕ and ν are known.

Normally when applying the Sokolovski method to a ϕ-constant material one works into the stress field from the boundary stress condition on the sand surface AC in Fig. 30(b) having imposed a very small surcharge to that surface. From this condition alone and a knowledge of the soil density ρ (assumed constant) and of ϕ, it is then possible to calculate the directions of the stress characteristics and the magnitudes of the stresses and in particular the values of these quantities on line AG. The next step is to determine the extent of the zone ABF and the position of the curve AF can be determined from a knowledge of the local angle of wall friction δ' at the top A of the wall. This fixes the extent of the radial fan between AG and AF. It is now assumed that near A the radial lines for a very short distance near A are straight. Starting from A and from the knowledge of the magnitudes and directions of the stresses on line AG, the same information can be calculated for all points within the sector AGF. In particular the magnitudes and directions of the stresses are now known on AF. From this information and from a knowledge of the distribution of δ' on the wall AB, the magnitudes and directions of the stresses can be determined at all points within sector ABF. In particular the normal σ_w and shear τ_w stresses on the wall can be determined. In Fig. 30(b) the size of the wall is the same as in Figs 30(c) and (a) which show respectively the observed and a simple

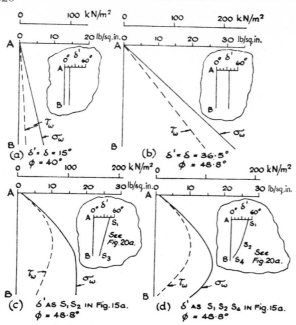

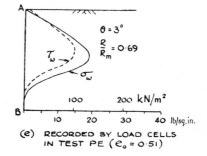

Fig. 33. (a-d) Normal σ_w and shear τ_w stresses on wall AB predicted by Sokolovski (1965) method assuming soil failing everywhere at $\varphi = 40°$ or $49°$ for δ' distributions shown in insets. (e) σ_w and τ_w recorded by load cells as largest region of soil attains $\varphi_{max} = 49°$ near top half of wall

assumed zero-extension line field. All three diagrams can be taken as relevant to the conditions of test PH after the wall has rotated about its toe through $\theta = 3°$ into the sand. Inspection of the observed velocity characteristics (zero-extension lines) of Fig. 30(c) suggests that $\nu = 20°$ throughout most of the deforming sand and this value of ν has been used in constructing the assumed velocity characteristics of Fig. 30(a). The most appropriate value of ϕ to associate with $\nu = 20°$ (which corresponds to $\dot{v}/\dot{\gamma} = 0.346$) was obtained by extrapolating the curve AB in Fig. 14(b) to point D, and the corresponding value of ϕ is 49°. This value of $\phi = 49°$ has been used in constructing the stress characteristics of Fig. 30(b) and it is necessary to assume that the stress ratio corresponding to this value of ϕ is simultaneously generated throughout the whole of the sector ABGC in Fig. 30(b). This may be compared with the corresponding assumption for the velocity characteristics which require that all the soil within the sector ABEC in Fig. 30(a) is dilating uniformly. While this latter assumption is more likely to be realized than the former, it is evident from the model test data already presented that any theory should take account of the variation of the mobilized ϕ and ν at different points within the sand at each and every stage of wall displacement. Before indicating how this can be done, by making use simultaneously of stress and velocity characteristics, let us consider the influence of the variation of the angle of wall friction on the magnitude of the wall contact stresses as predicted by the Sokolovski method for a material of constant ϕ.

If the Code of Practice values of $\phi = 40°$ and $\delta = 15°$ are taken and it is assumed that the local angle of wall friction δ' is everywhere equal to 15° as shown by the inset to Fig. 33(a), then the resultant predicted distributions of σ_w and τ_w on the wall are as shown in the main part of Fig. 33(a). If now it is assumed that $\phi = 49°$ then the predicted stresses for $\delta = \delta' = 36.5°$, which was the average value measured when $\theta = 3°$ in test PE (see Fig. 18(b)), are as shown in Fig. 33(b). (For convenience of comparison of the predicted and observed stresses Fig. 18(b), showing the stress distribution as measured by load cells when $\theta = 3°$ in test PE, is reproduced in Fig. 33(e).) If now the observed values of δ' shown in Fig. 20(a) are approximated by the line S_1S_3 and used in the Sokolovski analysis then the predicted stress distribution is as shown in Fig. 33(c).   Finally if the curve $S_1S_2S_4$ in Fig. 20(a) is used instead to represent the variation of δ' on the wall then the predicted stress distribution becomes as shown in Fig. 33(d).   It is interesting now significantly different are these two stress distributions and that this has been caused solely by a small modification to the distribution of δ'.   The stress characteristics corresponding to Fig. 33(c) are shown in Fig. 30(b) and variations of δ' have a significant influence only on the region ABF, with a slight effect on sector AFG and none on AGC.   If the assumed distribution of δ' is made to agree more closely with the observed values in Fig. 20(a) than does curve $S_1S_2S_4$, then neighbouring stress characteristics of the same family in region ABF intersect, which of course is impossible.   One important conclusion that was drawn from this work was that, if the Sokolovski method is to be modified to take account of the variation of ϕ throughout the sand mass at any stage of a test then, it will only be reliable if the distribution of δ' on the wall is known or can be satisfactorily predicted.   It is not sufficient to know the average overall value δ.

Indication of a more realistic method of predicting contact stress distribution after wall displacement

In addition to simple methods of predicting stress fields such as that outlined for an assumed shape for the velocity field, the Cambridge group has for some time been studying more realistic methods of solving such problems.   One promising method is being worked on by I. A. A. Smith, A. Serrano and B. L. Tennekoon under the supervision of Dr R. G. James. The immediate objective is to obtain the load–displacement relationship for any structure, e.g. walls, sheet pile walls, foundations and anchors, in contact with sand.   Before the application of any load from the superstructure it is assumed that the initial conditions within the sand, namely initial voids ratio e_0, initial mean stress level s_0 and initial stress ratio $(t/s)_0$ are known at all points within the mass of sand that will be deformed.   They need not be uniform. Small increments of load or of movement of the superstructure are then applied successively to the sand.   The stress and strain conditions throughout the sand are determined at the end of each increment and due account is taken of the changes of stress ratio, mean stress level and dilation rates at each point of the sand mass during that increment.   Consequently the method permits the prediction of progressive failure throughout the mass.

It is assumed that the sand is a rigid work-hardening plastic material with successive yield loci of the type shown in Fig. 11, which are relevant up to the attainment of the limiting stress ratio (corresponding to the Coulomb ϕ_{max}) but not thereafter.   Further it is presumed that at all times the principal axes of stress and of strain rate coincide.   Pending the time when any simplifying relationship between stresses and strains can be found for the sand, the following information as obtained from the simple shear apparatus is being used.

> (a) The family of yield loci for each initial voids ratio e_0 of the sand.   Cole (1967) found that the K_0 values are approximately linearly related to e_0.
>
> (b) The stress ratio t/s–shear strain γ relationship is known for all mean stress levels s and initial voids ratios e_0.
>
> (c) The volumetric strain v–shear strain γ relationships are known for all mean stress levels s and initial voids ratios e_0.

In addition to having to know the initial conditions within the sand just before the first increment of wall movement it is necessary to assume for this first increment only a distribution for the local angle of wall friction δ', or alternatively that the soil does not slip on the wall.   This condition, coupled with the fact that v_0 can be obtained from the v–γ curve observed in the simple shear apparatus when testing a sample at the initial voids ratio e_0 and mean stress level s_0, fixes the value of ξ_w (the direction of $\dot{\epsilon}_1$) and hence of ψ_w (the direction of σ_1) on the wall.

Further, just before the first increment of wall movement, the relevant value of ϕ_0 might be taken as that corresponding to the K_0 line in Fig. 11. All the relevant information is now available to construct the stress characteristics for this first increment. From these the velocity characteristics for the first increment can be constructed since they intersect the stress characteristics everywhere at $\frac{1}{2}(\phi_0 - \nu_0)$. Now knowing the wall displacement increment (velocity V_w) and that the sand is stationary below one velocity characteristic, it is possible to compute the velocity of the sand at each node of the velocity characteristics. Hence the strain increments (especially the values of γ and ξ) are known everywhere and from these and the data listed in (b) and (c) it is possible to determine the stress ratio t/s (i.e. ϕ_{mob}), the dilation rate ν at every point in the sand and ξ_w (and hence ψ_w) on the wall. Both ϕ_{mob} and ν are now no longer constant throughout the sand but differ from point to point. Taking these values of ϕ_{mob} everywhere and from a knowledge of ξ_w a new stress characteristic field can be determined. For this it is necessary to use the extended Sokolovski equations developed by I. A. A. Smith. These contain terms which allow for the variation of ϕ throughout the sand and when used in finite–difference form they can also take account of the variation of the density of the sand. From the new stress characteristics the new velocity characteristics can be found. To determine the new strains it is necessary to use a new set of equations, developed by A. Serrano, which relate strains to velocities and take account of the variation of ν throughout the sand. From the strains the new values of ϕ_{mob} and ν can be found from the data in (b) and (c). The whole cycle has to be repeated again and again (iterated) until there is no further change in the resultant stress and velocity characteristics. The resultant strains and stresses at this stage are the correct values at the end of the first increment of wall movement.

The second increment of wall movement can now be applied and the whole procedure is similar to that for the first increment except that now the process starts from the velocity characteristics as determined at the end of the first increment.

The act of putting the theoretical programme outlined into practice is a major computing task which is being undertaken at Cambridge and also by Serrano in Spain. During this process many variations on the proposed theme will be included. In particular it is hoped that the new data provided by Stroud, from his tests on the sand at low stress levels in the Mk 7 simple shear apparatus, will not only provide more dependable experimental results, but may lead to considerable simplification in our representation of the stress–strain relationships of the sand. It is possible, now that the critical state line has been confirmed for sand, that more use can be made of the fundamental parameters associated with this line. A first attempt to do this was made by Wroth and Bassett (1965) and was extended and simplified by Bassett (1967). All this information will make it possible to reduce the assumptions that have been made in the theoretical programme.

Once the theoretical programme has been made to work satisfactorily for all initial conditions of the sand for one problem, it can readily be extended to other problems such as that of the footing shown in Fig. 1 even if no restraint is placed on the footing. The predictions must then be compared with model test data and at Cambridge we have as yet only completed a series of such tests of the wall rotating about its top or its toe into the sand and of a flat footing being pushed vertically downwards on to the surface of the sand. We are at present engaged on tests in which an instrumented wall is rotated about its top or toe away from the sand and also when it is being translated into the sand. All such tests can be carried out in the apparatus shown in Fig. 16. It is only when we have been able to predict satisfactorily what is seen to happen in the models that our theories can be extended to field problems. We should also then be able to have real confidence in, and know the limitation of the range of application of, simplified approaches to problems. To achieve this simplification I think we will have to develop the art of predicting zero-extension line fields in a similar manner to D. W. Taylor's for flow nets in seepage problems. When doing this at field scale it is essential that we obtain in advance as much information as possible concerning the displacements and contact stress distributions, especially of the local angles of wall friction δ' on real structures. A version of the Cambridge type load cell has been developed by Dr E. C. Hambly for this purpose (Roscoe, 1969). It can be made to measure either effective or total normal stress as well as shear stress and can be made so robust that it can be built into the face of a driven pile. Dr R. H. G. Parry is carrying out preliminary tests to improve methods of measuring strains within soils under field conditions.

Once this has been achieved we will at last be in a position to predict load–displacement curves for foundations and can then design the superstructure and its foundation as a single unit.

RESTATEMENT OF MOHR–COULOMB FAILURE CRITERION AND CONSEQUENCES

One of the most important conclusions that may be drawn from the work already described is that it entails a radical change in the customary method of interpreting the Mohr–Coulomb criterion. Generally this criterion is stated as if it contains only one concept, although in fact it contains two namely

(a) any element of soil will fail when the diameter of the Mohr's circle of stress, representing the stress conditions in that element, has increased in size sufficiently to touch the Mohr–Coulomb envelope at two points defining identical stress ratios τ/σ

(b) the two planes through the element which then become rupture surfaces are those upon which this stress ratio τ/σ acts.

If the soil is cohesionless and the Mohr–Coulomb envelope is two straight lines of slope ϕ passing through the origin on a τ–σ diagram this statement can be simplified. Consider any point in a mass of such a sand. At any instant there are two planes through this point upon which the stress ratio τ/σ is the same and is greater than on any other plane through that point. The two concepts of the Mohr–Coulomb failure criterion are now

(a) the sand will fail at that point when the greatest stress ratio τ/σ reaches its limiting value $(\tau/\sigma)_{max} = \tan \phi$

(b) the two planes through the point along which rupture surfaces develop are those upon which $(\tau/\sigma)_{max}$ is attained.

It is suggested that the second concept is erroneous. For example if it were true then the rupture surfaces that would develop in the wall problem would all be parallel to the stress characteristics shown in Fig. 30(b). However, it has already been shown (see e.g. Figs 7 and 23) that rupture surfaces coincide with the directions of zero-extension. This means that rupture surfaces form along the zero-extension lines shown in Fig. 30(c) which were obtained from the observed displacement of the lead shot. Figs 30(c) and (b) can only be made compatible if the Mohr–Coulomb criterion is restated in the form 'in any element within a soil mass a rupture surface will develop along a plane which is a direction of zero-extension at the instant when the stress ratio τ/σ on any other plane through that element attains a value corresponding to a point on the Mohr–Coulomb envelope'. τ and σ are now the shear and normal stresses respectively on this second plane and do not refer to the rupture surface.

Let Fig. 34(a) represent the Mohr's circle of stress for the conditions at a point P in the sand mass (see Fig. 34(c)). The stress ratio τ/σ corresponds to a point on the Mohr–Coulomb envelope on the two planes through P labelled stress characteristics in Fig. 34(c). These are at angles of $[45° - (\phi/2)]$ to the direction of the major principal stress σ_1 which makes an angle ψ with the vertical axis Ox. If the direction of the major principal strain rate $\dot{\epsilon}_1$ makes an angle ξ with the vertical axis Ox (see Fig. 34(b)) such that $\psi = \xi$, then the zero-extension directions are as shown in Fig. 34(c) at an angle of $[45° - (\nu/2)]$ to the direction of $\dot{\epsilon}_1$ and hence of σ_1. The angles between the stress characteristics and the zero-extension lines are $(\phi - \nu)/2$.

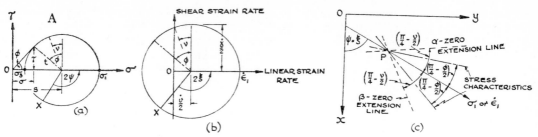

Fig. 34. Mohr's circle of (a) stress, (b) strain rate, for element of sand at point P dilating at rate ν and mobilizing a stress ratio φ, assuming principal axes of strain rate and of stress coincide. (c) Directions of zero–extension lines and of stress characteristics at point P

Although extensive use has already been made of this concept in outlining the methods for predicting load-displacement curves for walls, foundations and so on when ϕ and ν are variables, it also applies at the instant that ϕ_{max} and ν_{max} are simultaneously developed. Hence in carrying out conventional stability analyses in which a failure plane is assumed it is desirable to think of the failure surfaces as being zero-extension lines rather than being planes of maximum stress ratio τ/σ, where τ and σ are as defined in Fig. 34(a). At a free surface these rupture surfaces will make angles of $[45° - (\nu/2)]$ and not $[45° - (\phi/2)]$ to the direction of the major principal stress σ_1. The relevant stress ratio to apply in the analysis to the assumed rupture surface is that which occurs on a zero-extension line (corresponding to point A in Fig. 34(a)). This stress ratio is measured directly in a direct shear test such as in the simple shear apparatus in which the zero-extension lines are horizontal.

RELEVANCE OF OBSERVATIONS IN MODEL TESTS TO FULL-SCALE BEHAVIOUR

For the case of the wall rotating about its toe into the sand, model tests have been carried out on two different heights of wall. In both cases identical strain fields and identical wall contact stress distributions were observed at the same angle of wall rotation. The mean stress levels in one test were approximately double those of the other but the maximum in either was about 50 lb/sq. in. when scaled to a wall height of approximately 1 ft. According to Vesic and Clough (1968) there is no fundamental change in the stress–strain behaviour of six different types of sand until a mean stress level of 1500 lb/sq. in. is attained. As a mean stress level of 1500 lb/sq. in. is approached the dense sand would begin to behave in a similar manner to a loose sand at a lower stress level. The relevant initial voids ratio to use in a model test could be obtained from the model law developed by Roscoe and Poorooshasb (see Roscoe (1968a)). Despite this we would expect the pattern of behaviour observed in our model tests to be relevant to walls at least as high as 30 ft in the Leighton Buzzard sand.

Similar model tests at two different scales have been made for walls that rotate about their tops. In these a discontinuity grows into the sand from the toe and there is no simple correlation between the load and the wall displacement at the toe or the rotation of the wall. This is believed to be due to the fact that the thickness of the wedge shaped zone (e.g. Fig. 25(a)), within which the discontinuity develops, varies with wall height. If it were constant the displacement of the toe to attain peak load on the wall should be constant. From the evidence so far obtained we would only feel confident in predicting limits for the wall displacement at the toe, within which the peak load would develop, for wall heights up to 40 ft. This also applies to the walls that translate horizontally into the soil.

It has been shown by Roscoe (1968a) that the only satisfactory way of truly modelling to scale a prototype problem, in which the self-weight of the soil is significant, is to use a centrifuge. Self-weight of the soil is significant in almost every practical soil mechanics problem.

Fig. 35. View of one limb of $2\frac{1}{2}$ m radius centrifuge showing one sample container being adjusted and slip rings on vertical axle

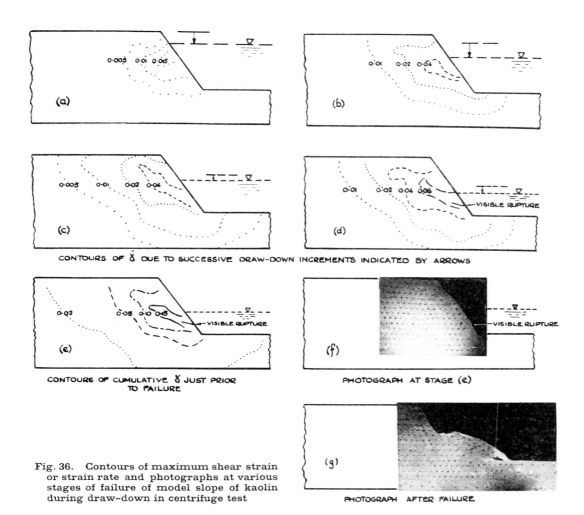

Fig. 36. Contours of maximum shear strain or strain rate and photographs at various stages of failure of model slope of kaolin during draw-down in centrifuge test

The essential feature of centrifugal testing is to keep the self-weight stresses identical at geometrically similar points in the model and the prototype.   Since the same stress patterns are imposed in both cases, the strain patterns must be identical.   Hence with the centrifuge it is possible to obtain answers immediately to full-scale problems without having to appeal to, or wait for the development of, any theory.

The early centrifuge work pioneered at Cambridge by A. N. Schofield (now Professor at University of Manchester Institute of Science and Technology) has been described by Avgherinos and Schofield (1969); it has subsequently been continued by L. J. Endicott.   A large centrifuge of 5 m operational radius is now being built at Cambridge; in the meantime Endicott has been carrying out tests on model slopes of clay in a $2\frac{1}{2}$ m radius centrifuge shown in Fig. 35.   Figs 36(a)–(d) show the contours of maximum shear strain increments $\dot{\gamma}$ during four stages of draw-down of the free water surface on a slope of height 15 cm.   The extent of each increment of draw-down is indicated by the vertical arrow.   The principal axes of strain in the clay near the slope rotate during draw-down and the contours of cumulative maximum shear strain γ at the stage of Fig. 36(d) are shown in Fig. 36(e).   These diagrams clearly show that the rupture develops progressively upwards from the toe and that the tension crack does not appear in the upper horizontal surface until it is approached by the rupture surface. Fig. 36(f) shows the development of a rupture surface from the toe before the appearance of a tension crack, while Fig. 36(g) shows conditions after failure.   This mode of failure has been observed in only two of 14 tests completed by Endicott; in the remaining 12 the rupture surface passed through the toe of the slope.   However, in all the tests these slopes failed progressively in the manner described (see Bjerrum, 1968).   Since most of the tests were made at an acceleration of 50 times that of gravity, Endicott's results are relevant to field slopes of a height of $7\frac{1}{2}$ m (25 ft).   The clay was saturated remoulded kaolin and the degree of overconsolidation at the mid-height of the slope was about 6.

The centrifuge is an extremely powerful tool of immediate value in practice since it can provide answers to problems in which the boundary value problems are too complicated for present methods of analysis, and further it is not necessary to know the stress–strain properties of the soil.   Recently Endicott completed a model test at a fraction of the cost of a trial embankment which was fully instrumented.   Since the time scale in the centrifuge in this test is reduced by about 3000 times Endicott was able to predict after a test lasting $3\frac{1}{2}$ h what may be observed in the field in several years' time.

CONCLUDING REMARKS

In this Paper I have only been able to present a few glimpses of some of the work that is now being carried out at Cambridge.   I have not discussed the outstanding work of Tovey (1970) on developing quantitative methods of measuring the degree of anisotropy of clays with the scanning electron microscope.   Nor have I mentioned the work of Walker (1967), Ting (1968) or Hawley (1970) on time effects in clays.   Far too little mention has been made of the distinguished work on the study of stresses and strains by people such as Professors de Josselin de Jong, P. W. Rowe, H. B. Poorooshasb, Dr J. Biarez and Messrs R. Butterfield and R. Harkness.   Despite these shortcomings I hope I have conveyed three main points.

The first point is the need, especially in research, for a radical change of outlook.   We should stop concentrating attention only on the shear strength of soils and think in terms of their stress–strain behaviour, especially at stress levels corresponding to working loads which will probably be less than half the values required to produce failure.   We must continue to develop laboratory and field test equipment to investigate the stress–strain behaviour of soils under as wide a range as possible of imposed stress and strain paths.   The axisymmetric triaxial test is one of many possible tools and imposes conditions on the soil which can rarely be strictly relevant to an element of soil in the field.   Any new test device that is developed should provide means of checking the assumptions made regarding the conditions it is supposed to impose on the soil. X- and γ-rays as well as boundary load cells can provide such means.

At the same time boundary value problems should continue to be investigated in the same detail at model scale in the laboratory. The centrifuge will provide much reliable evidence but can never fully replace a properly instrumented full-scale field test.

My second point is that I hope I have conveyed to the practising engineer the need for all this fundamental research and to seek his tolerance and occasionally his assistance while it is being sorted out. I have always rejected the idea that the best way to make progress is continually to apply small modifications to current methods. This entails restricting attention to specific problems, each of which can only be solved by making assumptions peculiar to that problem. This method may help to develop a reasonable intuition in its sponsors but it also tends to make them perpetuate the mistakes of their predecessors. We have now reached a stage at Cambridge where we urgently need opportunities to use our instruments in the field and would welcome co-operation from practising engineers in full-scale projects. There must be a two-way interchange of knowledge and information. We might well in the U.K. consider the development of a national institute for this purpose.

The third point I wish to make is the extent of the opportunities and the challenge that is now offered not only to workers in soils but also in any other particulate material. With the tools and methods so far developed at Cambridge and elsewhere we are only beginning. I am confident they can be developed for the further study of dynamic loading of particulate materials and their behaviour when flowing. Any young man starting research now in such materials cannot help but make significant discoveries with the facilities available.

ACKNOWLEDGEMENTS

At Cambridge we always work very much as a team in which each member has made his own significant contribution to the main aim of the research programme. For the past few years the team has consisted of about 40 members. On behalf of all the past and present members, and especially myself, I wish to thank Professor Sir John Baker for the continued and immeasurable support that he has given since the work began in 1945. The people who as members of the staff of the Engineering Department have given limitless service in the development of the group are Professor A. N. Schofield, Dr C. P. Wroth, Dr R. G. James, Mr R. E. Ward, Mrs R. H. Stock and more recently Dr R. H. G. Parry. I ask all the other members to accept my thanks, not only for their contributions but for the pleasure they have given me in endeavouring to keep up with their ideas. None of the work would have been possible without the manufacturing ingenuity of Mr A. A. Barker who has made every piece of equipment that the group has used. In all our recent designs we have been greatly helped by Mr P. W. Turner. I would also like to thank Dr R. G. James and Dr P. L. Bransby for the countless discussions we have had in the preparation of this Paper and Messrs E. D. Nisbet and E. R. Mudd for preparing the diagrams.

REFERENCES

ARTHUR, J. R. F., JAMES, R. G. & ROSCOE, K. H. (1964). The determination of stress fields during plane strain of a sand mass. *Géotechnique* **14**, No. 4, 283–308.
ARTHUR, J. R. F. & ROSCOE, K. H. (1961). An earth pressure cell for the measurement of normal and shear stresses. *Civ. Engng publ. Wks Rev.* **56**, No. 659, 765–770.
ARTHUR, J. R. F. & ROSCOE, K. H. (1965). An examination of the edge effects in plane-strain model earth pressure tests. *Proc. 6th Int. Conf. Soil Mech., Montreal* **2**, 363–367.
AVGHERINOS, P. J. & SCHOFIELD, A. N. (1969). Drawdown failures of centrifuged models. *Proc. 7th Int. Conf. Soil Mech., Mexico* **2**, 497–505.
BASSETT, R. H. (1967). Granular materials in the simple shear apparatus. Ph.D. thesis, University of Cambridge.

BJERRUM, L. (1968).   Progressive failure in slopes of over-consolidated plastic clay and clay shales.   *Proc. Am. Soc. civ. Engrs* **93**, SM5, 1–49.

BRANSBY, P. L. (1968).   Stress and strain in sand caused by rotation of a model wall.   Ph.D. thesis, University of Cambridge.

BURLAND, J. B. (1965).   Deformation of soft clay.   Ph.D. thesis, University of Cambridge.

BURLAND, J. B. & ROSCOE, K. H. (1969).   Local strains and pore pressures in a normally consolidated clay layer during one-dimensional consolidation.   *Géotechnique* **19**, No. 3, 335–356.

COLE, E. R. L. (1967).   The behaviour of soils in the simple shear apparatus.   Ph.D. thesis, University of Cambridge.

COUMOULOS, D. G. (1968).   A radiographic study of soils.   Ph.D. thesis, University of Cambridge.

DAVIS, E. H. (1968).   Theories of plasticity and the failure of soil masses.   In *Soil mechanics: selected topics* (ed. I. K. Lee), pp. 341–380.   London: Butterworths.

DE JONG, G. DE JOSSELIN (1959).   *Statics and kinematics in the failure zone of a granular material.*   Delft: Uitgeverig Waltman.

GEIRINGER, H. (1930).   Beitrag zum Vollständigen ebenen Plastizitätsproblem.   *Proc. 3rd Int. Congr. appl. Mech., Stockholm* **2**, 185–190.

HAMBLY, E. C. (1969).   A new true triaxial apparatus.   *Géotechnique* **19**, No. 2, 307–309.

HAMBLY, E. C. & ROSCOE, K. H. (1969).   Observations and predictions of stresses and strains during plane–strain of 'wet' clays.   *Proc. 7th Int. Conf. Soil Mech., Mexico* **1**, 173–181.

HANSEN, BENT (1958).   Line ruptures regarded as narrow rupture zones.   Basic equations based on kinematic considerations.   *Proc. Conf. Earth Pressure Probl., Brussels* **1**, 39–48.

HANSEN, J. BRINCH (1953).   *Earth pressure calculation.*   Copenhagen: Danish Technical Press

HARR, M. E. (1966).   *Foundations of theoretical soil mechanics*, pp. 217–225.   New York: McGraw-Hill.

HAWLEY, J. G. (1970).   The primary/secondary transition during the one-dimensional consolidation of saturated clay.   Submitted as Ph.D. thesis, University of Cambridge.

HVORSLEV, M. J. (1937).   Uber die Festigkeitseigenschaften gestörter bindiger Böden.   *Ingvidensk. Skr.* A, No. 45.   (English translation No. 69–5.   U.S. Waterways Experimental Station, Vicksburg, Miss., 1969.)

JAMES, R. G. (1965).   Stress and strain fields in sand.   Ph.D. thesis, University of Cambridge.

JAMES, R. G. & BRANSBY, P. L. (1970a).   Experimental and theoretical investigations of a passive earth pressure problem.   *Géotechnique* **20**, No. 1, 17–37.

JAMES, R. G. & BRANSBY, P. L. (1970b).   A velocity field for some passive earth pressure problems.   Submitted for publication.

KOLBUSZEWSKI, J. (1965).   Sand particles and their density.   *Symp. Densification particulate mater.*   Materials Sci. Club, London.

LORD, J. A. (1969).   Stresses and strains in an earth pressure problem.   Ph.D. thesis, University of Cambridge.

LUCIA, J. B. A. (1966).   Passive earth pressure and failure in sand.   Research project report, Mechanical Sciences Tripos, University of Cambridge.

MEYERHOF, G. G. (1951).   The ultimate bearing capacity of foundations.   *Géotechnique* **2**, 301–332.

MEYERHOF, G. G. (1953).   The bearing capacity of foundations under eccentric and inclined loads.   *Proc. 3rd Int. Conf. Soil Mech.* **1**, 440–445.

PARRY, R. H. G. (1956).   Strength and deformation of clay.   Ph.D. thesis, Imperial College of Science and Technology, University of London.

POOROOSHASB, H. B., HOLUBEC, I. & SHERBOURNE, A. N. (1967).   The yielding and flow of sand in triaxial compression.   *Can. Geotech. J.* **3**, No. 4, 179–190 and **4**, No. 4, 376–397.

RENDULIC, L. (1938).   Eine Betrachtung zur Frage der plastischen Grenzzustände.   *Bauingenieur* **19**, 159–164.

ROSCOE, K. H. (1957).   A comparison of tied and free pier foundations.   *Proc. 4th Int. Conf. Soil Mech., London* **1**, Part 3, 419–423.

ROSCOE, K. H. (1958).   Foundations for steel frames which have been designed according to the plastic theory of structures.   *Proc. Midland Soil Mech. Soc.* **2**, No. 12, 73–99.

ROSCOE, K. H. (1966).   Discussion on Session 7, Div. 5, *Proc. 6th Int. Conf. Soil Mech., Montreal* **3**, 522–524.

ROSCOE, K. H. (1967).   Panel discussion on Session 3, Shear strength of soil other than clay.   *Geotech. Conf., Oslo* **2**, 188–192.

ROSCOE, K. H. (1968a).   Soils and model tests.   *J. Strain Analysis* **3**, No. 1, 57–64.

ROSCOE, K. H. (1968b).   A note on the cutting of soils.   Paper presented at R.E.A.C. meeting at Cambridge, May, 1968.

ROSCOE, K. H. (1969).   Some soil mechanics concepts and the possibility of their wider application.   Paper 81, *Proc. Int. Conf. Struct., Solid Mech. Engng Des. civ. Engng Mater.*, University of Southampton.

ROSCOE, K. H., ARTHUR, J. R. F. & JAMES, R. G. (1963).   The determination of strains in soils by an X-ray method.   *Civ. Engng publ. Wks Rev.* **58**, No. 684, 876 and **58**, No. 685, 1009–1012.

ROSCOE, K. H., BASSETT, R. H. & COLE, E. R. L. (1967).   Principal axes observed during simple shear of a sand.   *Proc. Geotech. Conf., Oslo* **1**, 231–7.

ROSCOE, K. H. & BURLAND, J. B. (1968).   On the generalised stress–strain behaviour of 'wet' clay.   In *Engineering plasticity* (ed. J. Heyman & F. A. Leckie), pp. 535–609, Cambridge University Press.

ROSCOE, K. H. & SCHOFIELD, A. N. (1956).   Stability of short pier foundations in sand.   Proceedings of the symposium on plastic theory of structures in Cambridge.   *Br. Weld. J.* **3**, No. 8, 343–354.

ROWE, P. W. (1962).   The stress-dilatancy relation for static equilibrium of an assembly of particles in contact.   *Proc. Roy. Soc.* A, **269**, 500–527.

Rowe, P. W. & Peaker, K. (1965). Passive earth pressure measurements. *Géotechnique* **15**, No. 1, 57–78.

Saada, A. S. (1968). A pneumatic computer for testing cross-anisotropic materials. *Mater. Res. Stand. Am. Soc. Test. Mater.* **8**, No. 1, 17–23.

Schofield, A. N. & Wroth, C. P. (1968). *Critical state soil mechanics*, pp. 310. New York: McGraw-Hill.

Shield, R. T. (1953). Stress and velocity field in soil mechanics. Brown University, Tech. Rep. No. 81 for O.A.N.A.R. (also *J. Math. Phys.* **33**, 144).

Sokolovski, V. V. (1965). *Statics of granular media*, 270 pp. Oxford: Pergamon Press.

Stroud, M. A. (1970). The behaviour of sand at low stress levels in the simple shear apparatus. Submitted as Ph.D. thesis, University of Cambridge.

Terzaghi, K. (1943). *Theoretical soil mechanics*, 510 pp. New York: Wiley.

Ting, W. H. (1968). Some effects of history on the stress–strain behaviour of kaolin. Ph.D. thesis, University of Cambridge.

Tovey, N. K. (1970). Electronmicroscopy of clays. Ph.D. thesis, University of Cambridge.

Vesic, A. S. & Clough, G. W. (1968). Behaviour of granular materials under high stresses. *Proc. Am. Soc. civ. Engrs* **94**, SM3, 661–688.

Walker, L. K. (1967). The deformation of clay as a time-dependent process. Ph.D. thesis, University of Cambridge.

Wroth, C. P. & Bassett, R. H. (1965). A stress–strain relationship for the shearing behaviour of a sand. *Géotechnique* **15**, No. 1, 32–56.